This book belongs to:

About Captain Cillian™

Ahoy readers! Thank you for buying my learning adventure book.

My name is Captain Cillian and I am a fun friendly sailor from Ireland. I love exploring many ports and sailing the seas and oceans.

My learning adventure books and games will take you on a journey of discovery around Ireland and the world! On each adventure, we will encounter many challenges and gain rewards. You will **Explore, Learn, Create** and **Play.**

My learning adventure gifts are available online at **captaincillian.com** Here you will find lots of activities to enjoy with your friends, family or with teachers in the classroom, or bring Captain Cillian with you on your holidays!

I'm light, easy to carry and I love exploring!

Captain Cillian™

Captain Cillian woke up from a deep sleep in County **Sligo**. It was a warm, **windy day**. "**Good morning** friends, gather around, today I have an interesting challenge for us. We are all going **surfing**!" smiled Captain Cillian.

"What do you mean, Captain Cillian? I don't know how to surf," moaned Pirate Ben.

"Don't worry, we are meeting my cousin Ciara and she is a super surfer. She will show us the tricks of the waves. Okay crew, all aboard the **ship**, let's sail to Strandhill, a famous **beach** in County Sligo," said Captain Cillian.

Sligo

EXPLORE IRELAND

Sligo

County Sligo is situated in the north-west of Ireland on the Atlantic Coast. It has a beautiful coastal landscape and a mountain called Benbulben. Sligo is famous for an Irish poet called William Butler Yeats!

English Words	Focail Ghaeilge
Good morning	Dia duit ar maidin
Beach	Trá
A windy day	Lá gaofar
Surfing	Surfáil
Ship	Long

LEARN IRISH

3

Captain Cillian and the crew set sail. As they approached Strandhill, the crew could see **sand** for miles, stretched across the Sligo coast. The **water** beside the beach was very shallow. They decided to drop **anchor** out on the bay and take their small **dinghy** boat to shore.

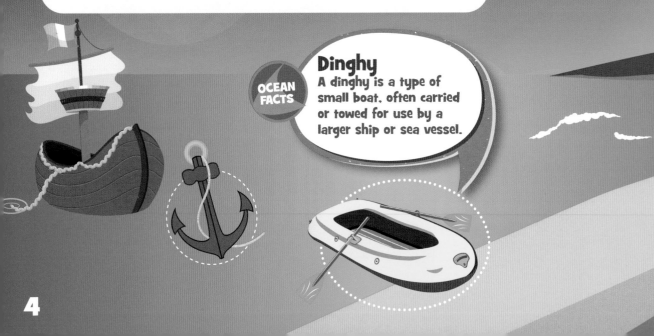

OCEAN FACTS

Dinghy
A dinghy is a type of small boat, often carried or towed for use by a larger ship or sea vessel.

English Words	Focail Ghaeilge
Sand	Gaineamh
Water	Uisce
Anchor	Ancaire

LEARN IRISH

EXPLORE IRELAND

Strandhill

Strandhill is situated on the Cúil Irra peninsula, which is 5 miles west of Sligo town on the Wild Atlantic Way. A lot of the landscape around Strandhill is covered in sand dunes.

They all climbed out of the dinghy and ran on to the beach. "Let's play tag in this wide open space," smiled Freddy Monkey.

"Great idea, but first we need to locate my cousin Ciara," said Captain Cillian.

Captain Cillian put on his magical blue cape. Then deep in his cape pocket he searched for his magic whistle. He blew into the whistle three times. A gust of wind lifted sand from the beach, high into the air.

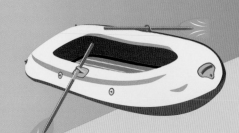

English Words	**Focail Ghaeilge**
Magical blue cape	Clóca draíochta gorm
Pocket	Póca
Great idea	Smaoineamh iontach

LEARN IRISH

Suddenly, behind a sand dune, a pink **beach house** appeared, made of **wood** with a tin roof.

The little house had a large wooden porch with pots of flowers and a comfortable sun chair.

Surf boards were lined up outside the beach house. On the deck sat Ciara, relaxing on a sun chair and enjoying a fruit cocktail!

"Ahoy, cousin Cillian, what brings you up to my beautiful beach?" said Ciara.

"Hello Ciara, great to see you cousin! We want to learn how to surf. Can you teach us, please?" smiled Captain Cillian.

"Okay, no problem guys! We need to get you some surf gear. Pick up some board shorts or wet suits and a surfboard from the beach house. There are two types of boards we are going to have fun with today: a Boogie Board and a Surf Board!" laughed Ciara.

English Words	Focail Ghaeilge
Wood	Adhmad
Beach house	Teach trá
Surf board	Clár surfála
Pink	Bándearg

LEARN IRISH

OCEAN FACTS

Surfing

Surfing is a water sport. The surfer rides on a board on a moving wave towards the shore. Surfers can also body board. This is when a surfer lies on their belly on the board.

"Surfing is all about riding the waves. To surf we need wind to create the waves. Wind generates waves that occur on the surface of oceans, seas, lakes, rivers, and canals or even on small puddles and ponds!" explained Ciara.

"What happens is really interesting!
When the wind blows over a water surface,
it creates a wave. The waves in the oceans can
travel thousands of miles before reaching land!
Wind waves come in all sizes, from small little ripples,
to waves over 100 feet (30 metres) high!"
continued Ciara.

"Surfers are always looking for the ultimate wave, to ride them high in the ocean and bring them into shore. It is very exciting when you learn to catch your first wave!" smiled Ciara.

"Oh, this is brilliant," shouts Pirate Ben. "I love learning new tricks. Surfing may bring me closer to more hidden caves and treasure on the coast! Let's get on these boards and out into the wild Atlantic Ocean!".

LEARN IRISH

English Words	Focail Ghaeilge
Atlantic Ocean	An tAigéan Atlantach
The sea	An fharraige
Lakes	Lochanna
Rivers	Aibhneacha
Canals	Canáil

LEARN IRISH

Along with speaking, reading, and writing, listening is one of the four skills we need to learn languages such as English and Irish and many more!

"**Slow down**, Pirate Ben," said Captain Cillian. "We need to learn how to manage the **surf board** first and practise the techniques before we dive into the sea. So **listen everybody** and pay attention to Ciara, our teacher."

The crew sat on the beach, listening and watching Ciara. She explained how to stand on the board, lie on your belly, hold the board properly and ride with the waves to shore. "Okay we are ready, let's do it!" said Captain Cillian.

Everyone grabbed a surfboard and ran to the edge of the sea.

"Oh, it's a bit chilly," cried Freddy Monkey.

English Words	Focail Ghaeilge
Slow down	Tóg go mall é
Surf board	Clár surfála
Listen everybody	Éistigí gach duine
Belly	Bolg

Starfish

Starfish or Sea Stars are spiny skinned Sea Urchins. They cannot swim and they do not use gills to breathe. There are over 2,000 species of Starfish in the world! They are found in the deep blue sea.

English Words	Focail Ghaeilge
Swimming	Ag snámh
Starfish	Crosán
Crabs	Portáin
Seaweed	Feamainn

"Just dive in and start swimming, you will warm up in 60 seconds!" said Ciara.

They all practised different surfing positions, floating and standing on the boards in the shallow part of the water. Lots of laughter could be heard for miles!

"I can see some starfish and crabs! Very cool," said Pirate Ben.

"I see you've met my friends, the Spider Crabs!" said Ciara. "The Spider Crab is the largest crab found in Irish waters. It measures 20 centimetres across the shell and their legs are 50 centimetres long or more! Spider crabs live in sand and around the beach rocks. They like shallow water zones, but they also live in deep waters of 120 metres!" explained Ciara.

Captain Cillian and friends had such fun surfing the waves at Strandhill with Ciara all day, playing tag on the beach, chasing crabs and examining the starfish and the seaweed with big magnifying glasses.

Later in the evening they all sat down to rest on the beach chairs and enjoyed some orange juice. Ciara made a barbeque of baked **potatoes**, beans, carrots and homemade **beef burgers**. For dessert, they all enjoyed some delicious vanilla **ice-cream** in a cone with hot **chocolate** sauce!

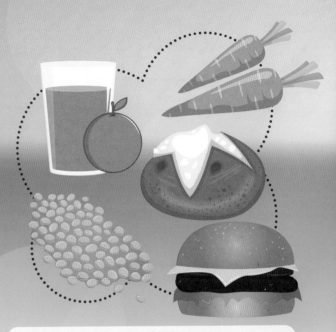

English Words	Focail Ghaeilge
Potatoes	Prátaí
Carrots	Cairéid
Beef burger	Burgar mairteola
Ice-cream	Uachtar reoite
Chocolate	Seacláid

LEARN IRISH

"Yum, this is delicious Ciara, you are the best cook in County Sligo and maybe the whole of Ireland!" Pirate Ben chuckled.

After a big dinner, everyone was very tired. Outside the beach house there were some hammocks connected up to the trees. The crew picked one each and jumped inside.

Ciara's Beach House

Lying down on the hammock, Captain Cillian
gazed out to sea. It was **a clear night** and you
could see the North Star shining brightly.
He watched the waves come in and out to shore,
so peacefully.

"Did you know, friends, at **night time** the North Star remains in the same spot
while the other stars circle around it!" explained Captain Cillian.

"Fascinating!" said Pirate Ben.

"Thank you cousin Ciara for an amazing day" said Captain Cillian.

"Oh I do love the sea and the surprises it brings every day. Good night, sleep tight, to all my learning adventure buddies!" smiled Captain Cillian.

Leabharlanna Poiblí Chathair Baile Átha Cliath
Dublin City Public Libraries

English Words	Focail Ghaeilge	LEARN IRISH
A clear night	Oíche gheal	
Night time	Oíche	
I love the sea	Is breá liom an fharraige	
Surprise	Iontas	
Adventure	Eachtraíocht	
Sleep	Codladh	

19

1. Mark on the map the location where cousin Ciara lives.

2. List four new Irish words you learned on this adventure?

   1.

   2.

   3.

   4.

3. What is surfing?

   ....

....

4. What was Captain Cillian wearing when he was surfing (see page 17)?

    ....

5. Together with your friends, family or teacher, take a trip to the beach or park and find two interesting objects to talk about. Then create a fun game that Captain Cillian and his friends would play too!

6. Create your own surfboard and share with your friends or in the classroom (see page 22). Visit www.captaincillian.com for competitions.

7. Act out this Captain Cillian story with your friends or create your very own story using
    *   summer beach wear and sun hats
    *   a cardboard box and cereal boxes
    *   a marker, sissors and glue (ask a grown-up to help)
    *   paints
    *   chairs
    *   a bed sheet
    *   and lots of interesting objects you can find at the beach or in your home to create an imaginary beach.

Create your own surfboards

...with your favourite colours.

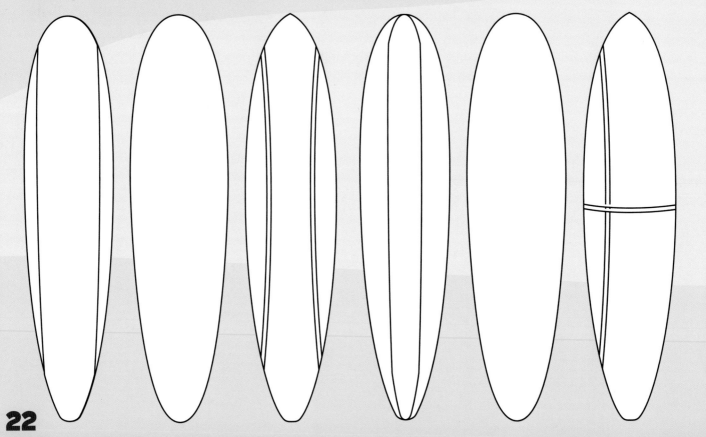

Colour me in

... with your favourite colours.

Word Search

Find these words in the puzzle below.

ATLANTIC   PIRATE

BEACH   SLIGO

DINGHY   WATER

MAGICAL

U	Q	C	Z	N	N	I	O
D	F	I	Q	X	I	P	O
K	I	T	Q	B	J	I	G
U	V	N	E	E	I	R	I
H	M	A	G	I	C	A	L
J	C	L	O	H	O	T	S
H	X	T	B	K	Y	E	Q
B	M	A	R	E	T	A	W

23

Words, Sounds and Clothes with Captain Cillian

Fas-cin-a-ting
Ham-mock
Tech-niques

Words that come up a lot

English Word	I like	I see	I am
Focal Gaeilge	Is maith liom	Feicim	Tá mé

English Word	Focal Gaeilge	Sounds Like
Skirt	Sciorta	Shkerta
Dress	Gúna	Goona
Trousers	Bríste	Breeshtee
Coat	Cóta	Koh-tha
Shoes	Bróga	Brohga
Shirt	Léine	Layna
Pyjamas	Pitseamaí	Pitshamee
Socks	Stocaí	Stukee
Hat	Hata	Hotta

Religion and Ethics for OCR

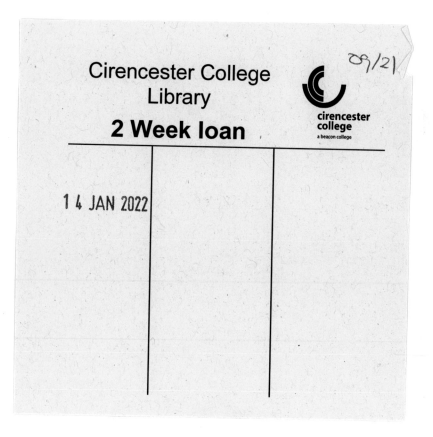
Cirencester College, GL7 1XA
Telephone: 01285 640994

10656216

Copyright © Mark Coffey and Dennis Brown 2016

The right of Mark Coffey and Dennis Brown to be identified as Authors of this Work has been asserted in accordance with the UK Copyright, Designs and Patents Act 1988.

First published in 2016 by Polity Press
Reprinted in 2019, 2020

Polity Press
65 Bridge Street
Cambridge CB2 1UR, UK

Polity Press
350 Main Street
Malden, MA 02148, USA

ISBN-13: 978-1-5095-1015-3
ISBN-13: 978-1-5095-1016-0 (pb)

A catalogue record for this book is available from the British Library.

Typeset in 9.5pt on 13pt Utopia by Servis Filmsetting Ltd, Stockport, Cheshire
Printed and bound in the UK by TJ Books Limited, Padstow, Cornwall

The publisher has used its best endeavours to ensure that the URLs for external websites referred to in this book are correct and active at the time of going to press. However, the publisher has no responsibility for the websites and can make no guarantee that a site will remain live or that the content is or will remain appropriate.

Every effort has been made to trace all copyright holders, but if any have been inadvertently overlooked the publisher will be pleased to include any necessary credits in any subsequent reprint or edition.

For further information on Polity, visit our website: politybooks.com

MARK COFFEY AND DENNIS BROWN

RELIGION AND ETHICS FOR OCR

THE COMPLETE RESOURCE FOR COMPONENT 02 OF THE NEW AS AND A LEVEL SPECIFICATIONS

OCR
Oxford Cambridge and RSA
An OCR endorsed textbook

polity

Contents

Acknowledgements

This book has been a labour of love for the authors and we could not have accomplished the finished product without the help of many people. We would like to thank everyone at Polity Press who has been involved in the project, especially Pascal Porcheron, Leigh Mueller and Neil de Cort, who have worked tirelessly with us and have shown enthusiasm, creativity and patience in their editorial and production role at every stage.

Thanks are also due to Polity's anonymous readers for their helpful comments on various chapters in the early stages, as well as our 'Guinea-pigs' – several years of sixth-form students at The Manchester Grammar School who have played a valuable part in the book's evolution, providing us with honest and sometimes forthright feedback, and sharpened the book's clarity and exercises.

Mark Coffey would also like to thank various teachers along the way: John and Margaret Parry, inspiring sixth-form English and RS teachers who resisted the temptation to concentrate on exam technique and encouraged him to think critically and independently; Professors E. David Cook, David Clough and Nigel Biggar, whose expertise and skill as thinkers, writers and teachers also trained and guided earlier attempts at learning to write on ethics. Thanks also go to Mark's parents, Bob and Mina, who helped with the indexing and proofreading of this book, and to his brother, Professor John Coffey, who first inspired him to think about ethics, philosophy and theology. Their wisdom, kindness, friendship and faith are an inspiration. In addition, we both remember our dear young friend and late colleague at Manchester Grammar School, Matthew Bennett, whose warmth, wisdom and wit, as well as his writing, were among his many gifts that we miss.

The authors and publishers are grateful to all who gave permission to reproduce copyright material. While every attempt has been made to acknowledge all the sources we have drawn upon, we would like to apologise if any omissions have been made and would invite any such copyright holders to contact Polity Press, so that these may be rectified in future editions.

Foreword

Why should you study Ethics? You may well have thought about this already, but here are some reasons why we think you will enjoy and benefit from studying this subject.

The quick answer is that you are studying an Ethics specification for A Level. But why did you choose it? Perhaps it was a negative choice – you did not want to study Physics and you were not interested or suited to some other subjects and Ethics was the only one left to choose. Hopefully, it was a more positive reason – you will have noticed that ethical issues appear in newspapers and on TV a lot – rape, theft, murder, war, abortion, environmental crises and medical dilemmas seem to be discussed very frequently. With all these issues, there always seem to be many different and differing opinions. Some people talk about rules to be obeyed; others talk about the consequences of our actions; still others talk about what their religion says.

All these different approaches can be very confusing. Whose opinion should we follow? Is there one correct answer to ethical questions? How are we to find out?

The twentieth-century Existentialist philosopher Albert Camus said that 'a man without ethics is like a wild beast loosed upon this world'. One of the aims of this book is to teach you how many people – some from the past and some from the present – have attempted and do attempt not to be 'wild beasts' in their dealings with other people. What Camus was trying to say was that a code of ethics is essential to allow a society to function properly. Without such a code of ethics, there would be no society and people would simply do what they wanted to, regardless of what anyone else thought. This would result in chaos and anarchy.

Ethics is important. This is why you should study it. Studying ethical theories like Utilitarianism, Natural Law and Kantianism will help you to discover and discuss the principles upon which people base the decisions they make from day to day on important issues like abortion, euthanasia, war, business and the environment. When you read what other people have said about these issues, you will gradually form your own views about the same issues. Whilst everyone has a right to an opinion, democracy will be healthier and more civil if it is thought through and informed by rational argument.

As you work through this book, you will be challenged to think long and hard about difficult theories and issues. We do not apologise for this. We want to stretch you to think through these theories and issues. We hope, however, that by the end of your study of Ethics, you will also have enjoyed the journey as far as we have taken it in this book. Ethics, of course, is dynamic. Because human nature and the world we live in are always changing, new situations and examples come to light and force us to go back to first principles again, and to re-think our position on any issue. This is both the joy and the challenge of ethics – no two cases are ever the same, so we have to keep thinking and making decisions with every new case. We hope that you will buy into this journey – we enjoy it and hope that you will too.

How to Use This Book

Obviously we want you to enjoy reading and learning as much about ethics as possible and have designed this book so that it will help you not just to pass your exam, but to achieve the best grade possible. As you will have noticed, the chapters follow the structure of the AS and A Level qualifications very carefully and each chapter is designed to be relatively self-contained and to cover the knowledge and the skills you will need to succeed in the Religious Ethics section of your AS/A Level Religious Studies.

To this end we have highlighted important terms in the margins. They are also included in a comprehensive Glossary at the back of the book, which you should use for revision purposes when it comes to preparing for your exams. The list of Further Reading at the end of each chapter will direct you to specific sources of information on individual topics – pursuing these will be a terrific way to extend your knowledge and also to explore further the topics that interest you.

The chapter summaries outline the key points that you should know after studying each chapter and these can be used as revision checklists as you complete the work in each chapter. If you do not feel confident in everything outlined in the summary then you should read back through the chapter again to refresh your memory. At the end of each topic, some 'thought points' are included to help you revise the topic. You should attempt these as they will really help you practise for your exams and also give you an indication of just how ready you are.

Each chapter also contains a number of exercises to get you thinking about the topic in question, as well as Discussion Questions for you to talk through with your fellow students and your teacher. These are especially important, as debating some of the issues in the book really is the best way to learn about them and to figure out your own opinions on the various ways of thinking about ethics.

Websites

There are a range of websites mentioned throughout the book, and, while you always need to proceed with caution when using sources from the web, it will provide a great resource to further your knowledge.

Ethical Thinkers' Timeline

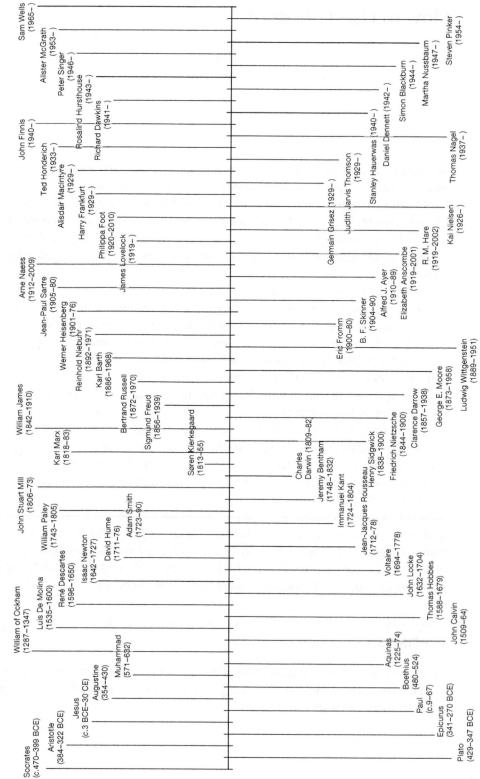

Introduction:
The OCR Specification and Exam Technique

Honing your skills

Welcome to your course in Ethics for OCR Religious Studies. A Level is a step up from GCSEs and the essay-writing at the heart of it calls for a range of skills and techniques as well as fluency in your style. Mastering technical terms, providing examples and having a good grasp of the strengths and weaknesses of theories are all part of the mature essayist's work. In short, taking the mystery out of exam success is our aim in this chapter.

Planning lots of skeleton outlines to past paper questions will help you to take a broad question and focus it down to a relevant and well-crafted argument. Practice trains you to select examples, reasons and evidence. It also keeps you focused, assists with avoiding tangents or fallacies, and helps you to spot gaps in your revision. Timed essays in class will also train you to allocate minutes in proportion to the marks available and to work out how many paragraphs you can reasonably write in the two hours available for planning and writing three essays.

This chapter should serve as a guide as you learn to research and plan your essays. Remembering that irrelevancy and running out of time are two major reasons for underperformance, essay skills are at the heart of your success in this subject. Making lots of essay plans and structuring them in paragraphs will help to hone your skills as an essay writer. We begin by flagging up some key elements in essay writing.

Crafting your essay argument

Interpret the focus of the question together with any terms or value judgements implicit in it.

Decide on your *thesis* (the broad argument you are going to advance taking into account any qualifications you might offer to the terms of the question – e.g. 'In my assessment, this is not an either–or situation, but a both–and one').

Weigh up the *extent* to which you agree with any assertion made in the question – is it true of all or some forms? Are you aware of other *perspectives* that could be taken?

Be clear on the counterargument and key reasons and examples *opposed* to your thesis + evaluation of strengths and weaknesses of these. Showing your awareness of this builds the credibility of your own position.

Then set out the reasoning of key thinkers and arguments *for* your thesis and evaluation of strengths and weaknesses of these.

Evaluate arguments and counterarguments and (if you have time) bring them into dialogue.

Make your personal response explicit, with phrases like 'it is my contention that', or 'in my assessment, there are obvious strengths in the Situation ethicists' view over the position taken by that of a Natural Lawyer because. . .'

Summarise the reasons for your concluding judgement.

Dialogue not monologue

Aristotle commented that 'it is a mark of the educated mind to be able to entertain a thought without accepting it'. One of the lessons to learn as you move from GCSE/IGCSE to A Level is that arguments that oppose your own conclusion deserve a fair hearing, and their criticisms of your position require you to respond to them. Avoid setting up straw-men opponents that are easy to demolish. Seek to understand the weaknesses of your position and arrive at a well-reasoned and balanced conclusion.

Essential skills and strategies for success

Please note that all comments concerning techniques, strategies and skills needed for success in the AS and A Level examinations are the views of the authors, not of the exam board (OCR).

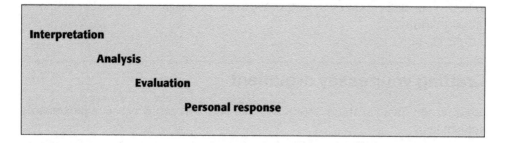

Interpretation

    Analysis

        Evaluation

            Personal response

One of the important ways that AS and A Level differ from GCSE is the technique for formulating and writing essays. At GCSE, there is much more of a focus on rote-learning. To some degree it is possible to prepare answers in advance, remember the information then write it in your examination. This is a strategy that will not work at AS or A Level.

If you wish to achieve high marks in the essays you write at this level, you will need to learn a number of important new skills and techniques.

There are two assessment objectives (AO1 and AO2), details of which are listed on pages 15-16 (for AS Level) and pages 18-19 (for A Level). Learning to understand what these assessment objectives mean will help you a lot in the way you write essays. They will help you to interpret and analyse information, and to assess and evaluate theories and their application to issues. You will need to develop an independent mind and critical awareness of strengths and weaknesses so that you can make your own personal response to the question you have been asked.

AS Level	75 minutes	Two 30-mark questions	60 marks in total
A Level	2 hours	Three 40-mark questions	120 marks in total

The change from the old specification is also clear when you look at the *weighting* of assessment in the new AS and A Level, where the marks shift significantly:

From >>>>>>>>>>>>>>>>> To	
Knowledge and understanding concepts and terms.	Analysis, interpretation and evaluation.
Pre-2017 assessments	**Post-2017 assessments**
AS AO2 marks worth up to 10/35	AS AO2 marks worth up to 50%
A2 AO2 marks worth up to 14/35	A Level AO2 marks worth up to 60%

Getting to grips with AO2 skills

This shift requires you to sharpen your skills of interpretation and analysis of the terms in the question. Thorough knowledge and understanding ought to be the foundation of your success. But experience of doing past paper questions will sharpen your skills in:

- interpreting key terms, trigger words and value judgements over rival positions
- selecting and deploying relevant theories and thinkers, examples and arguments
- seeing how your judgement may rest on interpreting the question precisely

- evaluating the strengths and weaknesses of rival positions concisely
- making focused and concise comparisons and contrasts and supplying good examples
- identifying fallacies, assumptions, errors or claims that are scientifically or rationally unsound or just incoherent
- coming to a personal response regarding, for example, whether a theory is the 'most useful', 'best approach', 'effective in applying principles'
- using technical language fluently.

So, after you've learned each section of the course, you need to practise, practise, practise essay technique. Test and homework essays are not just for consolidating your knowledge. Rather, they are where you develop as a thinker and sharpen skills of selection and structuring a coherent argument. Essays are to humanities students as experiments are to science students. They are where you learn the discipline of sifting, sequencing and assessing the material put before you. In guiding the reader/examiner through the process of your thinking, it is helpful to use transitional phrases that *explicitly* set out your *personal response* to the question for the reader, together with *your own* interpretation, analysis, argument and evaluation of the question. Setting out a clear plan and structure to your argument avoids repetition, makes your logic clearer and ought to be more persuasive. The use of good examples or astute interfacing of theory and issue identify higher-grade candidates. Whilst you do not need to have a formal stock of transitional phrases up your sleeve, you do need to bring *your personal response* to the question to the forefront of your essay.

Reading and planning your essay

Homework essays are time-consuming and labour-intensive. It is tempting to skim read in preparation or even to write them straight off without research and planning. But teachers and examiners can tell apart those students who have taken the time to read and plan their essays from those who have not done so. Reading builds your vocabulary and understanding of concepts. It sharpens your writing style and offers you a wider range of examples. If this all seems too much like hard work, there are lots of good online audio resources to listen to.

Essay Weaknesses	Essay Strengths
• Pre-rehearsed answers that ignore the specific wording of the question. Irrelevance and poor timing are the key reasons students underperform.	• Your own personal response as you analyse and evaluate arguments and demonstrate independent reasoning and judgment.
• Generalisations (e.g. all Catholics are pacifists) or lists of ideas without examples and explanations.	• Close attention to the wording of questions and key words.
• Incoherent or longwinded arguments that do not transition the essay thesis from paragraph to paragraph. Your essay should weave the threads of the argument together coherently.	• Clear, practical examples and a sound ability to engage theory in practice.
	• Good grasp of concepts and distinctions. E.g. a clear understanding of philosophical grammar in distinguishing 'infer' from 'imply', 'refute' from 'deny', or 'a priori', 'a posteriori', etc.
• Evaluation left untill the conclusion rather than woven throughout essay in analysis of strengths and weaknesses.	• A balance between breadth and depth guided by the terms of the question.
• Confusion or conflation of ideas belonging to two distinct thinkers, e.g. Bentham and Mill.	• Good use of specific cases and, where appropriate, biblical references.
	• Clear logical structure and tightly argued paragraphs that do not waffle.
	• Clear analysis of strengths and weaknesses of rival positions in assessing their merits.
	• Excellent engagement between ethical theory and practical issues.

Elements of Essay Writing: Consider how you can sharpen these in making an informed, coherent and persuasive argument

- *A sentence* is a grammatical structure ending in a full stop. Avoid packing too many clauses into your sentences and keep your expression clear – style and substance go together.
- *A paragraph* is a collection of sentences grouped around one purpose or theme. Single-sentence or full-page paragraphs sound alarm bells. You should organise your argument into a step-by-step logical argument.
- To do this, it is best to brainstorm your essay into a series of steps and then to *shuffle your paragraphs* to find the most *logical order* to your essay. For example, you might begin with the weaker position or the one you disagree with, noting its strengths and the critical questions it raises for the position you wish to advance.

Every view deserves a fair hearing in the court of your essay, so do not be too quick to dismiss opposing positions and to assert the strengths of your own view. A critically considered conclusion will carry more credibility.

- Remember that *key terms* in the question are often *contested* – where this is the case, do not be too quick to settle their meanings – let the rival definitions wrestle over their meaning and context. For example, the question of when 'life' begins or 'life' ends in the abortion and euthanasia debates hinges partly on what criteria we use to decide these life-and-death issues.

- *Introduction.* Interpret the question's key words/phrases, and set out your broad position in the essay. Lead your reader by the hand. Unpack the question, set out your thesis point by point and think of essays as dialogues between ideas – not monologues or, worse still, rants. Be concise and clear about structure.

- *Links/transitions* between paragraphs. Avoid a repetitive style. Try to avoid the same stock phrases – style matters. (See the examples offered below.)

- *Evidence.* Your *general* argument needs *particular* examples both to illustrate it and to give the reasons grip. These can take the form of academic authorities who advance a position or demonstrations of how a theory proves to be more or less workable in practice. Balanced arguments can give you more credibility through your impartial handling of the evidence.

- *Include examples, case studies and quotes.* These illustrate your essay and develop a more engaging style.

- *Quotations* are important. For each essay topic, learn five or so quotes that will enhance your style by showing a familiarity with primary sources.

- *Paragraphs*

   Signposts at the beginning – give the markers a clear sense of your structure as they scan your answer by stating your main argument in the opening sentence of your essay.

   Intermediate conclusions at the end – arguments can subtly go off the rails if they do not keep on course with the focus of the question. Recapping what your examples, evidence and reasons have established in a sub-conclusion (one or two sentences) allows you to move the argument forward. You may even take a different course, persuading the reader that, though the initial position had its merits, it was mistaken, inadequate or needed revision. Sub-conclusions act like intermediate conclusions to establish shifts in the argument, like switches that move your train onto a new set of tracks.

- *Fluency with technical vocabulary.* Be aware of key vocabulary from glossaries and indexes in your textbook and have a clear idea of trigger words in questions (see below).

- *Scholars, textual sources, statistics.* Be accurate and selective – let the reasoning drive the essay. Evidence and examples ought to make an essay's reasoning more persuasive and engaging. Read textbooks – they will make you more fluent with ideas.

- *Arguments and counterarguments.* These should form a dialogue in your essay.

At times this can lead to a layering of a weakness identified, a response, then a further weakness that clinches the argument in favour of one side. If you were asked whether Utilitarianism is more practical than Virtue Ethics when applied to business ethics, for example, you could present strengths and weaknesses separately but also have a paragraph where some dialogue and debate entered into the argument. This layering of reasons and responses creates a dialogue rather than a monologue, and builds more credibility for your evaluative conclusions.

- *Theory Summaries – the way to tame the abstract.* Top students bullet point the key elements of abstract theories in their revision notes and clearly define the meaning(s) of key concepts. They deliver these concisely and clearly in exam essays. Weaker students ramble because they have not read and short-noted enough to understand the theories fully. The timed conditions of the exam are not the place to wrestle with your understanding.

- *Conclusion.* Here's where you summarise your argument rather than embarking on a new one. Looking back, all paragraphs in the essay should lead logically to the conclusion.

- *Review your homework essays.* It may seem like a novel idea, but if it's a homework essay, don't hand it in without first re-reading it! On this proof reading, check it for spelling and grammar errors. Then ask yourself whether your explanations are clear in their understanding of concepts and theories. Also try to be self-critical about whether you've relevantly addressed the question, reflected a range of perspectives, and structured a well-evidenced argument in the right sequence or order. If not, then re-edit it. It is tempting to think that it is your teacher's job to rewrite your essay for you, but this is like putting the oil randomly on a canvas and expecting your art teacher to make a painting of it! You are learning to be an INDEPENDENT thinker, so critical self-review is the way to mature as an essay writer.

Transitional phrases

As mentioned above, one element of becoming a good essay writer is to transition from one paragraph to the next in such a way as to lead your reader through the steps in your thought. This avoids repetition, makes your logic clearer and ought to make it more persuasive. Structure, substance and style all help to engage a marker and make their job easier, so that it is likely that they will be more favourably disposed while reading your essay.

Whilst you do not need to have a formal stock of transitional phrases up your sleeve, you do need to work on the style and structure of your homework essays so that you mature as an essay writer, offering a logical progression from one paragraph to another. Below is a list of exemplar phrases that illustrate this process. But be sure to select from, and deploy, your pre-rehearsed material in the right way, to address the exact terms of the question presented to you, or you will lose marks.

Scaffolding your essay

To facilitate this, it's useful to have in mind some scaffolding to your essay. Structure shows through in paragraphing (with signpost sentences at the start, and sub-conclusions at the end).
Interpret the key terms in the question.
Set up the contrasts and comparisons in your mind.
Weave evaluative judgements about strengths and weaknesses into every sub-conclusion of your essay – don't leave it until the final concluding paragraph.

If you find it helpful, here are some examples of transitional phrases to bring your personal response to the forefront of:

* *your opening thesis statement*
* *sub-conclusions at the close of each of your paragraphs*
* *your main conclusion.*

Introductions

The key terms of the question are contested by different moral theories, and it is my contention that . . .
My thesis in this essay will be that the terms in the question . . .
At the outset of this essay, I wish to clarify the contested terms in the essay title.
Various theories interpret the phrase 'X' in the essay title differently . . .
With respect to the term 'useful' / 'helpful' / 'successful', I would judge that X theory is, in comparison with Y theory, preferable because . . .

Setting out your personal thesis/assessment

I agree with Philosopher X who makes a strong case for . . .
Personally, I would argue that a weakness of X's theory is that . . .
I find the argument of X more persuasive than that of Y in terms of . . .
In my view, X's example of . . . is a useful starting point for considering the . . .
Although this is a matter of debate, and is certainly unprovable, I would argue that . . . because . . .
I am persuaded by X's more radical approach to this issue.
Regardless of the individual criticisms that can be made of X's proposal, I still think that it holds up under scrutiny.
In my assessment, this theory has the advantage(s) that . . .
In my judgement, X cogently defends the view that . . .

Expressing what you see to be difficulties with a position/ positions

In my estimation, X does not properly account for . . .

It may be objected to X's position that . . .

I consider X's position to be indefensible at the point at which . . .

X's assumption that . . . does not, in my judgement, hold up to criticism and is easily disproved.

In applying this theory to the issue at hand, its weaknesses become evident.

Not all arguments presented by Aquinas have survived scrutiny. . .

Several problems appear with this position.

That argument needs to be made cautiously, given the . . .

This dismissal of Natural Law because teleology is problematic after Darwin is too simplistic.

The argument is undermined by the fact that . . .

A more fruitful line of argument is . . .

A different position/contrasting view

While all of this may be true enough, I side with the opposing position set out in X . . .

In my view, X has responded to Y by marshalling good evidence to the contrary.

After evaluating the evidence, I would argue that X is correct in asserting that Y was wrong when he insisted that . . .

On the other side of the issue, X contends that . . ., and I find her argument persuasive.

As for Y . . . I am still more persuaded by the argument of X.

In my judgement, while this is a valiant effort, it does not ultimately succeed.

This is a plausible idea, but I would argue that it fails to explain . . .

In contrast, an alternative argument, which is in my opinion a stronger one, is put forward by X . . .

Conclusions/summaries

The contrasts and comparative assessment that I have set out lead me to conclude that the position/theory of X is more useful / practical / principled / consistent and rational / ethically robust than that of . . .

In concluding, it has been my contention in this essay that . . .

Despite the counterarguments to my opening thesis, I see no compelling reason to doubt the view that . . .

In summary, I have tried to make a case for . . .

Note taking throughout your course

As you go along, keep bullet point short-notes on comparisons and contrasts, similarities and differences, between theories. You need to be conversant with these. Also write down questions you have regarding the material your teacher covers, or that you would ask of theories and thinkers. Bring these up in lessons. Much of evaluative essay writing involves the requirement to

Compare common ground between theories and
Contrast distinctive features/contested approaches to practical ethical issues to form evidence-based judgements

Evaluate strengths and weaknesses throughout the essay

Strengths	Weaknesses
Reasons + evidence and examples	Reasons + evidence and examples
Similarities	**Differences**
Reasons + evidence and examples	Reasons + evidence and examples

Exercise

Photocopy several opinion or editorial pieces from quality newspapers. Then...

(1) Ask yourself whether the writer has given a fair-minded assessment of alternative or opposing views rather than misrepresented them (the straw-man fallacy).
(2) Highlight key words and phrases from each paragraph to identify the skeletal outline of the argument.
(3) Critically evaluate whether you think other evidence or information about context or more specific examples/case studies are necessary to support the author's argument – are the conclusions overdrawn (more conclusions drawn out than reasons and evidence put in)?

Be strategic about your planning and preparation

- Think about your style – be concise and target the question's focus in your sights.
- Make sure your information is accurate and relevant. Arrive at your concluding judgement(s) only after a balanced comparison of the strengths and weaknesses of theories.
- Mine books and web links for examples and case studies to illustrate your essays (though let the reasoning drive the essay, not the examples).

Mind mapping

Try setting out all of the angles from which you can think of questions being asked. You should become familiar with the specification itself, as this has all the content that you can be tested on. It will also offer you a sort of guarantee that you are ready to handle any question thrown at you.

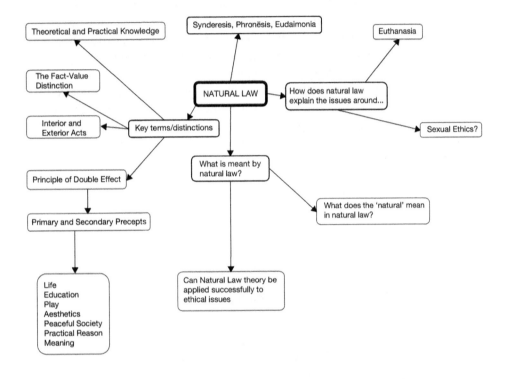

Why essays make you employable

Essay writing might seem like a real chore. Yet in developing transferable skills of persuasiveness, analysis and creative thinking, you are becoming more employable. As you read around theories and issues, you will find your fluency with ideas and your capacity to extract relevant data from your research growing with each essay. It is precisely these skills in selecting and deploying relevant and precise evidence and arguments that make graduates in the humanities so employable.

Not losing the wood for the trees – seeing the big picture of your argument

To use an analogy, you can get lost in the woods of concepts and abstract arguments with no visible way out. Equally, you might feel the need to airlift your wayward argument out of the forest in the concluding paragraph as you realise that you have not relevantly addressed the terms of the question. Yet a safer way out of the forest may be to leave stores of food there: to have well-rehearsed key points ready to go once you've selected what is relevant to the question. Excellent selection and deployment of relevant reasons, examples, thinkers, strengths and weaknesses are crucial to achieving a top grade.

Before you actually start writing an essay, whether as homework or in an exam, it is important to think carefully about both the content and its structure. This will be easier if you have used mind mapping techniques or some similar way of noting the information for a topic. Set out key terms, examples, key quotes, relevant thinkers, arguments and analytical points. Doing this will help to prepare you for any essay on a topic that you may be set.

Doing well in exams is a feat of memory – use bullet points, acronyms and mnemonics to help your recall become exam-proof.

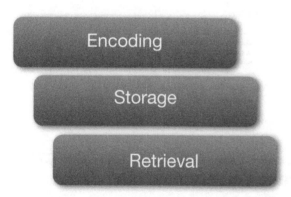

Exams are not just about understanding theories and applying them. They are also timed tests of your recall. Under such pressure, you need to find a process or system for encoding the information that will make it easy to retrieve. Lists of key principles and concepts in theories, as well as evaluative lists of strengths and weaknesses, should be memorised. This is best done in a concise orderly way using mind maps or bullet points, or with the aid of acronyms and mnemonics.

The two websites listed below may assist you in generating acronyms and mnemonics.

Acronym	Mnemonic
An acronym is an abbreviation using the first letter of each word. For example AIDS is an acronym for Acquired Immuno-Deficiency Syndrome	A mnemonic is a short phrase that you use to help remember something. So 'Richard Of York Goes Battling In Vain' helps me to remember the colours of the rainbow – red, orange, yellow, green, blue, indigo, violet
Acronym generator: www.cs.uoregon.edu/Research/paracomp/anym/	Phonetic mnemonic generator: www.remarkablemarbles.com/memory/phonetic-mnemonic-generator

We have included the grade descriptors for OCR Religious Studies at AS and A Level to help you to understand how your work will be graded. When you receive back a marked essay, it is worth looking up your level and taking the time to see whether and how you could improve on your level next time.

Final note: as your teacher marks your essays, identify the level you are presently at and be clear about what you need to do to improve. The Levels of Response grids below may be helpful.

AS Religious Studies and A Level Religious Studies

You will choose to study either
AS Religious Studies **OR** A Level Religious Studies.
These are two separate qualifications that are self-contained. In both cases, the AS and A Level Religion and Ethics component of Religious Studies amounts to 33.3 per cent of the course alongside the other two other sections of the course, namely Philosophy of Religion and Developments in Religious Thought.

An overview of the major differences is provided below.

	AS Level	A Level
Course studied over	1 year	2 years
Length of exam	75 minutes	120 minutes
% of marks for AO2 Analysis and evaluation	50%	60%

Details of the two courses are listed below:
For students taking an AS Level course, their end-of-course exam will be made up of 30-mark questions (they answer two questions from three options).

AS Level Religion and Ethics H173 for first assessment in 2017

Learners will study:

(1) Normative Ethical Theories: Religious Approaches – Natural Law and Situation Ethics

(2) Normative Ethical Theories: Deontological – Kantian Ethics

Teleological – Utilitarianism

(3) Applied Ethics: Natural Law and Situation Ethics to Euthanasia

Kantian Ethics and Utilitarianism to Business Ethics

AO1 – 50%	Demonstrate knowledge and understanding of religion and belief, including:
	• religious, philosophical and/or ethical thought and teaching
	• influence of beliefs, teachings and practices on individuals, communities and societies
	• cause and significance of similarities and differences in belief, teaching and practice
	• approaches to the study of religion and belief.
AO2 – 50%	Analyse and evaluate aspects of, and approaches to, religion and belief, including their significance, influence and study.

For students taking an A Level course, their end-of-course exam will be made up of 40-mark questions (they answer three questions from four options). Given that the same material may be examined at AS Level (in 30-mark questions) and at A Level (in 40-mark questions), the end-of-chapter 'Thought Points' are relevant for both AS and A Level students.

The key difference between AS and A Level is that, whereas the AS Level descriptors only go to level 5 (for Very Good), at A Level, there is an extra level 6 descriptor (for Excellence). This recognises the greater level of maturity which students may have developed in their second year of study. The weighting also shifts from 50:50 to 60:40 in favour of AO2 (assessment and evaluation). Here it is worth considering the terms used to describe a top-flight essay:

For AO1

An **excellent** demonstration of knowledge and understanding in response to the question:

- fully comprehends the demands of, and focuses on, the question throughout
- excellent selection of relevant material which is skilfully used
- accurate and highly detailed knowledge which demonstrates deep understanding through a complex and nuanced approach to the material used

Mark Scheme

Level (Mark)	Levels of Response for AS Level Religious Studies: Assessment Objective 2 (AO2) *Analyse and evaluate aspects of, and approaches to, religion and belief, including their significance, influence and study*	Note: The descriptors below must be considered in the context of all elements of Assessment Objective 2 (AO2) and the indicative content in the mark scheme.
5 (13–15)	A **very good** demonstration of analysis and evaluation in response to the question: • clear and convincing argument • successful and clear analysis and evaluation • views very well stated, coherently developed and justified • answers the question set competently • accurate and appropriate use of technical terms and subject vocabulary. • a very good range of scholarly views, academic approaches and sources of wisdom and authority used to support analysis and evaluation *Assessment of Extended Response: There is a well-developed and sustained line of reasoning which is coherent, relevant and logically structured.*	
4 (10–12)	A **good** demonstration of analysis and evaluation in response to the question: • argument is generally successful and clear • generally successful analysis and evaluation • views well stated, with some development and justification • answers the question set well • mostly accurate and appropriate use of technical terms and subject vocabulary. • a good range of scholarly views, academic approaches and sources of wisdom and authority are used to support analysis and evaluation *Assessment of Extended Response: There is a well-developed line of reasoning which is clear, relevant and logically structured*	
3 (7–9)	A **satisfactory** demonstration of analysis and/evaluation in response to the question: • some successful argument • partially successful analysis and evaluation • views asserted but often not fully justified • mostly answers the set question • generally appropriate use of technical terms and subject vocabulary. • a satisfactory range of scholarly views, academic approaches and sources of wisdom and authority are used to support analysis and evaluation with only partial success *Assessment of Extended Response: There is a line of reasoning presented which is mostly relevant and which has some structure.*	
2 (4–6)	A **basic** demonstration of analysis and evaluation in response to the question: • some argument attempted, not always successful • little successful analysis and evaluation • views asserted but with little justification • only partially answers the question • some accurate, but limited, use of technical terms and appropriate subject vocabulary. • a limited range of scholarly views, academic approaches and sources of wisdom and authority to support analysis and evaluation with little success *Assessment of Extended Response: There is a line of reasoning which has some relevance and which is presented with limited structure.*	
1 (1–3)	A **weak** demonstration of analysis and evaluation in response to the question: • very little argument attempted • very little successful analysis and evaluation • views asserted with very little justification • unsuccessful in answering the question • very little use of technical terms or subject vocabulary. • very little or no use of scholarly views, academic approaches and sources of wisdom and authority to support analysis and evaluation *Assessment of Extended Response: The information is communicated in a basic/unstructured way.*	
0 (0)	No creditworthy response	

Mark Scheme

Level (Mark)	Levels of Response for AS Level Religious Studies: Assessment Objective 1 (AO1) *Demonstrate knowledge and understanding of religion and belief, including:* • *Religious, philosophical and/or ethical thought and teaching* • *Approaches to the study of religion and belief*	Note: The descriptors below must be considered in the context of all listed strands of Assessment Objectives 1 (AO1) and the indicative content in the mark scheme.
5 (13–15)	A **very good** demonstration of knowledge and understanding in response to the question: • focuses on the precise question throughout • very good selection of relevant material which is used appropriately • accurate, and detailed knowledge which demonstrates very good understanding through either the breadth or depth of material used • accurate and appropriate use of technical terms and subject vocabulary. A very good range of scholarly views, academic approaches, and/or sources of wisdom and authority are used to demonstrate knowledge and understanding	
4 (10–12)	A **good** demonstration of knowledge and understanding in response to the question: • addresses the question well • good selection of relevant material, used appropriately on the whole • mostly accurate knowledge which demonstrates good understanding of the material used, which should have reasonable amounts of depth or breadth • mostly accurate and appropriate use of technical terms and subject vocabulary. A good range of scholarly views, academic approaches, and/or sources of wisdom and authority are used to demonstrate knowledge and understanding	
3 (7–9)	A **satisfactory** demonstration of knowledge and understanding in response to the question: • generally addresses the question • mostly sound selection of mostly relevant material • some accurate knowledge which demonstrates sound understanding through the material used, which might however be lacking in depth or breadth • generally appropriate use of technical terms and subject vocabulary. A satisfactory range of scholarly views, academic approaches, and/or sources of wisdom and authority are used to demonstrate knowledge and understanding with only partial success	
2 (4–6)	A **basic** demonstration of knowledge and understanding in response to the question: • might address the general topic rather than the question directly • limited selection of partially relevant material • some accurate, but limited, knowledge which demonstrates partial understanding • some accurate, but limited, use of technical terms and appropriate subject vocabulary. A limited range of scholarly views, academic approaches, and/or sources of wisdom and authority are used to demonstrate knowledge and understanding with little success	
1 (1–3)	A **weak** demonstration of knowledge and understanding in response to the question: • almost completely ignores the question • very little relevant material selected • knowledge very limited, demonstrating little understanding • very little use of technical terms or subject vocabulary. A very little or no use of scholarly views, academic approaches and/or sources of wisdom and authority to demonstrate knowledge and understanding	
0 (0)	No creditworthy response	

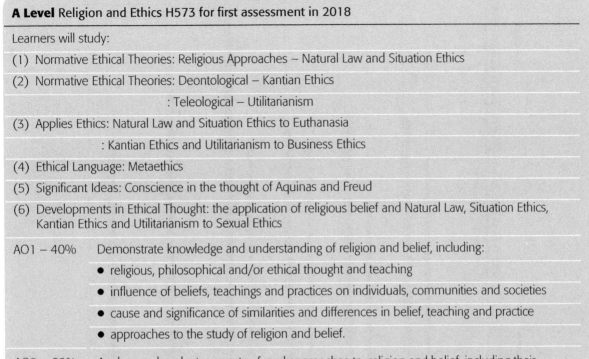

A **Level** Religion and Ethics H573 for first assessment in 2018

Learners will study:

(1) Normative Ethical Theories: Religious Approaches – Natural Law and Situation Ethics

(2) Normative Ethical Theories: Deontological – Kantian Ethics

: Teleological – Utilitarianism

(3) Applies Ethics: Natural Law and Situation Ethics to Euthanasia

: Kantian Ethics and Utilitarianism to Business Ethics

(4) Ethical Language: Metaethics

(5) Significant Ideas: Conscience in the thought of Aquinas and Freud

(6) Developments in Ethical Thought: the application of religious belief and Natural Law, Situation Ethics, Kantian Ethics and Utilitarianism to Sexual Ethics

AO1 – 40%   Demonstrate knowledge and understanding of religion and belief, including:

- religious, philosophical and/or ethical thought and teaching
- influence of beliefs, teachings and practices on individuals, communities and societies
- cause and significance of similarities and differences in belief, teaching and practice
- approaches to the study of religion and belief.

AO2 – 60%   Analyse and evaluate aspects of, and approaches to, religion and belief, including their significance, influence and study.

- thorough, accurate and precise use of technical terms and vocabulary in context
- extensive range of scholarly views, academic approaches, and/or sources of wisdom and authority are used to demonstrate knowledge and understanding

For AO2

An **excellent** demonstration of analysis and evaluation in response to the question:

- excellent, clear and successful argument
- confident and insightful critical analysis and detailed evaluation of the issue
- views skilfully and clearly stated, coherently developed and justified
- answers the question set precisely throughout
- thorough, accurate and precise use of technical terms and vocabulary in context
- extensive range of scholarly views, academic approaches and sources of wisdom and authority used to support analysis and evaluation

Level (Mark)	Levels of Response for A Level Religious Studies: Assessment Objective 1 (AO1) *Demonstrate knowledge and understanding of religion and belief, including:* • *Religious, philosophical and/or ethical thought and teaching* • *Approaches to the study of religion and belief*	Note: The descriptors below must be considered in the context of all listed strands of Assessment Objectives 1 (AO1) and the indicative content in the mark scheme.
6 (14–16)	An **excellent** demonstration of knowledge and understanding in response to the question: • fully comprehends the demands of, and focuses on, the question throughout • excellent selection of relevant material which is skilfully used • accurate and highly detailed knowledge which demonstrates deep understanding through a complex and nuanced approach to the material used • thorough, accurate and precise use of technical terms and vocabulary in context • extensive range of scholarly views, academic approaches, and/or sources of wisdom and authority are used to demonstrate knowledge and understanding	
5 (11–13)	A **very good** demonstration of knowledge and understanding in response to the question: • focuses on the precise question throughout • very good selection of relevant material which is used appropriately • accurate, and detailed knowledge which demonstrates very good understanding through either the breadth or depth of material used • accurate and appropriate use of technical terms and subject vocabulary. • a very good range of scholarly views, academic approaches, and/or sources of wisdom and authority are used to demonstrate knowledge and understanding	
4 (8–10)	A **good** demonstration of knowledge and understanding in response to the question: • addresses the question well • good selection of relevant material, used appropriately on the whole • mostly accurate knowledge which demonstrates good understanding of the material used, which should have reasonable amounts of depth or breadth • mostly accurate and appropriate use of technical terms and subject vocabulary. • a good range of scholarly views, academic approaches, and/or sources of wisdom and authority are used to demonstrate knowledge and understanding	
3 (5–7)	A **satisfactory** demonstration of knowledge and understanding in response to the question: • generally addresses the question • mostly sound selection of mostly relevant material • some accurate knowledge which demonstrates sound understanding through the material used, which might however be lacking in depth or breadth • generally appropriate use of technical terms and subject vocabulary. • A satisfactory range of scholarly views, academic approaches, and/or sources of wisdom and authority are used to demonstrate knowledge and understanding	
2 (3–4)	A **basic** demonstration of knowledge and understanding in response to the question: • might address the general topic rather than the question directly • limited selection of partially relevant material • some accurate, but limited, knowledge which demonstrates partial understanding • some accurate, but limited, use of technical terms and appropriate subject vocabulary. • a limited range of scholarly views, academic approaches, and/or sources of wisdom and authority are used to demonstrate knowledge and understanding with only partial success	
1 (1–2)	A **weak** demonstration of knowledge and understanding in response to the question: • almost completely ignores the question • very little relevant material selected • knowledge very limited, demonstrating little understanding • very little use of technical terms or subject vocabulary. • very little or no use of scholarly views, academic approaches and/or sources of wisdom and authority to demonstrate knowledge and understanding with little success	
0 (0)	No creditworthy response	

Mark Scheme

Level (Mark)	Levels of Response for A Level Religious Studies: Assessment Objective 2 (AO2) *Analyse and evaluate aspects of, and approaches to, religion and belief, including their significance, influence and study*	Note: The descriptors below must be considered in the context of all elements of Assessment Objective 2 (AO2) and the indicative content in the mark scheme.
6 (21–24)	An **excellent** demonstration of analysis and evaluation in response to the question: • excellent, clear and successful argument • confident and insightful critical analysis and detailed evaluation of the issue • views skilfully and clearly stated, coherently developed and justified • answers the question set precisely throughout • thorough, accurate and precise use of technical terms and vocabulary in context • extensive range of scholarly views, academic approaches and sources of wisdom and authority used to support analysis and evaluation *Assessment of Extended Response: There is an excellent line of reasoning, well-developed and sustained, which is coherent, relevant and logically structured.*	
5 (17–20)	A **very good** demonstration of analysis and evaluation in response to the question: • clear argument which is mostly successful • successful and clear analysis and evaluation • views very well stated, coherently developed and justified • answers the question set competently • accurate and appropriate use of technical terms and subject vocabulary. • a very good range of scholarly views, academic approaches and sources of wisdom and authority used to support analysis and evaluation *Assessment of Extended Response: There is a well-developed and sustained line of reasoning which is coherent, relevant and logically structured.*	
4 (13–16)	A **good** demonstration of analysis and evaluation in response to the question: • argument is generally successful and clear • generally successful analysis and evaluation • views well stated, with some development and justification • answers the question set well • mostly accurate and appropriate use of technical terms and subject vocabulary. • a good range of scholarly views, academic approaches and sources of wisdom and authority are used to support analysis and evaluation *Assessment of Extended Response: There is a well-developed line of reasoning which is clear, relevant and logically structured*	
3 (9–12)	A **satisfactory** demonstration of analysis and/evaluation in response to the question: • some successful argument • partially successful analysis and evaluation • views asserted but often not fully justified • mostly answers the set question • generally appropriate use of technical terms and subject vocabulary. • a satisfactory range of scholarly views, academic approaches and sources of wisdom and authority are used to support analysis and evaluation with only partial success *Assessment of Extended Response: There is a line of reasoning presented which is mostly relevant and which has some structure.*	
2 (5–8)	A **basic** demonstration of analysis and evaluation in response to the question: • some argument attempted, not always successful • little successful analysis and evaluation • views asserted but with little justification • only partially answers the question • some accurate, but limited, use of technical terms and appropriate subject vocabulary. • a limited range of scholarly views, academic approaches and sources of wisdom and authority to support analysis and evaluation with little success *Assessment of Extended Response: There is a line of reasoning which has some relevance and which is presented with limited structure.*	
1 (1–4)	A **weak** demonstration of analysis and evaluation in response to the question: • very little argument attempted • very little successful analysis and evaluation • views asserted with very little justification • unsuccessful in answering the question • very little use of technical terms or subject vocabulary. • very little or no use of scholarly views, academic approaches and sources of wisdom and authority to support analysis and evaluation *Assessment of Extended Response: The information is communicated in a basic/unstructured way.*	
0 (0)	No creditworthy response	

Assessment of Extended Response: There is an excellent line of reasoning, well-developed and sustained, which is coherent, relevant and logically structured.

A Level candidates achieving excellence in their answers (the level six descriptors listed above) show a familiarity with scholarship informed by wider reading. This gives them fluency with technical vocabulary and allows for an intelligent interpretation of the question to deliver a thoroughly relevant answer that pays close attention to its wording. Avoiding potted summaries of thinkers, they show a skill in selecting and deploying material together with a nuanced understanding of thinkers. Top candidates understand classic thinkers and their contemporary interpreters to the extent that, though they wrote centuries before the particular issues that arise in modern ethical debates, they can present a nuanced account of how their thought may apply to these. Accomplished essay writers exhibit accuracy, precision and depth of understanding together with a breadth of perspective that allows for a variety of views to be compared and contrasted in a sophisticated manner. They have fingertip familiarity with a range of scholarship, but have digested it to the extent that they can advance their own thesis and position on any given question, arguing cogently for their own judgements in a persuasive way. Most importantly, assessment and evaluation at both AS and A Level isn't restricted to the conclusion, but woven throughout essays. A discerning writer makes informed judgements as to the relative strengths and weaknesses of theories throughout the essay. Their critical analysis is coherent and persuasively reasoned through from a clear thesis statement to a successful conclusion.

Philosophy as the history of ideas

One distinctive feature of this textbook lies in its attention to the history of ideas. Ideas are not treated as though they float around in the abstract. They emerge from and give impetus to movements and periods of change. Technology such as the printing press at the time of the Protestant Reformation was to distribute ideas across Europe at a pace that had never been seen before. Just think that, a little over 100 years after Karl Marx's death, one-third of the world's people would be living under the influence of his thought. The advent of the modern state, accounting practices and the growth of Utilitarian thought is hardly coincidental. Attention to the history of ideas along with the analysis of primary texts is central to the study of Philosophy at university. But even in A Level study, it brings Moral Philosophy and Ethics to life if you can see how the biographies, times and ideas of key thinkers interact.

So keep in mind the current of ideas and a sense that thinkers are often moved to write in opposition to influential movements or writers of their day. Kant, for example, wrote that Hume awoke him from his 'dogmatic slumbers'. He was moved to justify his knowledge claims and to meet Hume's scepticism. So, as you read through the chapters, try to situate thinkers in their periods and enquire into the changing times in which ideas emerge. Often it is the artists, poets, engineers and inventors who innovate change; as Simon and Garfunkel sang, 'the words of the prophets are written on the subway walls'. The philosophers may not be the first to get there, but they do articulate new social, political, religious or cultural movements in language, and make these ideas more clearly understood. So refer back to the timeline on page **x** as you read through this book and seek to build up a mental picture of when key thinkers are writing and how their context may shape their ideas or account for what they're reacting to or how they innovate.

Preliminary note on some key distinctions in ethics

As we begin to examine key debates in Moral Philosophy, it is useful to keep in mind three branches of the study of Moral Philosophy.

1   *Practical or applied ethics*

Practical ethics looks at the specifics of how ethical judgements and reasoning work out in real-life issues. It is here where the theories you are studying prove themselves or fall short as they are applied to issues such as euthanasia and business ethics.

2   *Normative ethics*

Normative ethics sets out standards or principles by which character or actions can be judged or evaluated. Ethical principles and criteria offer a means of judging how we ought to act (e.g. Kantian, Utilitarian, Virtue, Natural Law ethics). Normative ethical theories broadly divide between
  deontological – ethics based on principles which are more fixed and absolute in determining behaviour, e.g. Kantian, Natural Law; and
  teleological – ethics based on optimising outcomes or consequences, e.g. Utilitarianism and Situation Ethics.

3   *Meta-ethics*
Meta-ethics is the study of the meaning of moral terms (e.g. justice, goodness) and metaphysical questions (beyond scientific scope) such as 'Is morality objective?', 'Are there moral facts?' or 'Is there a relationship between morality and human happiness and flourishing?' It is *analysis* rather than action – the study of the meaning of the terms and concepts used in moral judgements. It is sometimes described as the epistemology (the justification of what we can be said to know) of ethics because the very meaning of terms such as 'good' and 'bad', 'right' and 'wrong' is so debatable. Meaning (semantics) and justification (epistemology) are inter-related in terms of critical debate and analysis. '*Meta*' is a Greek word meaning 'around' and deals with questions surrounding the meaning of ethical terms and the question of moral realism.

Deontological vs teleological approaches to ethics

Deontological ethics focus on duty (from the Greek, '*deon*', meaning 'what is true', or 'duty'), motives, and the rightness or wrongness of actions or rules rather than their justification in terms of consequences. Such theories view 'goodness' in terms of adherence to law, duty or motives, actions being right or wrong in themselves, as opposed to actions being instrumentally good, the end goal justifying the means of achieving it.

Philosophers distinguish between act and rule deontological theories. Although we will cover these in more detail in the chapter on Kantian Ethics, in brief, *act-deontologists* judge the rightness of their actions on the basis of what any just and impartial person would do in the same particular set of circumstances. By contrast, *rule-deontologists* follow fixed principles or rules that apply regardless of their ability to deliver favourable outcomes in specific cases. Immanuel Kant's Categorical Imperative offers one example of rule-deontology. Its fixed principle of acting with Good Will and in terms of universalising the rule by which one acts applies whether or not it promotes pleasure or pain. Kant is well aware of the human tendency to make exceptions to rules, for example when the obligations of a promise prove costly.

It may be supposed that deontological thought is seldom seen in areas of public policy, but this is not the case. Examples of deontological thinking are common to medical codes of conduct in the UK and internationally, such as:

- doctor–patient confidentiality (assuming that what is revealed does not break the law of the country concerned);
- anti-discrimination laws establishing rights to be treated fairly in accessing health, housing and education without regard to one's age, disability, creed, ethnic or racial origin, sexual orientation, gender, nationality, political affiliation, etc.

Furthermore, in the post-World War II Geneva Declaration (1948), the clause about a doctor not using his/her medical knowledge contrary to the laws of humanity was framed partly in response to cases such as that of the infamous Nazi doctor Mengele, known as the 'angel of death'. He oversaw a team of medical doctors whose torturous 'experiments' in the notorious 'Block 10' at Auschwitz concentration camp included many operations without anaesthetic, as a result of which nearly all 'patients' lost their lives painfully and within hours or days. The belief that doctors may at times be bound by their duty to a moral law that could ever call for civil disobedience in transcending unjust national laws is a deontological one.

Teleological ethics (from the Greek, '*telos*', meaning 'goal' or 'purpose') can, confusingly, be used in two distinct senses.

(a) Aristotle's ethics focuses on the purpose of actions and beings. In this sense of teleology, everything is aimed towards an end purpose. This may be because some divine being(s) designed them that way, or simply because living things by their nature, work towards certain goals (whether consciously or not).

Deontological ethics:
Deontological ethics are concerned with fulfilling our duty (**deon** in Greek means 'duty'), to obey the moral law, as opposed to justifying an action in terms of motives or consequences. Duty presupposes a fixed and universal law, and the spirit of this approach is captured in the phrase 'Let justice be done though the heavens fall.'

Teleological ethics:
Telos is the Greek word meaning 'goal' or 'end', and teleological ethics refers to moral statements based upon consequences. Actions are justified in terms of the favourable outcomes they result in.

(**b**) Teleology can more simply refer to acting on the basis of achieving certain consequences or outcomes.

So teleological theories agree that our actions are goal-orientated. For Eudaimonistic theories like Virtue Ethics (which use '*telos*' in the sense of (**a**)), that goal is human flourishing or happiness in seeking the virtuous life ('*eudaimonia*' means happiness in the sense of flourishing).

By contrast, others use '*telos*' in the sense of (**b**), in which that outcome is the maximisation of pleasure (Bentham), or preferences/ choices (Singer). Here, the end goal can justify the means and, rather than having intrinsic rights and wrongs, choices and actions are instrumental or useful in bringing about good outcomes. This gets complicated because Mill (a Utilitarian) also reads Aristotle and broadens out Bentham's idea of pleasure to be more eudaimonistic and to speak of happiness in its broader sense of human flourishing.

The philosopher Elizabeth Anscombe, who was heavily influenced by Aristotle, came up with the term 'consequentialism' to describe the second sense of teleology above (**b**). She was extremely critical of this position (and of Utilitarianism in general) for several reasons:

- It denied that there was any difference between actions that were intended and those that were foreseen but not intended.
- If right and wrong are to be decided purely by outcomes, then where does ends–means justification stop? Anscombe was appalled at the use of the atomic bomb on Nagasaki and Hiroshima on these grounds.
- Motives or intentions are vital to understanding human behaviour and responsibility, yet consequentialism gives little or no importance to them.
- If it is true that right and wrong are to be judged by the consequences of decisions, we don't need to be consistent in our choices or lives. Whilst consistency isn't an intrinsic good, if everyone works purely on a consequentialist basis, ethics becomes more inconsistent and has few enduring or basic values and principles.

In summary, think of Natural Law as a deontological theory, and teleological only in sense (a), but of Utilitarianism as teleological in sense (b).

SECTION I

NORMATIVE ETHICAL THEORIES: RELIGIOUS APPROACHES

CHAPTER

1 Natural Law

LEARNING OUTCOMES

To discuss issues raised by Aquinas' theory of Natural Law, including

- *telos*
- the four tiers of law
- the precepts
- whether or not Natural Law provides a helpful method of moral decision-making
- whether or not a judgement about something being good, bad, right or wrong can be based on its success or failure in achieving its *telos*
- whether or not the universe as a whole is designed with a *telos*, or human nature has an orientation towards the good
- whether or not the doctrine of double effect can be used to justify an action, as in killing someone as an act of self-defence

Malala Yousafzai. When the Taliban occupied the Swat Valley in Pakistan and attempted to ban girls from attending school, through writing a blog on the BBC website, Malala became an activist campaigning for her right to an education. After threats intended to silence her, on 9 October 2012, a gunman asked her name, then fired three shots at her from his pistol. **The Taliban gunman had force, so why did they fear Malala speaking out? Article 26 of the UN Declaration of Human Rights states that everyone has the right to an education. Are rights invented or self-evidently true?**

Malala Yousafzai in 2014

Law and justice

Do you have a moral duty to disobey unjust laws?
What gives law its authority?

Whenever we ask questions like 'What gives laws their legitimacy?', 'Do we have a duty to disobey unjust laws?', or 'Is there an objective standard (e.g. human reason or God) by which we can judge good and evil?', we are drawn into an age-old discussion of Natural Law. In ancient Greece, the Stoics used the term 'logos' to mean the ordering principle of the universe. Ethics was objectively grounded in the very nature of reality. Natural law was a kind of universal moral gravity. Socrates had paid the ultimate price for his belief in the just rule of law – he had accepted the unjust death sentence of an Athenian court. Determined not to accept an offer from friends to bribe guards to secure his escape, he refused to undermine the rule of Athenian law which he had spent his life advocating, even when its unjust judgement went against him. For Socrates and Plato, politics was a form of social ethics. The laws and judgements of Athenian courts were just insofar as they conformed to the eternal form of justice. Their unjust judgement on his teacher and mentor Socrates was to trigger Plato's lifelong quest for the eternal and universal justice by which such travesties could themselves be judged.

Plato (429–347 BCE), whose name may result from the width (*platos*) of his shoulders, was from a noble family who had political and poetic ambitions for him. Instead, he opted for philosophy and became a devoted pupil of Socrates, whose unjust death sentence at the hands of the Athenian court in 399 caused him to leave Athens. He was motivated to seek the perfect form of justice and attempted to train philosopher-kings who could implement this. Socrates speaks in most of Plato's dialogues and it is hard to distinguish the thought of one from the other. Plato founded the Academy, a school of philosophy in Athens. This is seen as the first university and it sought unchanging truth, Mathematics being central to this quest as it offered knowledge unspoilt by the changing physical world. For this reason, Plato placed the command 'let no-one ignorant of geometry enter here' above the entrance to his Academy. His work the *Republic* has a claim to being the most important political text in history. It sees politics as a form of social ethics and advocates the making of virtuous citizens through education. For Plato, defining ethical concepts clearly has a practical bearing on our lives. The questions he raised and his influence on Christian, Jewish and Islamic thought, not to mention Western philosophy and politics, led Alfred North Whitehead to comment that European philosophy is 'a series of footnotes to Plato'.

Developing this tradition in his *Nicomachean Ethics* (*NE*), the Greek philosopher Aristotle distinguished between *legal* justice and *natural* justice, 'which everywhere has the same force and does not exist by people's thinking this or that'. The Roman lawyer Cicero saw Roman laws as legitimate not because they were set down or 'posited' by authorities like the senate or emperor, but because they were grounded in a universal 'natural law' by which not only Roman citizens, but all humanity, were bound. In *De Republica*, he writes,

'True law is right reason in agreement with nature. It is applied universally and is unchanging and everlasting . . . there will be no different laws in Rome and in Athens, or different laws now and in the future, but one eternal and unchangeable law will be valid for all nations and all times.'

Natural Law is also evident in Paul's statement in Romans 2:14–16:

'When Gentiles, who do not have the Law, do by nature things required by the Law, they are a law for themselves, even though they do not have the Law, since they show the requirements of the Law are written on their hearts, their consciences bearing witness, and their thoughts now accusing, now excusing them.'

What do you think Paul meant by the above statement?   **N.B.** Gentiles are non-Jews

Moving on from the first century to the eighteenth, the opening line of the American Declaration of Independence refers to 'the Laws of Nature and of Nature's God' in grounding inalienable human rights: 'We hold these truths to be self-evident, that all men are created equal, that they are endowed by their Creator with certain unalienable Rights, that among these are Life, Liberty and the pursuit of Happiness.' The idea of a universal moral law appeared to be 'self-evident' though this may have owed much to the widely held belief in God.

Do you think this is a less 'self-evident' belief in today's world?

This belief in Natural Law and rights is a tradition that Martin Luther King drew on in his 1962 'Letter from a Birmingham Jail' in arguing that:

There are two types of laws: just and unjust. One has not only a legal but a moral responsibility to obey just laws. Conversely, one has a moral responsibility to disobey unjust laws. We should never forget that everything Adolf Hitler did in Germany was 'legal'. I submit that an individual who breaks a law that conscience tells him is unjust, and who willingly accepts the penalty of imprisonment in order to arouse the conscience of the community over his injustice, is in reality expressing the highest respect for law. . . . How does one determine whether a law is just or unjust? A just law is a man-made code that squares with the moral law or the law of God. An unjust law is a code that is out of harmony with the moral law. To put it in terms of St. Thomas Aquinas; an unjust law is a human law that is not rooted in eternal law and natural law.

Martin Luther King (1929–68) was an American clergyman and a leader in the African American civil rights movement. He led protests against segregation on buses in Montgomery in 1955 and confronted the brutal police of Birmingham, Alabama, with non-violent protests to focus national attention on the injustices of racial discrimination and segregation. King was an electrifying orator who said in his 'I have a dream' speech to over 250,000 in Washington (1963), 'When the architects of our republic wrote the magnificent words of the Constitution and the Declaration of Independence, they were signing a promissory note ... that all men - yes, black men as well as white men - would be guaranteed the unalienable rights of life, liberty, and the pursuit of happiness. It is obvious today that America has defaulted on this promissory note insofar as her citizens of color are concerned ... But we refuse to believe that the bank of justice is bankrupt.' In 1964, he received the Nobel Peace Prize and, in 1968, Congress was to pass the Civil Rights Act before his assassination on 29 March of the same year.

How might the language of MLK's words above be said to draw on an appeal to a moral law from which national laws gained their legitimacy and authority? What is it that makes rights unalienable (they can't be bought, sold or transferred), if it is not that they are 'endowed by the creator'?

Understanding Aquinas' Natural Law theory – four types of law

Aquinas' response to the kinds of questions asked at the start of the chapter was to distinguish between four types of law: eternal law, divine law, natural law and human law. As we see below, he saw human laws as just, or actions rational, insofar as they participate in the eternal law of the creator.

Eternal law was the mind or reason of God. This could be seen only in terms of its effects in Natural Law and in 'moving all things to their due end' (*Summa Theologica* (*ST*)). The wisdom of God was reflected in his creation and sustaining of nature but could not be known directly by man.

Divine law was revealed in the laws and moral precepts of scripture, providing a corrective to the fallenness of man. Aquinas believed that human reason was not so impaired by the fall as to be unable to think rightly about ethics. The revelation of scripture and the worship of the Church supplemented our understanding of the divine purposes and motivated our moral life with an inspiring vision of divine perfection and holiness. Yet it was not exhaustive in directing our moral conduct or applying to all circumstances, and here, natural and human law both express and supplement divine law.

As Aquinas writes, 'the theologian considers sin principally as an offence against God, whereas the moral philosopher considers it as being contrary to reason' (*Summa Theologica*, Ia IIae, 71, 6, ad5).

Natural Law is innate to all of nature which is ordered by the divine lawmaker. Morality is reason thinking rightly in humans, who, by their innate knowledge and natural inclination, can discern primary goods which are worth pursuing for their own end. God has ordered nature with essences/inclinations suited towards their purpose or end goals. Innate to human minds is the synderesis rule (that good is to be done and evil avoided).

Human law. Aquinas was no anarchist. He sought to underpin respect for proper human law and authority that sought the common good. What begins in nature is, through custom and usefulness, established in human laws through practical reasoning and experienced judgement (*phronēsis*). There can be unjust laws that are not rooted in Natural Law. As he writes, 'if in any point it deflects from the law of nature, it is no longer a law but a perversion of law' (ST I–II, Q.95, A.II).

Exercises

1. The ancient Greek philosopher Protagoras wrote that 'man is the measure of all things'. In contrast, Aquinas wrote that a law bears the character of a measure and since measures should be accurate and certain and human reasoning is not certain, no law can arise out of human reason. Instead, it must be measured by its participation in the eternal law.

   Do you think laws against murder are based on objective moral rules or on the subjective thoughts of humans?

2. Aquinas claimed that slavery, though 'devised by human reason for the benefit of human life, did not alter 'the law of nature . . . except by addition'.

   What problems might arise from the fact that we think that slavery is immoral today and yet Aquinas accepted it within his system of Natural Law?

Aquinas' medieval synthesis of Aristotle and Augustine – what he learned from each

Aquinas saw Natural Law as 'nothing else than the rational creature's participation in the eternal law'. He *synthesised* the 'new' knowledge of Aristotle's system of thought with that of the Bible and Augustine at a time when many thought it incompatible. He saw faith and reason, philosophy and theology as a collaborative search for truth. Revelation had nothing to fear from the insights of reason. Fallen as it was, man's reason had not been so impaired as to make the ethical life impossible. In the two sections that follow, we shall explore what he learned from Aristotle and from Augustine.

Aristotle (384–322 BCE)
Aristotle's father was the physician to the king of Macedonia and, like many parents today, wanted his son to be a doctor too. From eighteen years of age, Aristotle studied at Plato's Academy in Athens. Through his connections, he became a personal tutor to a thirteen-year-old who would become Alexander the Great, and Aristotle was later to set up his own school, The Lyceum, in Athens in 334 BCE as he began to diverge from Plato and develop his own ideas. Following Plato's death, his nephew became head of his Academy, rather than Aristotle (perhaps because, as a non-citizen, the latter could not own property in Athens). Aristotle is seen as an early empiricist. He comes to base judgements more on sense perceptions than pure reason, studying biology and classifying types of objects in the natural world. Where Plato's Academy had focused on subject matters like Geometry or the harmonics of sound, Aristotle was more practical, performing dissections (his father may have given him some lessons in medicine, even surgical technique) and categorising knowledge in a more systematic way. In some ways a precursor to science, though his findings here – more than his method – are obsolete, his writings on ethics, rhetoric and politics remain influential today.

In the Early Middle Ages, Muslim scholars had translated or preserved Aristotle's ancient-Greek writings in Arabic/Aramaic. The recovery of forty-two books where there had previously been two caused controversy. When these works differed from the Church's teaching on a personal God, an immortal soul or creation, some censorship occurred. In his *Summa Theologica* (1265–74), however, Aquinas sought to synthesise Aristotle with the Christian tradition.

From Aristotle, Aquinas learned that . . .

Nature is goal directed

Telos:
The goal or end purpose of anything. All of nature is seen in Aristotle's thought as directed towards a final end – as goal-orientated.

As Aristotle writes, 'Nature makes nothing without a purpose' (in his treatise *On the Soul*). Drawing on Aristotle's teleology, Aquinas believed that God's eternal law had so devised the natural world and its creatures that they possessed a natural tendency to pursue the behaviour and goals appropriate to the natures he had given them. An acorn's purpose or end goal (*telos*) is to grow into an oak tree, and an oak tree flourishes with growth and produces more acorns. A 'good' eagle is one whose attributes (eyesight, talons, wing-span, strength) make it a supreme predator.

Aquinas' goal-orientated or teleological view of nature drew on Aristotle's account of the four causes.

For Aristotle, nature was directed towards an end – it was teleological (*telos* = goal/ end). We need to pay attention to our nature or form, the second kind of cause. We are bodily, social and rational beings, so it follows that we should ask after the goals and habits that allow our potential to be fully actualised. Aristotle uses the word *kalon* meaning beautiful/good in respect of good acts or habits that allow us to realise fully our essential nature. Attending to our purpose or end goals relates to the third and fourth causes. The 'good life' (**eudaimonia** refers to the good or flourishing life) is to be spent training our habits and desires (in some sense, the efficient cause of character growth in virtue) to the rational end of flourishing rather than stunting our development (final cause).

1 Material cause (matter)	What is it made of? Marble	
2 Formal cause (form)	What are its characteristics? Sculpted marble in human form.	
3 Efficient cause (source)	What brought it about? Sculpted by Michelangelo	
4 Final cause (purpose)	To depict the biblical king/ make money	

Seeing the four cases in Michelangelo's *David*

Aristotle held a goal-orientated or teleological view of nature. The potential of every object or being in the material world was fulfilled when directed towards its proper purpose or end. The unmoved mover was the ultimate cause, everything else was moving arrowlike to its intended target.

Aristotle would agree with the warning that sometimes appears on TV – 'Do not try this at home on your own!'; how do you develop virtues like generosity or justice, humility or compassion on your own? We need families, communities, even states, to thrive in and fully express our natures.

For Aristotle, the supreme expression of the final cause of nature was the unmoved mover. As the highest conceivable good, God's being was fully actualised – perfectly fulfilled potential. In contrast to the divine, the natural world was constantly changing and full of potential – for example, infants have the potential to grow into adults. Nature is dynamic and Aristotle argued that nature's order, beauty and goodness were not due to mere chance. Nature was, in its essence and inclination, directed towards ends and purposes that fulfilled its potential. There was *logos* or a rational principle (for Aquinas this was the mind of God) ordering nature.

Humans possess a rational soul that can recognise God's law

The soul was the essence of a thing for Aristotle. Within it was contained the potentiality for growth or the actualisation of its essence. The essence of man was his rational soul. The rational soul was able to intuit the Natural Law. Thought and intellect are what set mankind apart as being capable of contemplation in art, maths and science, and as possessing the capacity to will goals and train their habits. Here Aristotle distinguished between the three kinds of soul shown in the table.

1 The soul of material things	2 The soul of animals	3 The soul of humans
Vegetative	Appetitive	Rational mind (nous)
(Potential for nutrition, growth and reproduction)	((1) + potential for sensation, movement, reproduction and training of offspring)	((1, 2) + potential for practical and theoretical reasoning and intellectual and moral virtues (the latter being the ordering of the will through habitual training to govern the appetites), and for worshipping God)

True happiness or flourishing (*eudaimonia*) is bound up with a virtuous life

Eudaimonia:
The good life – flourishing, fulfilment and happiness in a holistic sense – the flourishing of any form of life aimed at actualising its full potential

Aquinas saw that we desire happiness and that it is often realised in the fulfilment of our true potential. The highest of goals 'is always desirable in itself, and never for the sake of something else' (*NE* 1.7). For Aristotle, true fulfilment of human potential (*eudaimonia*) came in the pursuit of excellence (*arête*) in terms of moral and intellectual virtues. His *Nicomachean Ethics* was either edited by or dedicated to his son (Nicomachus), and drew together his notes from his school, the Lyceum. It taught the *interconnectedness of virtue and happiness*. The life well lived was dedicated to the fulfilment of the highest intellectual and moral virtues, for virtue is its own reward. In flourishing as a rational, social and moral being, it is our faculty of reason that most closely connects us with the divine, therefore 'We must . . . strain every nerve in order to live in accordance with the best thing in us' (*NE* 10.7). The paradox is that self-actualisation cannot be selfish. Our soul's good cannot be fulfilled with 'selfish' desire. The *polis* or peaceful and harmonious ordering of communities like the Greek city state of Athens is fundamental to the thriving of each citizen. So politics is really a form of social ethics. Through experience and practice, as well as by working with wise teachers, we develop the practical wisdom (*phronēsis*) to make wise judgements in any given situation.

Arête:
Virtue, or any good characteristic or excellence. *Arête* involves committed and purposeful training and practice usually under the tutelage of a master-practitioner.

From Augustine, Aquinas learned that. . .

Human nature and reason are corrupted by the Fall

As is evident from his *Confessions*, Augustine is very aware of the fallenness of human nature which, without divine grace, is incapable of living up to its own standards let alone God's, or of earning its own salvation. He drew on St Paul who wrote that 'what I do is not the good I want to do; no, the evil I do not want to do – this I keep on doing' (Romans 7:19). Evil is a privation of good, a falling short of the flourishing life. The problem here is that our will is moved not only by reason, but also by our desires – by

Augustine (354–430 BCE)
Augustine became Bishop of Hippo and remains the single most influential Christian theologian in the West outside of the New Testament writers. His *Confessions* offer a spiritual autobiography of striking insight and honesty. After a fairly hedonistic lifestyle, in his late twenties, he lived with a woman by whom he had a son, and he admits in his *Confessions* to God that, 'I delayed from day to day the conversion to you . . . even while I sought for it. I thought that I would be miserable if I were kept from a woman's arms.' Such quotes are taken by many to advocate virginity and take a low view of sex, starting a long tradition of guilt associated with sexuality. Yet it may be that Augustine's relationship had been with a freed slave, in which case the law would have forbidden him, as a Roman Citizen, from marrying her.

Augustine saw God as the source of all goodness and of no evil, but human nature, like the natural world, had a tendency to decay and to fall away from its eternal creator. Such is the corruption of the human will to obey divine commands that, without the assistance of God's grace, humankind would be powerless to fulfil them.

our loves. So, for Augustine, the moral life is not simply a question of knowing what makes for the flourishing life. It is also one of confession, divine grace and habitual training in virtue. We can see Augustine's influence in Aquinas' highlighting of *seven vices* (later termed deadly sins) – pride, greed, lust, envy, gluttony, anger and sloth, which corrupt the capacity of our reason to know the Natural Law.

Mankind's proper end is a harmonious relationship with his creator God

As Augustine famously put it, 'Thou hast made us for Thyself, O Lord, and our hearts are restless until they rest in Thee' (*Confessions*, ch. 1). For Augustine, the Fall has obscured humankind's vision of God. Despite this, reason and free will have not been lost. Here, the theological virtues of faith, hope and charity/love allow us to flourish fully in an ethical way in directing us to our ultimate end – *union with God given to us by his grace*. Aquinas sees that the cardinal virtues of temperance, wisdom, justice and courage will need to be transposed onto a higher level by the theological virtues of faith, hope and charity/love. As he puts it, 'Temperance is love keeping itself entire and incorrupt for God; fortitude is love bearing everything readily for God's sake; justice is love serving God only and therefore ruling all else well; prudence is love distinguishing between what helps it towards God and what might hinder it' (*On the morals of the Catholic Church*, XV). Moral virtues lead us to God as the source behind Natural Law and our ultimate end. As C. S. Lewis put it, 'The human mind has no more power of inventing a new value than of imagining a new primary colour, or, indeed, of creating a new sun and a new sky for it to move in' (Lewis, *The Abolition of Man*, Clarendon Press, 1943). Yet mankind's imperfect happiness and fulfilment in this life were an indication that our souls were created for another life beyond death. This should direct our reason to the heavenly and eternal beatific vision of God as the ultimate source and satisfaction of human desire.

Aquinas' *Summa Theologica* became a central text in European universities of the Middle Ages. Here we consider several key terms in his work.

Thomas Aquinas (1225–1274)

Thomas Aquinas, the most significant theologian/philosopher of the medieval period, was canonised (declared a saint by the Catholic Church) in 1323. Born in a castle to the Count of Aquino, his family were bitterly opposed to him becoming a Dominican friar (a monk devoted to study). They had ambitions for him to rise to a powerful position in the Church. His brothers are even said to have kidnapped him, keeping him for more than a year in the family castle. Having begun his studies aged five at the Abbey of Montecassino, he went to the University of Naples and then entered the Dominican Order. Nicknamed the 'dumb ox', perhaps because of his size and possibly his weight, his academic flair soon became evident. At his death aged no more than fifty, he had penned around 8 million words in commentaries and works of natural theology. His *Summa Theologica* was to synthesise the scientific reason of Aristotle (on whose works Aquinas had written commentaries) with Christian teaching on faith and scripture. He wanted to integrate revelation and human reason and see them as compatible. Many truths (including knowledge of the existence of God and the moral law) can be arrived at through human reason and logic, independent of revelation. Thomism (the name for his school of thought) still remains central to Roman Catholic theology and ethics.

The Synderesis Principle

The Synderesis Principle 'that good should be done and evil avoided' (*ST* II, I, 94 art. 2) is innately known by our conscience. According to Aquinas, this is our inner knowledge of and natural disposition towards doing good and avoiding evil – one that is innate – a natural disposition of humans to understand the first principles of morality. For Aquinas, all creation is ordered by God's eternal law and each part of it expresses its essential nature in its inclination towards the Natural Law. For example, a 'flourishing' eagle is an efficient predator. As rational creatures, human beings possess reason and free will. Reason directs us towards our proper ends and the actions that lead to them.

The distinction between real and apparent goods

Aquinas distinguishes between real goods (which direct us to the happiness or flourishing that results from fulfilling our essential natures in accordance with the precepts of the Natural Law), and apparent goods (where a lack of practical judgement or virtue misdirects our actions towards ends that we mistakenly take to be good). One example he offers is 'A fornicator seeks a pleasure which involves him in moral guilt' (*Summa Theologica*, 1a, 19, 9). What is sinful here is that the fornicator who engages in sexual intercourse with an unmarried woman pursues pleasure as an end in itself. For Aquinas, the proper end of sexual intercourse is reproduction and, should a pregnancy occur as a result of fornication, the father may avoid his responsibilities as a parent. Real goods direct us towards the proper ends that preserve and promote the flourishing of human nature.

Pleasure is not a primary good, and the pleasure paradox is that if we make it an end in itself, it recedes from us, as anyone who's eaten too much chocolate will know. Humans naturally incline towards courses of action in which 'good is to be done and pursued and evil to be avoided'; few intentionally and wholeheartedly pursue evil ends, yet we may choose a bad action under the appearance of a good one. Examples would be wilfully doing evil so that good may come of it (e.g. giving a terminally ill patient a lethal injection to end their suffering) yet breaking the Primary Precept of preserving life.

Primary and Secondary Precepts and how they are derived

Primary Precepts concern the goals towards which human action gravitates (e.g. the preservation of life). These are absolute and universal principles that are self-evident and express natural human inclinations. Aquinas sees natural human inclinations as directing us to certain precepts:

> **Primary Precepts:** Arrived at by observing the goals towards which human action tends to gravitate

- to preserve life and health
- to live in an ordered society
- to worship God
- to learn and seek truth and educate offspring
- to reproduce.

Secondary Precepts are derived from Primary Precepts through practical reasoning and consider what ought to be done in a more specific way. Primary Precepts are descriptive of natural inclinations, whereas secondary ones are prescriptive, having the force of a duty or command. Primary Precepts are absolute and universal, whereas secondary ones can vary widely based on the circumstances of time or place. For example, how in practice, we educate or look after our health has varied greatly according to time and place. Examples of Secondary Precepts may be seen below:

> **Secondary Precepts:** These make Primary Precepts normative in terms of what ought to be done (e.g. provision of shelter, healthcare, protection for the vulnerable). Through practical knowledge, the primary goods come to be applied.

Do not legalise euthanasia.
Education ought not to be denied to people on the grounds of wealth or gender.
Do not waste your opportunities to learn by being lazy.
Obey just laws and authorities.
Work for the common good of your community and society.

Phronēsis – practical reasoning and judgement

To understand how these primary goods come to be applied, we need to grasp Aristotle's distinction between theoretical and practical knowledge. Theoretical knowledge is abstract and intellectual, but practical reason, wisdom or judgement (***phronēsis***) is necessary if we are to avoid being unduly swayed by our passions and do the right things for the right reasons at the right time. Such practical wisdom develops through virtuous habits that dispose us to act rationally; right reason must be married to right desire. Aquinas defines virtue as 'a good habit bearing on activity', so a combination of reason, virtuous inclination and conscience together help us to arrive at practical judgements in the specific cases. The virtues strengthen our practical rationality – for example, prudence and temperance inform our judgements and train us to desire the right things.

> ***Phronēsis:*** Practical judgement or wisdom generally built up through experience and observation, and seen in judgements that find the mean or middle course between deficiency and excess

Motives matter – the distinction between exterior and interior acts

Aquinas makes another distinction between interior acts (intentions or motives) and exterior acts (actions). A kind act (e.g. giving alms for charity) may be motivated by a wholly selfish intent (for vainglory or to buy favour or obligation). As rational creatures, we are responsible for both our desires and our motives according to Aquinas. The intention that wills the act determines whether it is good or evil. Exterior acts can be evil in themselves, such as adultery or theft, but as Jesus identifies in the Sermon on the Mount, the rightness of a deed or act springs from the inner motive – 'he who looks at a woman lustfully has already committed adultery with her in his heart' (Matthew 5:28).

The Doctrine of Double Effect

In the *Summa Theologica*, Aquinas addresses the problem of killing in self-defence. In using force when faced with life-threatening violence, a person both upholds and goes against the Primary Precept of preserving life. Aquinas addresses such cases in which the harmful effects are part and parcel of the good effect, by paying attention to the motives involved. Four criteria are set down to establish this:

The act to be done must be good in itself or at least indifferent.
The good effect must not be obtained by means of the bad effect.
The bad effect must not be intended for itself, only permitted.
There must be a proportionately grave reason for permitting the bad effect.

We will look at this principle in more detail in the chapters on abortion and euthanasia.

Proportionalism – a revision of Natural Law, or consequentialism creeping into it?

The more absolute character of Natural Law can appear to lead to harsh and unbending decisions. Yet it has a long tradition of casuistry (taking general moral principles and considering how best to apply them to particular cases). A controversial example of this type of thinking is seen in **Proportionalism** (a view popularised by Bernard Hoose in a book of the same title and also by Richard McCormick). This position is seen as a kind of middle way between consequentialism and deontological ethics. In unavoidable circumstances where both good and evil will result from an action, the proportion between the two is weighed in choosing the lesser of two evils.

Some examples of Proportionalism may be seen in Just War theory, in which violence may be used to bring about peaceful ends, or in a case where the theft of food would prevent starvation from hunger (both of which Aquinas sanctions). Hoose extends this. In ectopic pregnancies, for example, the embryo mostly implants in the fallopian tube. If this ruptures, internal bleeding could result in the death of the mother, whilst lasering the embryo would destroy it without threatening her future fertility. Hoose argues for this as the lesser of two evils, a proportionate response. The treatment is being done with the primary intention of saving life but in full knowledge that it would go against the Primary Precept of preserving life (in terms of the embryo). Here certain goods of character, such as dignity, integrity or justice, are being served. For Proportionalists, this is not consequentialist reasoning but the application of Natural Law in practical reasoning to bring about a proportionate good as opposed to the cruel inflexibility of exceptionless laws. The Catholic Church has, however, condemned proportionalism as a form of consequentialism (see the encyclicals *Veritatis Splendor* (*The Splendour of Truth*, 1993, s. 75), and *Evangelium Vitae* (*The Gospel of Life*, 1995, art. 68).

Exercise

Write out the terms opposite on a series of cards. In 1 minute, describe or define them without mentioning the actual word on the card. See how many correct terms your fellow students can come up with.

The final cause
The efficient cause
The eternal law
Natural Law
Real and apparent goods
The Synderesis Principle
Phronēsis
Arêté
Eudaimonia
Interior and exterior acts
Primary Precepts
Secondary Precepts
The Doctrine of Double Effect
Proportionalism

Criticisms of Natural Law theory

Evolutionary science has led to a widespread rejection of final causes or purpose in nature

It may be argued that Aquinas' thirteenth-century belief in nature as purposive and goal-orientated becomes obsolete after Darwin. In *On the Origin of Species* (1859), Darwin argued that nature evolved in the competition for survival. Natural selection is the blind watchmaker – unsighted and uncaring. So whilst Aristotle's knowledge may have been new in Aquinas' day, the idea that we can see in nature that the essence of everything is ordered to a purpose or goal by the unmoved mover is by no means obvious in modern science.

The Fact–Value Gap

Natural Law attempts to move from the facts about the essential nature of the world to values about how we ought to live in it: from descriptions of the essential nature of things in the world to prescriptions about how we ought to act or behave. For David Hume, there is a gap between these two types of statement. We simply do not 'see' moral facts. The factual statement 'People lie' is different from the value judge-ment 'You ought to tell the truth.' As James Rachels puts it, 'It may be that sex does produce babies, but it does not follow that sex ought or ought not to be engaged in only for that purpose. Facts are one thing, values are another' (Rachels 2006, p. 52). Take the use of Natural Law theory to condemn homosexuality on the grounds that the natural order of sexual relations is heterosexual and open to reproduction. Can what is 'good' be identified as being 'natural' without begging the question 'Is what is natural good?' We may observe that 'the function of the eye is to see', but the state-ment that 'the function of human sexuality is reproduction' seems to make a moral judgement when it involves ruling out barrier methods of contraception as contrary to nature.

The list of basic human goods varies across time and cultures

The atheist philosopher Kai Nielsen dismisses Aquinas' out-dated view of a fixed or essential human nature. In his view, Natural Law theory is to be rejected along with medieval physics and cosmology. Science, history and anthropology dismiss the idea of a single human nature common to humankind across time and place. Aquinas saw homosexuality as unnatural, and yet it is observable in non-human animals.

Cultural anthropology shows us just how variable human values and goods turn out to be. The prohibition on usury (interest on loans) was praised in a feudal age when the aristocratic class rarely borrowed, but with the increasing wealth of finan-ciers and industrialists, the prohibition on usury ended. Some recent Natural Law scholars have even added marriage as a basic good.

Its absolutism leads to negative consequences

Utilitarians believe that they can weigh basic goods against one another on the scales of pleasure and pain. While we may be tempted to find the foundations for human rights in Natural Law, morality seems far from rooted in self-evident natural princi-ples that are universally agreeable. In particular, Natural Law's aversion to making moral decisions based on consequences (except in the **Doctrine of Double Effect**) makes decision-making in dilemmas very difficult to calculate. Utilitarians are far happier to weigh conflicting goods on the scales of pleasure and pain and steel themselves as they trade off compassion against promise-keeping, or preserving life against truth-telling, in achieving the best outcome. Modern citizens generally approach ethical theories from the angle 'What should I do in this dilemma?' rather than 'How do I pursue a flourishing and worthwhile life?'

The Doctrine of Double Effect and Proportionalism recognise the serious dangers of principles or rules that can lead to greater suffering. With the world population at 7 billion and rising fast, if every life has to be preserved, and not only abortion but also contraception are forbidden, this can lead to overpopulation, suffering and poverty. An absolutist view of the Primary Precept of life (its preservation and reproduction) can lead to policies that do little to address the spread of HIV/AIDS or the suffering of the dying. If the promotion of contraception rather than sexual abstinence were undertaken, the spread of HIV could be lessened. If euthanasia were legalised, many terminally ill patients could be granted an end to pain which is, in their view, unbearable and pointless. Of course such logic runs counter to the absolutism of the Primary Precepts.

Natural Law theory is too closely allied to the Roman Catholic Church

The Catholic Church's justification for viewing abortion, euthanasia, contraception and IVF as morally wrong, as well as the emphasis on marriage as a basic good, is rooted in Natural Law thinking. As Peter Singer comments, Natural Law is 'The semi-official philosophy of the Roman Catholic Church to this day' (*Practical Ethics*, p. 243). The papal encyclicals on the ethics of the sanctity of life – see *Humanae Vitae* (*Human Life*; 1968), *Veritatis Splendor* (*The Splendour of Truth*, 1993), and *Evangelium Vitae* (*The Gospel of Life*; 1995) – are all based on Natural Law principles. While some secular thinkers are drawn to it (e.g. the philosopher Jeffrey Stout at Princeton), others, such as Singer, are suspicious that it is a veiled attempt to present Church teachings as common sense.

A theological objection: the fallen reason of mankind is not free and it is optimistic to think that it naturally inclines to doing good and avoiding evil or that it only goes wrong when mistakenly aiming at apparent rather than real goods

Drawing on Augustine, the protestant theologians Karl Barth and Reinhold Niebuhr questioned the faith that Aquinas' Natural Law placed in the moral reasoning of fallen human beings. Aquinas believed that, despite the fall, mankind retained an innate tendency to do good and avoid evil (the *Synderesis* Principle) and morality was reason thinking rightly.

Niebuhr argued that it is not simply the virtue of love that was corrupted at the fall, but also human justice and free will. Human beings are creatures made in the image of God. Yet they are also sinners, as is taught in Calvin's doctrine of total depravity. Reason's powers to discern good from evil are corrupted by pride and self-interest.

Karl Barth saw Natural Law as man seeking autonomy or independence from God's commands. Barth's friend, the German theologian Dietrich Bonhoeffer, even argued that ethics, or knowledge of good and evil, began at the fall. He believed that ethics represented an attempt to become our own creators, separate from God, and to know right from wrong not in relation to God but autonomously from him. In this view, ethics ought to reconnect with God, and emphasise the need for divine grace through Christ's atoning death, the revelation of scripture, and the Holy Spirit's inner work in convincing the conscience and renewing the will.

Karl Barth (1886–1968)

Karl Barth was a Swiss-German theologian who wrote *The Barmen Declaration* (1934), the Confessing Church's rejection of Nazism and its attempt to control the state church. He refused to sign the oath of allegiance to Hitler and had to leave his German lectureship in Bonn to take up one in his native Switzerland (in Basel). He saw nineteenth-century liberal theology, biblical studies and philosophy of religion as accommodating God's mystery to natural reason and thereby taming and domesticating God. Modern man sought to 'bolt and bar himself against revelation'. Yet, for Barth, apart from God's revelation in Christ's incarnation and through scripture and his Spirit, God remained wholly other. He agreed with Kierkegaard about the 'infinite qualitative distinction between God and mankind'. That so many of his highly educated university teachers and peers should capitulate so easily to the Nazi regime revealed for Barth just how accommodated they were to the spirit of the age. Barth believed that any capacity he and his fellow-theologian Dietrich Bonhoeffer had to see the idolatry of the Nazi state and Hitler came through attention to the 'strange new world of scripture', which revealed the divine command and named the injustices of the day for what they were.

Exercise

Which of the six criticisms of Natural Law theory do you find the most serious challenges to the theory? Choose three and explain why you have chosen them.

Taking it further: the revival of Natural Law
John Finnis (1940–), Germain Grisez (1929–)

With all of the above objections, it might look as though Natural Law is indefensible today. Yet the work of several thinkers has led to a revival of this theory in a form that meets many of these criticisms. Aquinas' approach to Natural Law said 'This is your essential human nature – now be who you are.' This tends to produce an ethic that is conformist and heavy on 'Do not' precepts, focusing on laws not persons. By contrast, the new Natural Law theorists accept Hume's distinction between 'fact' and 'value' statements. They work inductively through practical reasoning, first identifying basic goods that make for human flourishing, then applying these to specific circumstances.

Princeton Law professor Robert George has also argued that the foundations of legal theory cannot simply rest on legal positivism (the view that law rests on the authority of society/ its legislators rather than upon any necessary connection with morality).

The philosopher John Finnis

Table 2   Natural Law theory: the pros and cons

Pros	Cons
• It has a long tradition over many cultures – Jewish, Greek, Roman, etc. It can also provide a basis for dialogue in a multicultural society. It points to what is common to human nature and seeks an orderly society and world.	• Evolutionary science has rejected final causes and goal-orientated purposes in nature.
• It is based on reason and does not require scriptural revelation or laws. Just by using practical reasoning and observation of what activities human nature inclines towards, most of the Primary Precepts are clear and the Secondary ones derivable.	• The fact–value gap. Natural Law is guilty of leaping from descriptions of the essential nature of things in the world (facts) to prescriptions about how they ought to act or behave (values).
• It offers a foundation for law that gives it legitimacy and can account for why certain actions are universally and intrinsically wrong, e.g. torture. This allows for moral judgements to transcend cultural differences. The UN Declaration of Human Rights expresses this universality and absolute nature of ethics.	• The list of basic goods varies across time and culture.
• It is morally realist and offers a basis for universal moral principles. If one assumes there to be a fixed human nature and eternal moral law built into the universe, then the fact–value distinction can be rejected.	• Natural Law theory is too closely allied to the Catholic Church. Why should secular minds accept traditional sources of moral authority? They claim that the idea of a fixed essence to human nature and morality is used to argue for arbitrary limits to human freedom.
• It offers a holistic account of character, intentions and actions as well as finding a natural harmony between community and co-operative practice over individualism.	• Protestant theologians have questioned Aquinas' belief in the natural inclination of human nature to do good and avoid evil. Is Natural Law too optimistic about the human capacity to act morally under its own reason and not solely by divine grace?

In his view, it is crucial to guarantee human rights with a more secure moral foundation than that they are currently agreed by the powers that be.

Finnis usefully develops the idea of **phronēsis** in nine principles of practical reasoning to offer a clearer idea of how to move from Primary Precepts (what he calls basic goods) to Secondary Precepts.

1. *Good* is to be done and evil avoided in a purposeful and rational way. Have a life plan and pursue it with commitment of time, energy and resources.
2. Do not discount as of no value or *exaggerate* any of the basic human goods.
3. Be *impartial* in dealing with others and do not discount or exaggerate the value of other people's participation in human goods.

4. Avoid becoming fanatical about your own projects – keep a sense of *perspective* and be able to detach yourself from your immediate goals and see wider perspectives.
5. Be creative and committed, and think about the *consequences* of your actions.
6. Be *efficient* – do not waste opportunities or overlook foreseeable bad consequences of your choices. Material resources, time and energy are limited, so use them wisely.
7. Foster the *common* good of your community.
8. Do not justify going against any basic good by arguing that the *end* justifies the means.
9. Do not go against your *conscience*. For example, do not pursue apparent goods knowing them to be only the simulations of real goods even when they bring about real emotions or satisfactions.

Old Style Natural Law theory	Finnis–Grisez School of Natural Law theory
Logic is deductive. (from essential nature to action)	Logic is inductive. (from practical reason rather than human motives, urges and inclinations)
Heavy on prohibitions	Develops practical rationality to deal better with dilemmas
Conformist and too rigid	A rich and flexible understanding of the human good that moves from facts to values through practical reasoning.

FURTHER READING

Aristotle *Physics* II 3

Thomas Aquinas *Summa Theologica* I-II 93–5

Peter Baron (2012) *Kant and Natural Law*. PushMe Press

Catechism of the Catholic Church 1954–1960

John Finnis (1979) *Natural Law and Natural Rights*. Clarendon Press

Robert P. George (2009) *In Defence of Natural Law*. Oxford University Press

Stanley J. Grenz (1997) *The Moral Quest*. Apollos, IVP

James Rachels (2002) *The Elements of Moral Philosophy*. McGraw-Hill

Stanford Encyclopedia of Philosophy (2005, rev. 2011) 'Aquinas' Moral, Political and Legal Philosophy', *http://plato.stanford.edu/entries/aquinas-moral-political/*

Peter and Charlotte Vardy (2012) *Ethics Matters*. SCM Press, ch. 5

Thought Points

(1) Do you agree that the strengths of Natural Law outweigh its weaknesses?

(2) How could it be argued that Natural Law theory is not useful for solving ethical problems?

(3) Assess the strengths and weaknesses of Natural Law theory when it is applied to issues raised by sexual ethics.

(4) 'Natural Law has no serious weaknesses.' List reasons why some people might agree with this statement.

(5) Compare and contrast the views of Natural Law theorists with those of Situation ethicists on euthanasia.

(6) To what extent is Natural Law theory too rigid a theory to apply to discussions in sexual ethics?

(7) 'Whether a person is good or bad may be judged by their success or failure in achieving their telos.' Discuss this statement with your class.

(8) 'The Doctrine of Double Effect can justify active voluntary euthanasia.' List arguments for and against this statement.

CHAPTER

2 Situation Ethics

LEARNING OUTCOMES

To discuss issues raised by Fletcher's theory of Situation Ethics, including

- *agape*, the six principles
- the four working principles
- conscience
- whether or not Situation Ethics provides a helpful method of moral decision-making
- whether or not an ethical judgement about something being good, bad, right or wrong can be based on the extent to which, in any given situation, *agape* is best served
- whether Fletcher's understanding of *agape* is really religious or whether it means nothing more than wanting the best for the person involved in a given situation
- whether or not the rejection of absolute rules by Situation Ethics makes moral decision-making entirely individualistic and relativist

Is Christian ethics relativist or absolutist?

There is a story from the first century BCE of two leading Rabbis who interpreted the law very differently. It is said that a Gentile came to each of them asking them to teach him the whole Torah in the time he could stand on one foot. Rabbi Shamma drove him away with his measuring stick. By contrast, Rabbi Hillel converted the Gentile by telling him: 'That which is hateful to you, do not do to your neighbour. That is the whole Torah; the rest is commentary.'

Situation Ethics: A radical Christian-based Utilitarian moral theory, developed by Joseph Fletcher. The only absolute moral principle is to do 'the most loving thing in any situation'.

In the Sermon on the Mount, Jesus also opposes the harsh legalism of his day, suggesting that the spirit of the law is more to do with the true motives that lie behind actions than mere lip service obedience to the law. It is on this basis that more relativist interpretations of Christian ethics arise, one famous version being **Situation Ethics**.

Situation Ethics

In 1966, the Episcopalian priest Joseph Fletcher (who later became a professor of social ethics) wrote an 'explosive book' entitled *Situation Ethics: The New Morality*. In his controversial work, Fletcher set out 'act agapism' as a kind of Christian parallel to Act Utilitarianism in which love applies directly to situational judgements and not to rules. The morality of actions is to be judged on their consequences rather than on obedience to divine commands. Situationism's 'pragmatic–empirical temper' sees conscience as a verb instead of a noun, as the reason making moral judgements prior to a contextual decision rather than some mysterious inner faculty or external source (such as the Holy Spirit) which passes judgement after the event.

Fletcher's radical approach offered a third way between the *legalism* of rigid laws and absolute rules that often did more harm than good, on the one hand, and an irresponsible rejection of any moral law in *antinomianism* (*nomos* = 'law' in Greek) with its ad hoc approach threatening inconsistency and even moral anarchy, on the other. *Situationism* charted a middle course of 'principled relativism'. Fletcher spoke of the one law of *agape* ('selfless love'), drawing on the wisdom (*sophia*) of the Church and culture, and applying these in the *kairos* or moment of decision. Love decided 'then and there', using moral principles as 'rules of thumb'. His was a radically contextual ethic which worked empirically and inductively from the facts and circumstances of a particular case, building upon a minimal number of principles (four) and propositions (six).

These are:

Four working principles

Pragmatism
Drawing on the American pragmatists James, Dewey and Peirce, the focus of ethics should be on what works – that is, what brings about goodness, flourishing, or beneficial consequences. This is not about establishing universal rules or norms, but, in the specific context of a decision, to consider the *summum bonum* or highest good, which is the serving of love. Concrete rather than abstract decisions are informed by the facts of the situation and the likely consequences resulting from it.

Relativism
Absolute rules that prohibit ('Never do x'), or prescribe ('Always do y') are absent from Situation Ethics. Instead, all ethical judgements are relative to agapeic love. Yet, as Fletcher writes, Christian situationism 'relativizes the absolute, it does not absolutize the relative!' Fletcher sets out three polarities which are in tension in Christian ethics – law and love, authority and experience, and fixity and freedom. Seeing these in 'fruitful tension' and approaching moral decisions in humility is the way forward. The 'why' remains the same, whereas the 'what' and the 'how' may change depending on the circumstances.

Positivism
Following Hume, Fletcher acknowledges that the gap between facts and values means that 'We cannot verify moral choices. They may be vindicated, but not validated.' As in

Anselm's phrase 'I do not seek to understand in order that I may believe, but I believe in order that I may understand' (*Credo ut intelligam*), he considers value judgements in ethics to be a decision we commit to living by rather than a statement to be proven. The leap of faith Fletcher proposes is to regard love (*agape*) as an axiomatic value. Here he takes 1 John 1:4's 'God is love' to be defined in terms of God's love in Christ and our love as a response to this ('We love because he first loved us.' – 1 John 4:19). Such faith commitments are the essence of Christian ethics for Fletcher. Unlike natural theology's claim that reason underpins its beliefs, Fletcher sees such commitments as voluntary.

Personalism
We ought to put people, as opposed to objects, rules, authorities or tradition, at the heart of our value system. This draws on Martin Buber's distinction between I–it relationships (which can result in the use of people as objects or a means to an end) and I–thou relationships that are characterised by reverence and respect. As we are made in the image of a personal God, we should remember that 'things are to be used; people are to be loved'. For Fletcher, the Holy Spirit is present wherever love is at work in those of any faith or none. He quotes William Temple's statement that 'the atheist who is moved by love is moved by the spirit of God'.

Six propositions

1. Only love is intrinsically good. It is the 'regulative principle of Christian ethics' typified in the sacrificial and selfless death of Christ on the cross. To be known as Christ's disciple is to love one's neighbour, for, as Augustine says, 'in order to know whether a man is a good man one does not ask what he believes or what he hopes but how he loves' (quoted in Fletcher, *Situation Ethics*, Westminster John Knox Press, 1966, p. 63).
2. Love is the only ruling norm of Christian decision-making. Fletcher takes the collision between Jesus and the Pharisees to be over legalism – in particular, whether the love of God and one's neighbour are to govern the interpretation of all other laws. Jesus' disciples pluck grain on the Sabbath and fail to observe certain fast days, and he frequently touches those who are diseased and ritually unclean. Love governs his reading of the law. As Augustine put it, 'Love with care and then what you will, do' (p. 79).
3. Love and justice are the same, because justice is love distributed. Prudence and practical wisdom (*phronēsis*) are valued in the virtue tradition and Fletcher gives the example of a field commander who has to decide whether a platoon or company or even a regiment is expendable. Love is rational, not purely emotive – at times it carefully calculates the outcomes and distributions of good. Agapeic love is not 'one-to-one' but 'multi-lateral' in its love of all neighbours, and 'optimific' in a manner that sounds very much like Utilitarianism with its equal consideration of interests. Fletcher would respond by asserting that the agapeic calculus (the greatest amount of neighbour welfare for the largest number of neighbours possible) goes further than the Hedonic Calculus in its obligations to serve others. Furthermore, he argues that where laws are unjust (e.g. in the segregation laws), civil disobedience can be a duty of justice understood agapeically.

4. Love wills the neighbour's good whether we like him or not. Love should not be sentimentalised because *agape* is not *eros* (intimate or romantic love) or *phileo* (friendship) – forms of love in which we are attracted by our emotions and a reciprocity or benefit we gain from the relationship. *Agape* is benevolent in that it seeks to love its enemies and to will them good and not evil. Love can be hard-headed (as when 'a nurse in a military hospital deliberately makes wounded soldiers hate her enough to motivate them to get them on their feet again' or when a priest turns away beggars, for, as the *Didaché* (4:5) says, 'Do not be one who opens his hands to receive, or closes them when it is time to give').

5. Only the end justifies the means – this end is love. Legalism is prone to sticking to principles and rules out of a mistaken sense of duty far removed from the original intention behind the law. When nurses lie to schizophrenics to keep them calm for treatment or when Bonhoeffer rejected his pacifism to take part in the plot to assassinate Hitler, the end of love justified the means undertaken. Bonhoeffer happily takes on the Jesuitical maxim 'Finis sanctificat media' ('the end justifies or sanctifies the means'). Jesus legitimised King David taking the showbread from the temple in desperate circumstances (Matthew 12:4), unlawful as this was. Fletcher gives the example of a Romanian Jewish doctor who saved the lives of 3,000 pregnant Jewish women prisoners admitted to a concentration camp by aborting their embryos. Regardless of our view of abortion, the end of saving 3,000 lives justified this means.

6. Love's decisions are made situationally not prescriptively – it decides there and then. Law may offer security and limit the room for error that trusting human freedom over decisions might introduce. It may be that, as we do not know the future, decisions like Captain Scott's to stretcher an injured man from the South Pole, which may have cost him his life and that of his team, was the right one at the time. Equally, the choice of the seaman in charge of a lifeboat overloaded with seven crew and thirty-two passengers in 1941 to throw most of the males into the sea off Newfoundland resulted in his conviction for murder. As Fletcher writes, 'Situation ethics says it was bravely sinful, it was a good thing.' The universals of Situationism are love for God's sake and for one's neighbours. The '*kairos* factors' of the when, the where, the which, the how are down to the particulars of the dilemma.

The moral life – we are what we habitually do, or how to survive in a crisis

Fletcher sets out a case of sacrificial adultery in which a World War II German prisoner of war can only bring about her release from a Ukrainian prison camp by becoming pregnant by a Russian guard (pp. 164ff.). She takes this course of action as she urgently wishes to be reunited with her family and to bring up her three children (plus her newborn, Dietrich, who is loved more than the rest because he brought about her freedom). Fletcher asks us to consider whether Mrs Bergmeier has done the right thing. He relates that, after Dietrich's christening, she asks the same question of her Lutheran pastor.

It is said that extreme cases make bad law, and one criticism of Situation Ethics is that Fletcher's examples build a moral system around exceptional cases that do not properly characterise the moral life. Virtue ethicists would remind us that the moral life has far more to do with trained habits of practice and inclinations of character and will than with intermittent and extreme dilemmas. In another example, Fletcher asserts that an unmarried couple 'living together' who love each other are more pleasing to God than a couple whose marriage is characterised by conflict and mutual disdain. Offensive and unorthodox in 1966, such a view appeared to move too easily with the spirit of the age.

Situation Ethics and the individual conscience

Fletcher saw conscience as the work of moral reasoning rather than a faculty in our heads or a mysterious inner voice. It is a verb not a noun, and he took its literal meaning of 'knowing together' to refer to the kind of practical reasoning that takes account of consequences and acts creatively with love and justice towards those affected. It directs action (is antecedent to events) rather than being a kind of confession box in the mind after actions, reactive and passing judgement from a fixed rulebook. The problem with working from abstract ideals of behaviour as set out in absolute principles and rules is that the actual reality of human lives and circumstances is often complex and varied. Social or pastoral care workers can experience rules as harsh when rigidly applied to the marginalised and vulnerable without taking their individual circumstances into account.

As a verb, active and dynamic, the Situationist's conscience is able to avoid the either–or 'pseudo-problems' of justice vs love, or faith vs works. Rather, faith is love, and love is justice distributed. Fletcher quotes Paul Tillich who writes: 'love without justice is a body without backbone' (*Situation Ethics*, SCM Press, 1966, p. 94). Moral manuals full of fixed principles do not express agapeic love in action. Instead, it has a 'pragmatic–empirical temper' in Situation Ethics, and the Situationist's conscience 'keeps principles sternly in their place, in the role of advisors without veto power!' (1966, p. 55). Aside from loving God through the love of one's neighbour, there are 'only maxims, never rules' (ibid.)

Critics see the root meaning of conscience ('knowing together with') as pointing away from individual judgements in particular circumstances and towards moral knowledge being social. They question whether subjective individuals can wisely discern the right course of action without reference to rules and the collective understanding embodied in principles. In much the same way as Rule Utilitarians would critique Act Utilitarianism, they would suggest that if our moral compass were broken or inaccurate, consulting fixed standards would help. In ethicist Neil Messer's assessment, 'it seems fairly clear that he [Fletcher] more or less lifts a secular philosophical theory off the shelf in order to spell out what might be understood by Christian love' (*Christian Ethics*, SCM, 2006, p. 82).

Strengths of Situation Ethics

1. Situation Ethics pays attention to the exceptional nature of dilemmas rather than being legalistic and inflexible.

2. In placing agapeic love at the heart of its ethic, it claims to restore the spirit of the law that Jesus spoke of in the Sermon on the Mount.
3. It is practical and realistic. It is a Christianised form of Act Utilitarianism that takes a realistic account of the fallen, broken and complex world, in which the right thing to do may not be obvious from pre-determined rules.
4. More comfortable with individual and subjective intuitions about identifying the loving thing to do than was Natural Law or Divine Command Ethics, it appealed to the liberalising spirit of the late 1960s in which Fletcher was writing.
5. It articulates what Christians working with the marginalised and vulnerable find so painfully inadequate about legalism; that the rules are applied harshly and uniformly without compassion or attention to individual circumstances.

Weaknesses of Situation Ethics

Ethicist Neil Messer judges that 'Fletcher's Situationism has not worn well and many Christian ethicists now regard it as little more than a historical curiosity . . . as a theological theory of ethics, it looks distinctly thin' (*Christian Ethics*, SCM, 2006, p. 81). Fletcher sees himself as part of a long tradition of writers and theologians who fought legalism in their day with an emphasis on love and realism (including St Paul (cf. 1 Corinthians 6:12), the author of 1 John, Augustine, Abelard, Aquinas, Luther, Leo Tolstoy, Emil Brunner, Paul Tillich, Reinhold Niebuhr and Paul Ramsey). He quotes, with approval, Augustine's famous maxim: 'Love with care, and then what you will, do' (p. 79). But one cannot help but see a very selective reading of these thinkers which interprets them as Situationists ahead of their time. In 1952, Pope Pius XII rejected Situation Ethics as opposing concrete circumstances to Natural Law and God's revealed will in scripture. He condemned it as altogether too individualistic and subjective.

Other common criticisms of Situation Ethics

1. *It sets people or love against rules*, thus failing to see that rules are essential to protect rights and limit harms done to people. Society requires extensive legislation to protect the vulnerable and it is naive to see laws or rules as legalistic because they can become inflexible in particular cases when (as Rule Utilitarians accept) they deliver better outcomes on an aggregated basis. Rules co-ordinate actions consistently and coherently (as in traffic laws), maintain trust (as in doctor–patient confidentiality) and reduce self-deception (because they guard individuals against self-interest or their limited perspective, and remind them of their duties).

   A contemporary of Fletcher's, Paul Ramsey, argued that rules often assist us in adjudicating between contradictory courses of action grounded in love. Ramsey's solution (in *Deeds and Rules in Christian Ethics*, 1967) was to reject Fletcher's *act agapeism* and propose a *rule agapeism* which entailed 'rules of practice' that operated in areas of human activity or institutions. Thus, the institution of marriage ought to embody love as a rule of practice. There should be a presumption against separation and divorce unless the burden of proof against this was overwhelmingly met (e.g. in persistent abuse or unfaithfulness). Similarly, in the rules governing the practice of a Just War, genocide and torture were ruled intrinsically immoral, but other actions were judged in terms of the proportional weighting of good and evil outcomes. Ramsey disapproved of the US policy of targeting cities in the Soviet Union with nuclear weapons, for example, arguing that they should be directed only against military targets.

One example of how difficult it is for well-intentioned people to agree about the loving thing to do can be seen in Fletcher's statement that 'On a vast scale of "agapeic calculus" President Truman made his decision about the A-bombs on Hiroshima and Nagasaki.' By contrast, the pacifist and founder of the Catholic worker movement, Dorothy Day, wrote of this event:

> Mr. Truman was jubilant. President Truman. True man; what a strange name, come to think of it. We refer to Jesus Christ as true God and true Man. He [Truman] went from table to table on the cruiser which was bringing him home from the Big Three conference, telling the great news; 'jubilant' the newspapers said. Jubilate Deo. We have killed 318,000 Japanese.
> (Day, *The Catholic Worker*, September 1945, 1: www.catholicworker.org/dorothyday/daytext.cfm?TextID=554)

Without rules or principles, is it possible for love to elicit from the context the right outcome?

2. Situation Ethics too readily slips into the antinomianism (being anti-law) it claims to avoid. If rules are never prescriptive, but simply to inform our judgements, individuals come to regard them as negotiable – as Kant would see it, given human nature, exceptions to rules quickly become the rule. This was why Pope Pius XII judged Situation Ethics to be 'an individualistic and subjective appeal to the concrete circumstances of actions to justify decisions in opposition to the Natural Law or God's revealed will'.

3. What may be needed is to revise the application or formulation of a rule rather than to abandon it. Rules caution us against treating our situation as unique because we look at it from a self-centred viewpoint. We ought to universalise all of our actions in like situations rather than justifying our breaking of rules on the basis of the uniqueness of our situation. New Testament ethics emphasises the *koinonia* or community, in which love is expressed through mutual obligations, duties of care and service. Situationism is in danger of morphing into the individualism of the age.

4. Fletcher's 'middle way' between legalism and antinomianism sounds eminently reasonable but ignores the long tradition of what medieval thought referred to as casuistry. This may have got a bad press as a way of finding loopholes while seeming to honour rules, but the Christian tradition has provided resources for applying and interpreting rules in the context of situations. One such example is the idea of proportionality in Aquinas' Just War theory. Here he argues that the force should be proportional to the evil remedied. As he writes, 'though proceeding from a good intention, an act may be rendered unlawful, if it be out of proportion to the end'. Another example might be the Doctrine of Double Effect in which the primary intention of any action is beneficent or therapeutic,

but foreseeable harmful effects may result. So rules need not be applied without regard to consequences, but motives remain important in justifying any exceptions to them.

5. Moral rules can prohibit actions that are intrinsically and absolutely wrong (for example, the prohibition on bestiality in Leviticus 20:16), or indiscriminate violence towards the innocent or genocide. To regard the rightness or wrongness of every action as dependent upon its context may relativise the absolute wrongness of some actions and thereby undermine the morally educative nature of law.

6. As with consequentialist ethics more generally, we cannot be sure of the outcome of our actions, so to put all of our eggs in this basket, so to speak, is risky. What if (in the case of sacrificial adultery above), the war's end would have resulted in the mother's release two months later? Situationism presupposes human capacities of intuition and discernment in a manner that fails to reckon with human weakness. The Christian doctrine of the Fall (with which Bonhoeffer begins his ethics) must take into account our finitude in calculating, predicting and controlling consequences, as well as the universal effects of sin.

FURTHER READING

John Arthur (2005) *Morality and Moral Controversies*. Pearson, 7th edition

Michael Banner (2009) *Christian Ethics: A Brief History*. Wiley-Blackwell

Malcolm Brown (2010) *Tensions in Christian Ethics*. SPCK

Joseph Fletcher (1966) *Situation Ethics: The New Morality*. SCM

Robin Gill (2011) *The Cambridge Companion to Christian Ethics*. Cambridge University Press

Richard Hays (1997) *Moral Vision of the New Testament: A Contemporary Introduction to New Testament Ethics*. Continuum

R. G. Jones (1984) *Groundwork of Christian Ethics*. Epworth Press

C. S. Lewis (1960, rev. 2016) *The Four Loves*. William Collins, ch. 6

D. Stephen Long (2010) *Christian Ethics: A Very Short Introduction*. Oxford University Press

Neil Messer (2006) *Christian Ethics*, SCM Study Guide. SCM

Sam Wells and Ben Quash (2010) *Introducing Christian Ethics*. Wiley-Blackwell

Thought Points

(1) List the strengths of Situation Ethics.

(2) Discuss the view that the weaknesses of Situation Ethics outweigh its strengths.

(3) Do you think that Situation Ethics is compatible with Natural Law? Explain the reasons for your answer.

(4) Explain your views on the statement that Situation Ethics is not really a Christian theory of ethics.

(5) Do you think that Situation Ethics gives any useful practical guidance in making moral decisions?

(6) Explain how it might be argued that Situation Ethics is the most Christian approach to moral decision-making.

(7) To what extent is Situation Ethics a more principled approach to moral decision-making than Preference Utilitarianism?

SECTION II

NORMATIVE ETHICAL THEORIES: SECULAR APPROACHES

3 Utilitarianism

LEARNING OUTCOMES

To understand key elements of Utilitarianism, including

- utility
- the hedonic calculus
- Act Utilitarianism
- Rule Utilitarianism

You will also discuss

- whether or not Utilitarianism provides a helpful method of moral decision-making
- whether or not an ethical judgement about something being good, bad, right or wrong can be based on the extent to which, in any given situation, utility is best served
- whether or not it is possible to measure good or pleasure and then reach a moral decision

Introduction

The seeds of Utilitarian thought can be traced back to the ancient Greek thinker Epicurus (341–270 BCE), who emphasised moderation in balancing pleasure and pain, or the Chinese philosopher Mo Tzu (420 BCE), who judged actions on the basis of their utility (useful consequences). Modern Utilitarianism grew up in a time of political upheaval under thinkers like Hume, Hutcheson and Sidgwick, and most notably with the ideas of Jeremy Bentham (1748–1832) and John Stuart Mill (1806–73). Bentham had much to say on subjects as diverse as prison reform, religion, poor relief, international law and animal welfare. A visionary far ahead of his time, he advocated universal voting rights and the decriminalisation of homosexuality. Philosopher Francis Hutcheson was to advocate 'applying a mathematical calculation to moral subjects', a phrase which indicates the altogether more empirical and non-utopian view of ethics in which Utilitarians supplied practical judgements in the real world of politics and dilemmas. Utilitarian ideas come to prominence in the late eighteenth and nineteenth centuries with the birth of the modern states like France and America. As James Rachels puts it:

the revolutions of 1848 showed the continuing power of the new ideas of 'liberty, equality, fraternity'; in America, a new country with a new kind of constitution was born, and its bloody civil war put an end, finally, to slavery in Western civilisation; and all the while, the industrial revolution was bringing about nothing less than a total restructuring of society.

(Rachels 2002, p. 39)

Jeremy Bentham (1748–1832)

Bentham's father was a prosperous lawyer who had ambitions for him to become Lord Chancellor. He studied Latin from three years of age and was found reading a history of England from his father's desk as a toddler. Rather than practising law, he looked at ways to improve upon it. After his father's death in 1792, his independent means allowed him to write between ten and twenty sheets a day for forty years, setting out his philosophical system and critiquing the laws of the day. University College London set up The Bentham Project in the 1960s to produce a scholarly edition of his works and correspondence, and they're now nearly done! He wrote on poor relief, international law, the decriminalisation of homosexuality, animal welfare and universal suffrage. His thought was to shape public policy in the decision-making of modern states.

Bentham's 'Auto-Icon' at UCL

The frontispiece of Thomas Hobbes' Leviathan, 1651. The body which possesses sovereign authority has the king as its head and is made up of individual citizens, whose bodies blur together in the social contract. Together, they balance Church and state power (bottom right and left). As Hobbes puts it, 'A multitude of men are made up of one person, when they are by one man, or one person, represented; so that it be done with the consent of that multitude in particular.'

Principle of Utility: A phrase first used by Jeremy Bentham in his *Introduction to the Principles and Morals of Legislation*, to refer to the principle that should govern society and bring the greatest amount of happiness to the greatest number of people. Bentham was a social reformer and wished that all members of society could achieve as much happiness (and avoid as much pain) as possible during their lives. This is the fundamental idea behind Utilitarianism.

It is far from coincidental that it was in this context that Utilitarian logic took hold. It offered a theory geared to the greatest good of the greatest number (the **Principle of Utility**), in which the interests of each were to count equally, and where, regardless of the diversity of people and opinions, there was a means for settling policy based upon outcomes that optimised choice or pleasure. The religious wars and the English Civil War of the seventeenth century gave greater momentum towards concentrating power in the hands of the state and settling disputes on a more secular basis. As Thomas Hobbes (1588–1679) had remarked in his political treatise *Leviathan*, without the governance of the state, the natural state of mankind is no utopia, but a 'warre of every man against every man' in which 'the life of man [is] solitary, poore, nasty, brutish, and short'. The laws of just states brought about order, but where they reflected the status quo of social hierarchies like the aristocracy or Church, Utilitarians called for a radical rethink. They were practical and political reformers, Bentham pressing for changes in the penal system and Mill (as an MP) presenting the 1868 Bill before Parliament calling for the vote for women. The influence of Utilitarianism grew with the rise of the social sciences (e.g., economics and sociology) and the policy decisions arising from this for growing nation states.

Classic Benthamite Utilitarianism

Supportive as Jeremy Bentham was of the American Revolution and, initially at least, of the French Revolution, he dismissed the intuitive belief of each in the natural rights of man as 'nonsense on stilts'. For Bentham, natural rights were a fiction. Rejecting religion, intuition or abstract rules as a secure basis for ethics, Bentham founded ethics on a principle of psychology. In two clear senses, he followed Hume. Firstly, he agreed that facts were different from values – you could not infer a moral 'ought' from a factual 'is'. Secondly, he saw human beings as being motivated chiefly by desires, not reasons. As he wrote, 'Nature has placed mankind under the governance of two sovereign masters, pain and pleasure. It is for them alone to point out what we ought to do, as well as to determine what we shall do' (Bentham, *The Principles of Morals and Legislation*, 2005 [1781]). Controversially, Bentham believed pleasure to be a 'simple and unitary concept' – even offering 'fifty-eight synonyms for pleasure' (MacIntyre, *A Short History of Ethics*, Routledge, 1971). For Bentham, goods such as knowledge, beauty and justice were all comparable in terms of pleasure and could be weighed on the same set of scales. As he wrote, 'Prejudice apart, the game of push-pin is of equal value with the arts and sciences of music and poetry.' Bentham was well aware of the criticism that this approach reduces all kinds of goods we value to the one set of scales – pleasure and pain. His response was to devise the 'Felicific' or '**Hedonic Calculus**' that brought a mathematical precision to optimising pleasure. The acronym FEDPPIC can help you to recall this.

Hedonic Calculus: This is also known as the Felicific Calculus. It refers to Bentham's quantitative method of determining what will provide the greatest good for the greatest number, and is therefore the moral thing to do. Its seven elements help an individual to add up the pros and cons of the possible consequences of an action.

Fecundity	How fertile will one pleasure be in producing others? An intense hit of an addictive drug may well be pleasurable but is almost certain to lead to pain (addiction, emotional and physical abuse).
Extent	When considering public policy, widening the view – how many are affected?
Duration	How long will the pleasure/pain go on for? The acquisition of knowledge (language, expertise) may be hard work at first, but learning how to read Shakespeare may lead to a lifetime of pleasure.

Purity	Some pleasures come at the expense of other people, or are ill-gotten (through cheating, exploiting).
Propinquity	How close or remote is a pleasure?
Intensity	The Epicureans advocated moderation in all things, and although we may be drawn to intense pleasures, this factor needs to be weighed against others. We cannot spend our lives bungee jumping, and intense drug-fuelled pleasures are short-lived.
Certainty	How guaranteed or predictable is the pleasure we aim at?

Bentham's independent wealth and legal training gave him the means and freedom to pursue his desire for reform in British law and politics. He famously designed a prison to increase efficiency in the surveillance of inmates. Known as the Panopticon, its guard could instanta-neously look into all of the individual prisoners' cells from his central view-ing platform without them knowing whether they were being watched or not. Julia Driver notes that 'in Port Arthur, Australia, where a model prison incorporating some panopticon features was built, prisoners would later complain that the psychological punishment was worse than the physi-cal punishment' (Driver, *Ethics: The Fundamentals*, Wiley-Blackwell, 2006, p. 43). Bentham certainly considered the detail of prison reform down to the size of prison beds and his penal reform advocated the moderation of sentences to the optimal level for both deterrence and reform (too short and the pain may not be sufficient to deter,

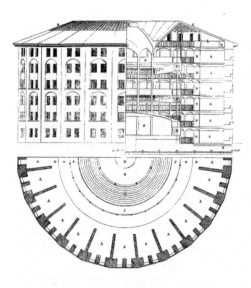

The Panopticon, Bentham's design for an institutional building

too long and an inmate may become institutionalised and reform may no longer be the object). Bentham would have favoured today's diminishing of sentences for good behaviour if this aided reform and prison order. Driver even infers that he might have agreed with the idea of the surveillance state if it could be shown to reduce crime. Utility or usefulness in achieving optimal consequences was the key. Bentham was unsentimental about conventional norms, bequeathing his body for medical research. This curious 'Auto-Icon' (today with a wax replacement for his own head) is still on view in University College London. Utilitarianism sought societal change through a practical-minded blend of political, legal and ethical reforms.

Classic Utilitarianism's emphasis on sentience (the ability to feel pleasure and pain) and on equality (each person's interests to count equally and none to count for more than one) was to have ramifications across many areas of practical ethics, including abortion, euthanasia, animal welfare and universal suffrage. Bentham anticipated many future reforms in the following passage:

> The day may come when the rest of the animal creation may acquire those rights which never could have been withheld from them but by the hand of tyranny. The French have already discovered that the blackness of the skin is no reason why a human being should be abandoned without redress to the caprice of the tormentor. It may one day come to be recognised that the number of the legs, the villosity of the skin, or the termination of the os sacrum are reasons equally insufficient for abandoning a sensitive being to the same fate. What else is it that should trace the insuperable line? Is it the faculty of reason, or perhaps the faculty of discourse? But a full grown horse or dog is beyond comparison a more rational, as well as more conversable animal, than an infant of a day or a week or even a month, old. But suppose they were otherwise, what would it avail? The question is not, Can they reason? Nor Can they talk? But Can they suffer?
>
> (Bentham, The Principles of Morals and Legislation *2005 [1781]*)

We've seen that, for Bentham, Utilitarian moral judgements were based upon three central ideas:

1. *Consequences matter* – good intentions can have disastrous outcomes, and agents who act selfishly can still bring about good ends. So not only are motives difficult to see rationally, conversely, outcomes are easier to model, make predictions about, and they deliver practically in a way that an ethics focused on the character of the agent rather than the outcome of an action fails to do.
2. *Minimising pain and maximising pleasure are and ought to be the sole goal of our actions* – though we may on the surface aim at knowledge, leisure, friendship, fame or wealth, these are just forms of pleasure for different tastes. As Bentham puts it, 'Prejudice apart, the game of push-pin is of equal value with the arts and sciences of music and poetry. If the game of push-pin furnish more pleasure, it is more valuable' (Bentham, *The Rationale of Reward*, 1830).
3. *Actions should aim at the greatest good of the greatest number* and each individual's interests are to count equally. Private happiness should be guided by public interest for Bentham, for, as MacIntyre puts it, 'society is nothing but a collection of individuals' (MacIntyre 1971, p. 232).

Each of these was to cause problems for classic quantitative Utilitarianism, which John Stuart Mill sought to remedy.

Exercise

Ask your teacher to bring in a chocolate bar as an object lesson. Then attempt to persuade them that it is in their interests to give you each a share of the chocolate bar to eat, by using each element of Bentham's Hedonic Calculus.

John Stuart Mill's qualitative Utilitarianism

John Stuart Mill recognised that not all pleasures and pains could be weighed quantitatively on the scales of the Hedonic Calculus. Here he was beginning to address problems that emerged from the three central tenets of classic Utilitarianism. If we are obliged in our every action to seek the greatest good of the greatest number, any luxury or personal enjoyment could be a cause of guilt. Because omitting to minimise the pain of others can be as bad in terms of consequences as deliberately causing pain, burn-out seems inevitable and some immediate questions arise:

J. S. Mill (1806–1873)

J. S. Mill was Britain's greatest nineteenth-century philosopher. A child prodigy, he spoke several languages before his teens and yet burnt out in his twenties, recovering from his depression through his love of the Romantic poets, especially Wordsworth. Politically liberal and empirical in his method, he believed in extending individual freedom through law and rational policies for social improvement that gave people freedom to pursue their own goals. His father's aim of educating a Utilitarian who could implement social change succeeded in his son John. In assessing human rights or social and political policies on the basis of their general usefulness to all, each individual's interests to count equally, Mill was progressive, naturalist and radical. In 1865 he became the MP for Westminster and championed equality for women, compulsory education, birth control and land reform in Ireland. With his wife Harriet Taylor, whom he admired as an intellectual equal, he wrote *The Subjugation of Women,* which remains an important text in the development of feminist thought.

---

1. Is pleasure the only good or is it just a by-product of other goods?
2. If we seek the optimisation of pleasure and the minimisation of pain for the greatest number, can this result in outcomes in which the interests of the majority are unjust towards those of the few?

John Stuart Mill's father, James Mill, was a disciple of Bentham's teaching. He home-schooled his sensitive young son rigorously in Greek, arithmetic and history, aiming to accelerate his intellectual development in order to achieve the greatest good of the greatest number. Yet, at twenty, Mill had a nervous breakdown, largely resulting from this hot-house life which stunted his social and emotional growth. In his recovery, the burdens and failures of Benthamite Utilitarianism became all too evident to Mill in three particular senses.

1. Aligning personal happiness with seeking the good of the greatest number proved elusive. If all of the reforms that Bentham and Mill's father dreamt of were to be achieved, would this fulfil his personal happiness? Mill was to rediscover his *joie de vivre* in the poetry of Wordsworth and Coleridge and in his friendship with Harriet Taylor, a married woman whom he met when he was aged twenty-four and whom, after a close personal friendship that raised Victorian eyebrows, he married a year after the death of her husband, in 1852. Mill could not live as

the 'mere calculating machine' of felicity that his father educated him to be. As he wrote in his autobiography, 'the habit of analysis has a tendency to wear away the feelings . . . Analytic habits [are] a perpetual worm at the root of the passions and the virtues.' Odd as Mill's home-schooling was, there was something in it which was symptomatic of a fault line that ran through Utilitarianism's focus on *acts* rather than *agents* (the character of the people behind them). Virtue Ethics places more value on motives, character and personal flourishing as bound up with that of the thriving of wider society. Bentham's calculations of felicity see society as individual units whose total happiness can be aggregated. That the theory should fail before its second generation on this front should serve to highlight the significance of our sympathy for our fellow human being as well as the dispositions of character that strengthen this. Life is not lived in abstract case studies, but in interpersonal ties and attachments. Mill saw the wider value to society of special relationships like family life, which were the seed bed of virtues like loyalty, empathy, kindness and obligation.

2. Bentham's quantitative and unitary idea of pleasure/pain proved inadequate. A pleasure pursued as an end in itself (like seeking pleasure by gorging oneself on chocolate) could be empty, whereas another pleasure (like gaining a love and understanding of a subject for itself by trying to get a good exam grade in it) could creep up on one 'by not making it the direct end'. As Mill wrote, 'Those only are happy (I thought) who have their minds fixed on some object other than their own happiness; on the happiness of others, on the improvement of mankind, even on some art or pursuit, followed not as a means, but as itself an ideal end.' (J. S. Mill, *Autobiography*, ed. Jack Stillinger, Oxford University Press, 1969). Mill was to reject the idea of pleasure as a simple concept as Bentham's quantitative Utilitarianism conceived it to be. Instead, he was to distinguish between *higher* (intellectual) and *lower* pleasures (of the body). As he wrote, 'Human beings have faculties more elevated than the animal appetites . . . It is better to be a human being dissatisfied than a pig satisfied; better to be Socrates dissatisfied than a fool satisfied. And if the fool, or the pig, are of a different opinion, it is because they only know their own side of the question' (Mill, *Utilitarianism*, ed. Roger Crisp, Oxford University Press, 1998, pp. 56–7). For Mill, Bentham's quantitative view of pleasure was open to injustices. In opposition to intuitive or common sense morality, it would seem to offer little ground on which to condemn a situation in which ten sadistic guards torture one masochist (who enjoys pain). More seriously, it could lead to the will of a majority oppressing a minority (as was the case with Nazi anti-Semitism, or when a racist majority in an economically depressed area scapegoats members of immigrant communities there). Mill responded by distinguishing pleasures and pains qualitatively. He argued for the somewhat elitist idea that the most competent judges (those who had experienced both pleasures of the mind or intellect and more bodily pleasures) would favour the former over the latter. Bentham may have rated push-pin higher than poetry, but Mill did not. Perhaps on the same basis, he would have elevated opera over football.

3. Where Bentham has a hedonic view of happiness as the overall balance of pleasure and pain in society (as a collection of individual units), Mill's thinking

becomes more eudaimonic. Pleasure as an intrinsic good is not just the sum total of pleasures and pains, but the good or flourishing life, which gives a greater place to virtue, relationships and other higher goods of the mind. The influence of the Romantic movement (Wordsworth and Coleridge in particular) and Aristotle's account of *eudaimonia* all serve to shape a more holistic view of happiness in Mill than Bentham offered: 'Virtue, according to the Utilitarian doctrine, is not naturally and originally part of the end, but it is capable of becoming so; and in those who love it disinterestedly it has become so, and is desired and cherished, not as a means to happiness, but as a part of their happiness' (Mill, *Utilitarianism*, pp. 35–6). Mill therefore recognised that people valued virtue as well as happiness as an 'authentic fact'.

The Hedonic paradox

In his book *The Methods of Ethics* (1874), philosopher Henry Sidgwick (1838–1900) noted the paradox that, if aimed at directly, pleasure vanishes. The disappointment or despair a recreational drug user might experience at the ever lessening effect of their substance abuse realises this paradox. Strangely, pleasure results indirectly. In his autobiography, Mill writes:

> But I now thought that this end [one's happiness] was only to be attained by not making it the direct end. Those only are happy (I thought) who have their minds fixed on some object other than their own happiness . . . Aiming thus at something else, they find happiness along the way . . . Ask yourself whether you are happy, and you cease to be so. (Mill *Autobiography*, 1909, p. 94)

So Mill's more eudaimonic version of Utilitarianism is influenced by Aristotle here in seeing pleasure as more holistic and not as an end in itself.

Act and Rule Utilitarianism

Act Utilitarians treat each situation on its merits, rather than entering into it with a commitment to generalised rules or principles, other than to act so as to produce the greatest good of the greatest number in the pursuit of pleasure and avoidance of pain. Bentham's Hedonic Calculus offered a ready reckoner to evaluate the likely outcome of one's decisions in particular circumstances. Act Utilitarians like David Lyons (*Forms and Limits of Utilitarianism*, 1965) argue that Rule Utilitarianism collapses into **Act Utilitarianism**. When exceptions to rules require that sub-rules be devised, or when they become burdensome or even cruel (e.g. when an estimated thirty women died each year prior to 1967 due to the ban on abortion), utility is not served. Rules have to be judged by their usefulness in maximising the greatest good of the greatest number. In contrast, Rule Utilitarians argue that a higher utility is achieved when the population as a whole follow laws and customs aimed at maximising the general happiness and minimising their pain, rather than if everyone does their own

Act Utilitarianism: This is Bentham's version of Utilitarianism, which operates by taking each situation on its own merits, wishing only to achieve the greatest good for the greatest number of people involved. There are no general rules, only the situation that applies to the individual.

calculation on an act-by-act basis. The individual therefore has to have strong reasons to break the law or bend rules that facilitate the greater good. Making exceptions for ourselves for selfish reasons breaks the Utilitarian principle that each individual's interests are to count equally.

Rule Utilitarianism seeks to follow those principles and rules that would maximise aggregate utility if universalised. After all, if Act Utilitarianism were to be universalised, this could have negative consequences. If each moral agent acted within the bounds of their own knowledge without a sense of the general rule or pattern of expected behaviour, the likely result would be far more disorder, unpredictability and less co-operation. This is not to say that all rules have to be absolute (without exceptions and qualifications). J. L. Austin defines Rule Utilitarianism in the principle 'Our rules would be fashioned on utility; our conduct on our rules' (quoted in J. L. Mackie, *Ethics, Inventing Right and Wrong*, Penguin Books, 1977, p. 136). That is to say that the total sum of happiness or preferences is better achieved if everyone follows rules rather than if they seek to calculate the best course of action at the time of each and every action they take. Consider the two cases below.

> **Rule Utilitarianism:** This is (arguably) Mill's version of Utilitarianism. The greatest good for the greatest number is achieved when everyone follows laws and customs that aim to maximise the happiness of everyone, not just some individuals.

1. Traffic laws. Stopping at a red light in a sleepy rural area when there is no traffic around can be a pain; if speeding to make it in time for a crucial interview would secure employment, then weighing the risks of breaking the speed limit against providing for one's children may make it seem worthwhile. But, overall, the aggregate safety and minimisation of pain is best achieved if everyone in the UK keeps to the Highway Code. Rules have developed as more traffic has taken to the roads to optimise the safe flow of traffic. Mill uses the example of sailors improving their calculations and course by using an Almanac rather than navigating by the stars. By analogy, rules and laws are the accumulated wisdom of past experience and collectively prove their worth by avoiding much suffering and conflict.

    If it was down to the individual to weigh up each act on the basis of its usefulness in terms of the greatest good of the greatest number, can you think of other cases where this could lead to injustices or risks and conflicts?

2. Imagine a fictional scenario in a racist town in which, as a result of one person's act of terrorism, there are riots and mob violence. Police round up a suspect who is a petty criminal and fits the profile. Would it be easier for an Act than a Rule Utilitarian to be tempted to imprison this individual even if they knew them to be innocent in respect of the terrorism charges, in order to preserve public order?

    Why may a Rule Utilitarian object more strenuously than an Act Utilitarian to this scenario?

Strong and Weak Rule Utilitarianism

Another distinction may be made regarding the importance attached to rules. Strong Rule Utilitarians emphasise the utility of rules to the extent that they should be held to even where they cause inconvenience, or even harm, in particular cases. There has to be an overwhelming reason to break them. Emergency vehicles like ambulances and fire engines may speed in built-up areas, for example, but a strong weight is attached to rules. By contrast, Weak Rule Utilitarians give more of a role to individual autonomy in moral decision-making. Rules ought to be adhered to, especially in cases where it is difficult to predict outcomes, or where we lack adequate information and have to take account of the general good. But there is more willingness to modify or bend them when they cause harm (for example, as when, in 2010, the Director of Public Prosecutions formally declared that he would not pursue cases of UK citizens assisting in a suicide by transporting a relative to the Dignitas clinic in Switzerland, as juries would not convict relatives acting on compassionate grounds and it was therefore a waste of taxpayers' money). The usefulness of rules and laws in minimising pain and maximising welfare would make reform rather than revolt an important goal of Rule Utilitarians. As an MP, John Stuart Mill campaigned for parliamentary reform, labour unions, proportional representation and equal political rights for women.

On Liberty – the importance of individual freedom in Mill's thought

The Statue of Liberty in New York Harbour has welcomed many generations of US immigrants with its symbolic promise of freedom. Political philosophers debate negative and positive versions of freedom and Mill saw that freedom can mean radically different things to different people.

We can liken the distinction between Act and Rule Utilitarianism to the respective approaches of the *judge* and the *legislator*. The judge conforms to a pre-established ruling, applying the statutes of the law. The legislator, however (and, as an MP, Mill knew this role firsthand), questions the principles that shape the laws. Stick too slavishly to the rules rather than their reasons, and you'll end up, writes Mill, 'like the old-fashioned German tacticians who were vanquished by Napoleon, or the physician who preferred that his patients should die by the rule rather than recover contrary to it' (*A System of Logic*, Book 6, ch. 12). For Mill, one of these was *the Harm Principle*, which gave greater weight to the interests of the individual. Law should not override the liberty of the individual unless they caused harm to others. In this sense, Mill's work *On Liberty* (1859) addressed some of the concerns about the 'tyranny of the majority' raised by Bentham's work. No longer could 'the greatest good of the greatest number' mean the curtailment of individual freedom purely on the wishes of the majority. Mill's idea of aggregate happiness (the greatest good of the greatest number, each individual's interests to count equally) recognises that, where individuals have liberty and thrive, the general happiness is increased. Losing the individual's happiness in the pursuit of the general happiness is to miss the point that 'each person's happiness is a good to that person, and the general happiness, therefore, a good to the aggregate of all persons' (as Mill argues in chapter 4 of *Utilitarianism*). He described a society in which everyone's sole duty was to live for the good of others as 'liberticide' (the killing of freedom). Instead, everyone ought to have the freedom to pursue happiness in their own way whilst respecting the freedom of others. So respect for the individual's freedom is crucial – to the extent that they pose no harm or threat to society, the law should not curb their liberties. As he writes, 'If all mankind minus one, were of one opinion, and only one person were of the contrary opinion, mankind would be no more justified in silencing that one person, than he, if he had the power, would be justified in silencing mankind' (*On Liberty*, p. 33).

Was Mill an Act or a Rule Utilitarian?

In opposition to the intuitionists, Mill saw observation and experience as the best predictors of consequences and the most objective measure of ethics. During the 'whole past duration of the human species', writes Mill, 'mankind have been learning by experience the tendencies of actions'. In this way, the rules and customs of conventional morality (e.g. 'Do not steal', 'Honour promises' or 'Do not murder') are like the 'landmarks and direction posts' that guide travellers who would, if left to their own devices (like the Act Utilitarian who ignores rules and relies on his/her own sense of direction at every turn), often take a wrong turn or lose their bearings. Landmarks, like rules, gain authority by reliably getting us to our end goal or destination. Mill offers an example in the form of sailors who 'cannot wait to calculate the Nautical Almanac. Being rational creatures, they go to sea with it ready calculated.' (*What Utilitarianism Is*, Chapter 2, 1883). So too, rather than testing every action, rules provide us with the foresight of generalisations. Rules may fall short of the fundamental principles of morality, but we all need landmarks and direction posts on the way to our ultimate destination. So training children with an ingrained respect for customary moral rules of thumb such as 'Violence never solves problems' or 'It's wrong to steal' is important. But when two such principles conflict – like 'It's wrong to lie' and 'Always act to protect those you love from strangers who intend them harm and ask you their whereabouts' – then you switch from a conventional to a critical level of ethical reasoning and consider consequences in this particular case. Here Mill would argue (opposing Kant's view) that you ought to lie to an axe-wielding killer who is after your friend's location, so he is not a strong devotee of rules. For Mill, the Principle of Utility provides us with the ultimate standard by which to judge 'all human conduct'. Customary rules and beliefs are to be judged and improved by using this standard as we see the consequences that follow from them. The terminology distinguishing Act and Rule Utilitarianism is later than Mill, and in setting out his basis for defending rights in Utilitarianism, Mill offers 'no other reason than general utility'. As he states:

QUICK QUESTION
If emergency services can jump red lights, should individuals do so if they judge that getting to a hospital on time might save a life?

justice is a name for certain moral requirements, which, regarded collectively, stand higher in the scale of social utility, and are therefore of more paramount obligation, than any others; though particular cases may occur in which some other social duty is so important, as to overrule any one of the general maxims of justice. Thus, to save a life, it may not only be allowable, but a duty, to steal, or take by force, the necessary food or medicine, or to kidnap, and compel to officiate, the only qualified medical practitioner.

Exercise

Can you briefly explain. . .
    Higher and lower pleasures
    Quality vs Quantity of pleasure
    Liberty and the Harm Principle
    Strong and weak Rule Utilitarianism

Discussion Questions

1. Bentham wrote that 'The community is a fictitious body, composed of the individual persons who are considered as constituting, as it were, its members. The interest of the community then is, what? – the sum of the interests of the several members who compose it.' Yet Mill emphasised the usefulness of rules and general happiness rather than calculating individual acts or individual private happiness. How does this deal with the criticism of Benthamite or Classic Utilitarianism that there is not enough time, before every action, to weigh up the consequences of every individual's decision to bring about the greatest happiness?
2. What objections might be raised against Mill's distinction between higher and lower pleasures and his idea of 'competent judges' who, having experience of both, can reliably tell us which are preferable?
3. If our actions are to be judged in terms of their usefulness in bringing about the greatest good of the greatest number, then whether it is right to tell the truth or to lie is dependent upon consequences. What does this do to one's personal integrity (Bernard Williams' objection)?
4. Peter Singer argues that: 'If it is in our power to prevent something bad from happening, without thereby sacrificing anything of comparable moral importance, we ought, morally, to do it.' Do you think of it as your duty to help starving children or victims of natural disasters when aid can save lives, or is this a charitable act which is praiseworthy, but whose omission is not equivalent to murder if you fail to do it?
5. As Utilitarianism judges actions in terms of their consequences, a great deal of weight must be attached to the assessment of potential risks and rewards in its calculations. How is this both a strength and a weakness in Utilitarian thought?

Stretch and challenge reading: Peter Singer

Peter Singer's shift from Preference Utilitarianism (and subjective values) to Hedonic Utilitarianism (and objective values)

Peter Singer stands in the tradition of the three great Utilitarians, Jeremy Bentham (1748–1832), John Stuart Mill (1806–73) and Henry Sidgwick (1838–1900). This tradition takes an empirical approach to ethics, basing it upon measurable outcomes, or the maximisation of pleasure (Bentham) / happiness (Mill). Utilitarian ideas came to prominence in the late eighteenth and nineteenth centuries with the birth of modern states like France and the US where free and democratic impulses came to the fore after the industrial revolution and World War I. Modern states restructured society with greater centralisation and bureaucratic measurement and control. Philosopher Francis Hutcheson was to advocate 'applying a mathematical calculation to moral subjects', a phrase which indicated a practically minded view of ethics focused on judging moral decisions by their utility (usefulness) in advancing certain outcomes.

Up until around 2011, Singer was a Preference Utilitarian who saw ethical judgements as subjective – that is to say that, rather than being true or false, they reflect the choices or desires/interests of individual humans or animals. Preference Utilitarians proceed by taking account of every sentient being affected by an action and aggregating (taking the sum total of) preferences, counting each's interests equally. Whilst human interests often do take precedence over those of animals, Singer has challenged the reasoning behind arbitrarily privileging the interests of our species in cases where this causes great animal suffering (e.g. in factory meat production or animal experimentation). So Preference Utilitarians reject Bentham's attempt to measure pleasure and pain quantitatively in his 'Hedonic Calculus'. They also see Mill's view that 'competent judges', who have experienced both pleasure and pain, would give greater weight to higher pleasures of the mind rather than lower bodily pleasures as rather elitist. It belongs to a patriarchal culture often seen in medical wards of the past where 'doctor knows best', or in the belief that political elites knew what was best for the masses and made their choices for them.

In *The Expanding Circle: Ethics, Evolution, and Moral Progress* (1982), Singer shows how kinship altruism, which is present in nature (for example in ant and ape colonies), has developed in evolutionary psychology and human reason, to expand our ethical concern to the wider consequences of our actions for other non-related humans. We ought to give far more weight to the interests or preferences of developing-world factory workers whose cheap labour we in the rich West exploit, together with 'resources' such as livestock and the planet itself. Our capacity for reasoning makes moral progress possible. We can act if the science of climate change warns us of impending disaster ahead, or rethink our consumer choices when we learn of the suffering the factory-farming industry inflicts on animals.

Here, there is a weakness in Preference Utilitarianism. Singer had sought to maximise the total number of satisfied preferences, but the egoist (who thinks only of their own interests) would ask 'Why?' Given the subjectivity of preferences (choices, personal opinions, or tastes), this language doesn't seem to give the same moral grip to the argument as moral objectivism does. Bentham's and Mill's hedonistic Utilitarianism, by contrast, in its emphasis on giving a value to pleasure and pain, is able to gain more traction in arguments with consumers of factory-farmed meat, or those reluctant to give to charities working in the developing world. Singer seeks to present the ethical life as fulfilling, but also as a rational one for human beings wanting to act consistently and not do to others what they wouldn't want done to them (or actively to do for others what they would want done to them).

Singer's recent book *The Point of View of the Universe: Sidgwick and Contemporary Ethics* (Oxford University Press, 2014) takes up Sidgwick's claim that humans should take an impartial, objectivist stance when considering their actions. Sidgwick reckoned that the 'profoundest problem of ethics' was the apparent rationality of both egoism and Utilitarianism. Reason alone cannot provide complete arguments for what we ought to do, but self-evident intuitions can supplement it. Sidgwick considered it to be self-evident that the good of one individual is equal to that of any other.

He set out three axioms or principles that he considered to be self-evident:

- an axiom of Justice – 'Whatever action any of us judges to be right for himself, he implicitly judges to be right for all similar persons in similar circumstances'
- an axiom of prudence – 'a smaller present good is not to be preferred to a greater future good'
- an axiom of benevolence – 'each one is morally bound to regard the good of any other individual as much as his own, except in so far as he judges it to be less, when impartially viewed, or less certainly knowable or attainable by him'.

Discussion Question

Do you consider Justice, prudence and benevolence to be self-evident to any rational person?

Influenced by Sidgwick and by Derek Parfit's two-volume book *On What Matters* (Oxford University Press, 2011), Singer now thinks that 'those who reject objectivism in ethics [are] on the defensive (see Peter Singer on Derek Parfit's *On What Matters* (13 June 2011), 'Does Anything Matter?' ABC Religion&Ethics, abc.net.au). Someone whose actions are purely selfish and who shows no consideration for those suffering in absolute poverty can be said to be objectively *wrong* – in increasing suffering rather than merely having *subjective* preferences disliked by others. To the extent that we can be rationally objective in ethics, we can then strengthen the argument that 'we rich people [should] give up some of our luxuries, ceasing to overheat the Earth's atmosphere, and taking care of this planet . . . so that it continues to support intelligent life'. Reason can lead us to see certain moral judgements as mistaken, and not just as matters of taste or preference. Arguably, the task of persuading people to change their lifestyle and actions is weakened if ethical judgements are subjectivist. And this task is central to the effective altruism movement Singer spearheads. Take the belief that we ought to help the poorest one billion people in the world who live on less than one dollar a day. Whilst my money may legally be mine, it is an accident of history (resulting in part, from colonisation, slavery and industrialisation) that I, as a citizen of a developed economy, have more wealth than the poorest in the world. Parfit argues that reason leads us to know that moral judgements can be false – for example, the belief that 'my money is my own and I have no obligations to children who die for lack of basic healthcare or through malnutrition'. Parfit sees Kantian and Utilitarian positions as climbing up different sides of the same mountain of objectivity in ethics.

For a Kantian, objectivity may take the form of:
'Everyone ought to follow the principles whose universal acceptance everyone could rationally will.'

Whilst for a Utilitarian, moral objectivity may take the form of:
'Everyone ought to follow optimific principles (ones which, if everyone acted on them, would make things go in the ways that would be impartially best), because these are the only principles that everyone could rationally will to be universal laws.'

So Singer has been persuaded that ethics assumes universalisability. Decisions ought not to be made from a self-serving point of view, but from an objective, impartial stance. Parfit seeks to defend a secular form of objectivity in ethics, in contrast to that of nihilists and subjectivists. His 2011 book reflects an increasing sense among philosophers that, to the extent that human behaviour is rationally motivated, we should have the good sense to see good arguments triumph over bad ones, and not simply shrug our shoulders and dismiss moral judgements as expressions of emotions.

Australian academic and activist Peter Singer (1946–)
Peter Singer is the Princeton Professor of Bioethics and arguably the most influential living philosopher. His book *Animal Liberation* (Vintage Press, 1995) – known as 'the Bible of the Animal Liberation Movement' – has sold over 500,000 copies, and his *Practical Ethics* (1993) is Cambridge University Press' most profitable philosophy text to date. On animal welfare, abortion, euthanasia, ecology, global trade and the war against terror, Singer is motivated to reduce the suffering of sentient beings. He gives 20 per cent of his income to charity and does not eat or wear any animal products. He is a vocal advocate of voluntary euthanasia and has been a pioneer of the effective altruism movement (see his TED talk and website www.thelifeyoucansave.org). Far from being an ivory-tower academic, Singer is an activist at heart, quoting with approval Marx's remark that 'The philosophers have only interpreted the world, in various ways. The point, however, is to change it' (*Theses on Feuerbach*). In a series of books such as *How Are We to Live? Ethics in an Age of Self Interest* (1995), *One World: The Ethics of Globalisation* (2004), *The Life You Can Save* (2010), *The Most Good You Can Do* (2015) and *Famine, Affluence and Morality* (2015), he has brought the Utilitarian tradition to bear on contemporary issues.

Strengths of Utilitarianism

Utilitarianism emerged with the growth of the nation state and it proved practical on three counts:

1. It found pragmatic *solutions to allocating scarce resources when massive demands were made*. The practical reasoning of Utilitarianism was *agreeable on secular grounds* and it sought to act impartially and *think globally* (*One World* is a title of a book by Singer along these lines). Its simple and unitary goal of maximising pleasure (Bentham/Mill) or preferences (Singer) offered a means of finding common ground in the public policy of diverse societies. Whatever disagreements of belief or culture exist, people can agree to the minimal requirement of minimising pain and maximising the greatest good (pleasure/preferences) of the greatest number. Consequentialist logic takes a hard-headed empirical look at dilemmas and moves away from abstract beliefs to find the optimal trade-off between conflicting preferences. Singer seeks to persuade consumers of meat, for example, that intensive factory farming of chickens, pigs or cattle makes their lives more of a burden than a benefit to them and that paying more at the supermarket to prevent this is worth it for the sake of justice. So where the process of finding common ground proves difficult, Utilitarians aim to inform our decisions on the basis of all available evidence and to help us reflect on the likely consequences of choices. As Singer writes, 'Ethics is practical or it is not ethics.'

    Utilitarianism has been from its inception, and is today, *reformist*. It questions the rationality of abstract and (as it often turns out) arbitrary rules, and brings a particular kind of clarity in banging heads together to work out solutions in a 'lowest common denominator' type way. Bentham worked on prison reform, Mill on the right for women to vote – to name just two campaigns. Singer was arrested for trying to photograph confined sows on a pig farm partly owned by the Australian prime minister and sat in a cage to draw attention to the plight of battery hens. He has campaigned on animal welfare and been on the receiving end of an assault, and angrily protests for his views on abortion, euthanasia and infanticide. Utilitarians do not content themselves with theorising – they are, and always have been, practical in their ethics.

2. Negative Utilitarianism's *emphasis on the priority of reducing unnecessary pain and suffering* clarifies what should be centre-stage in practical ethics. Famous contemporary Utilitarians like Peter Singer (*The Life You Can Save*, Picador, 2010) (www.thelifeyoucansave.com) and Toby Ord (www.givingwhatwecan.org) are putting their money where their mouth is and giving generously, reducing their global footprint and living as vegetarians whilst wearing non-animal products. They have encouraged thousands of people to give substantial percentages of their income to alleviating absolute poverty, thereby reducing the preventable deaths that so often result from it. Their conviction that, in investing their energies in an effort to reduce preventable suffering, 'the ethical life is not self-sacrifice, but self-fulfilment' (Singer, *How Are We to Live?*, Opus, 1995) seems to be an urgent and persuasive message.

3. Rather than begin with a whole raft of abstract metaphysical beliefs, *Utilitarian thought is empirical and informed by the human and natural sciences* such as psychology, social anthropology and neuro-biology. Utilitarians observe human psychology and the evolutionary traits of human behaviour rather than beginning with a fixed view of human nature, as Aristotle did. They work with the grain of both human self-interest and co-operation. Such an approach is informed and adaptable. Its solutions should prove workable and well evidenced.

Weaknesses of Utilitarianism

1. Ultimately, consequentialism must come back to *at least one non-consequential starting point*. In answer to the question 'What is a good outcome?', the answer 'pleasure' simply raises further questions, such as: What makes pleasure good as an end in itself? Is pleasure amorphous (taking one basic form that can be assessed quantitatively: 8 points for a Sky Dive, 5 for a good meal, 28 for getting into university, 40 for meeting the love of your life) or polymorphous (taking different forms that are not comparable, e.g. beauty, truth, goodness, justice, knowledge, family, friendship, and higher (aesthetic and intellectual) and lower (bodily) pleasures)?

2. Utilitarianism *moves from the 'is'*, or supposedly factual, observation that everyone seeks their own pleasure *to the 'ought'* statement of saying that they 'ought' to seek pleasure (albeit one in which individuals curb their private self-interest in favour of maximising pleasure for the greatest number). G. E. Moore's *Open Question Argument* applies here – if it makes sense to ask the question 'Sure this action maximises pleasure, but is it right?', then the definition commits the Naturalistic Fallacy: that because, by nature, people pursue pleasure and avoid pain, they ought to do so. If pleasure was an adequate definition of goodness, we would be asking a circular question like 'She's an unmarried woman, but is she a spinster?' John Stuart Mill regarded the general observation that each person desires their own happiness to be *a proof of Utilitarianism*. Yet an egoist could see their own happiness as subjectively good, without it logically following that they ought to will the general happiness. What the third great Utilitarian thinker, Henry Sidgwick, argued, in his book *The Methods of Ethics*, is that an egoist who sees their personal happiness as an objective good cannot logically argue that their happiness is 'more objectively desirable or more good than a similar happiness of any other person', so they must then agree with the Utilitarian that universal happiness is 'the real end of Reason, the absolutely Good'.

3. It is difficult to predict the future except by modelling it on past outcomes. Calculating consequences on models that assume the future will resemble the past can be risky. Should past generations whose nuclear power plants provided short-term energy while creating long-term leakage and danger be held accountable for the consequences they failed to predict? If predicting consequences is so crucial, surely the practical ethics of Utilitarianism cannot be left to ordinary people and belongs to highly specialised expert bureaucrats, making it elitist rather than

democratic as Bentham and Mill supposed it to be. And if we put all of our moral eggs in one basket (predicting good future outcomes for the greatest number), and it should turn out that our predictions were erroneous, then the basis of our decision-making turns out to be faulty. Take an Act-Utilitarian justification for the use of monkeys or apes in scientific experiments in which the medical benefits of a proposed drug treatment have been inflated and turn out to be non-existent. Here the deontologist may console themselves, in the event of a tragic outcome, that at least they stuck to what they believed to be right.

4. It has no *backward-looking reasons*. Some moral considerations have to do with the past, such as keeping promises. If I judge the rightness of an action purely on the basis of consequences, then this trivialises the breaking of promises in individual cases in which the utility of keeping them is low. An example of this might be returning a kindness done in the past.

5. The Harvard philosopher Robert Nozick presents an attack on **hedonism**, or the view that pleasure = goodness or an intrinsic good. As he writes:

> Suppose there were an experience machine that would give you any experience you desired. Superduper neuropsychologists could stimulate your brain so that you would think and feel you were writing a great novel, or making a friend, or reading an interesting book. All the time you would be floating in a tank, with electrodes attached to your brain. Should you plug into this machine for life, pre-programming your life experiences? Of course, while in the tank you won't know that you're there; you'll think that it is all actually happening. Would you plug in?
>
> (Nozick, *Anarchy, State and Utopia*, Basic Books, 1974)

If, as John Stuart Mill wrote, 'The utilitarian doctrine is that happiness is desirable, and the only thing desirable, as an end; all other things being desirable as a means to that end', then the answer may well be 'Yes!' Yet this would seem to be a shallow substitute for real life, a virtual world in no way comparable to what non-Utilitarians take to be the intrinsic goods of friendship, knowledge, beauty, etc.

6. A further problem is that pleasure is polymorphous – it takes many different forms. Where many systems of morality treat 'goods' of life, such as knowledge, beauty, truth, justice, life and health, etc., as separate and incommensurate (not able to be converted into comparable points on a scale), *Utilitarianism lumps every good onto the same set of scales and weighs them together.* Yet there's no guarantee that these goods are combinable in a simple exchange mechanism without losing something of their intrinsic worth. Your father's health is worth 10 points of a total 100 while you studying for a degree in engineering is worth 20, and you getting the limited family funding for a degree rather than your younger sister (who wanted to study fine art) is 30 on the scale. Sure, Utilitarianism can deliver policies on how to allocate scarce health resources when there is massive and conflicting demand, but, as Alasdair MacIntyre argues, 'the use of a conceptual fiction in a good cause does not make it any less of a fiction' (MacIntyre, *After Virtue*, University of Notre Dame Press, 2007).

7. Utilitarianism has a 'breathtaking systematisation' to its 'thin language, with 'too few feelings and thoughts to match the world as it really is' (a phrase used by Charles

Hedonism:
The term comes from *'hedone'*, the Greek word for 'happiness'. Hedonism is an ancient school of thought, allegedly founded by Aristippus of Cyrene, a pupil of Socrates, which argues that happiness is the highest good. In most forms of Hedonism, happiness is interpreted as 'pleasure'.

Taylor in *Sources of the Self*, Harvard University Press, 1992). It is happy to take a free ride on the intuitive, conventional morality which says 'if society follows principles and instils virtues whilst thinking morality objectively real, it will fare better on the whole'. Yet, at a critical level, pleasure and pain or people's preferences are the only intrinsic goods, and conventional morality is naively mistaken. So Utilitarianism is parasitic upon conventional morality, whilst at the same time accelerating its decline. The over-emphasis on impartial reasoning underestimates the power of compassion and devalues the special relationships with family and friends in which this empathy grows. Bernard Williams has argued that the impartial thinker that Utilitarianism idealises distances us from the interpersonal world of empathy, compassion and loyalties that is so valuable to us. Indeed it is in the soil of personal relationships that virtue grows and **egoism** is weeded out.

Egoism:
The belief that individuals have a moral duty to optimise the good consequences for themselves

Robert Solomon comments that American soldiers fighting in Cambodia in the 1960s who were not college-educated 'typically remained sensitive to and repulsed by the war crimes that had by then become a daily feature' of the war whereas college-educated recruits 'were able to rationalise these handily, using familiar Utilitarian arguments, cutting themselves off quite effectively not only from the guilt and shame but from the human tragedies they caused and witnessed': Solomon, 'Peter Singer's Expanding Circle' in *Singer and his Critics*, Wiley-Blackwell, 1999

8. *Utilitarianism is too morally demanding.* Philosophers distinguish *obligatory* from *supererogatory* actions. The former are required but the latter are above and beyond the call of duty, though all the more praiseworthy for that. As a consequentialist, Peter Singer believes that we are *responsible for omissions as well as commissions* – for what we fail to do as well as what we do. Furthermore, our responsibilities do not just relate to those close to us – to ignore a child dying on the other side of the world from a preventable disease which our disposable income could prevent or cure is no better than walking past a drowning child in a shallow pond on the way to our work. So, whilst a Utilitarian might feel obliged to give away as much of their disposable income to those living in absolute poverty as they possibly can, many would judge this to be morally praiseworthy, but not obligatory. Indeed, feeling guilty about every luxury purchase you make and every personal pleasure that does not pursue the greatest good of the greatest number could make for the very life that led to Mill's mental breakdown.

9. *Utilitarian commitments to total impartiality (the point of view of the universe) raise the problem of special relationships.* If we ought to give equal consideration and no special weight to any particular individual or group, what about our special obligations to family and friends? Whilst at the higher level of critical reason, this principle might appear to be a good one, at the intuitive level of our feelings of loyalty, attachment and love, does this make us less humane?

Discussion Questions

Imagine a case in which a surgeon finds himself with four patients on his ward, all of whom will die without a transplant in the next few weeks. One needs a new heart, another a new pair of lungs, another a liver, and a final one, a pancreas. A young homeless man with no traceable records or next of kin arrives on the ward unconscious, having fallen off a bicycle. It is touch and go whether the surgeon could save his life anyway and it looks like no-one will miss him, whereas four loving families visit their loved ones on the ward every day. The hospital is in a remote area and the surgeon on night duty is very skilful. He could extract all of the vital organs that night and transplant them the next day with the help of unsuspecting fellow surgeons who could be told that 'multiple donors had become available'.

1. What would an Act Utilitarian/a Rule Utilitarian do in the above situation?
2. Would they justify their action on the same basis?

FURTHER READING

Jeremy Bentham (2005 [1781]) *An Introduction to the Principles of Morals and Legislation.* Adamant Media Corporation

Krister Bykvist (2007) *Utilitarianism: A Guide for the Perplexed.* Continuum

John Stuart Mill (1998) *Utilitarianism*, ed. Roger Crisp. Oxford University Press

L. Pojman (2012) *Discovering Right and Wrong.* Wadsworth, ch. 7

Peter Singer (2011) *Practical Ethics.* Cambridge University Press

J. J. C. Smart and Bernard Williams (1973) *Utilitarianism For and Against* Cambridge University Press

Thought Points

(1) List the similarities and differences between Act and Rule Utilitarianism.

(2) List the strengths and weaknesses of Mill's theory of Utilitarianism.

(3) To what extent do you agree that it is impossible to make valid moral decisions on the basis of consequences?

(4) Discuss the view that Situation offers a more principled approach to moral decision-making than Act Utilitarianism.

(5) Explain how Utilitarianism might help to make a decision about business ethics.

(6) Explain how Singer's Preference Utilitarianism differs from Act and Rule Utilitarianism.

(7) Do you think that Utilitarianism is of any use in making moral decisions?

4 Kantian Ethics (Deontological)

Life and works

Immanuel Kant was born on 22 April 1724 in Königsberg, at that time the capital city of the province of East Prussia. It was a busy commercial city, with an important military port, and its own well-respected university. Kant was born into a working-class family; his father made saddles and harnesses, and his mother was the daughter of a harness-maker. The family were Pietist and Kant attended a Pietist school, the Collegium Fridericianum, until he was fifteen. Pietism was an evangelical branch of the Lutheran Church which emphasised the importance of Christian piety, a strong moral conscience and control of the passions. His mother, who died when he was thirteen, encouraged his intellect and imagination and taught him about nature and the starry heavens. His mother's religion was one of prayer, Bible study, quiet humility, and living out the golden rule in kindness to others. He judged her faith 'genuine' and 'not in the least enthusiastic' (fundamentalist), though he did rebel against the more zealous Pietism that sought to reform the mainstream German Lutheranism of his day. While at school, Kant reacted strongly against the Pietism of his youth and this may partially account for his later emphasis on rationality and autonomy. For Kant, religion ought to operate as 'religion within the boundaries of mere reason' (the title of one of his books, published in 1793). He turned to the Latin classics, which formed an important part of the school's curriculum. Later, Kant attended the University of Königsberg (known as the Albertina), where he quickly became fascinated by Philosophy, which was a compulsory first-year subject, studying Logic, Metaphysics, Ethics and Natural Law.

Immanuel Kant (1724–1804)

Immanuel Kant was a German philosopher at the heart of a movement known as the Enlightenment. He reacted against the evangelical Lutheran Pietism of his schooling, with its emphasis on religious devotion and biblical literalism. He valued reason independent of revelation or emotion, though he did imbibe his parents' values (they were harness-makers) of 'hard work, honesty . . . and independence'. Despite shaping modern Western philosophy, Kant never travelled any great distance from the Prussian port city of Königsberg. A bachelor, he kept to a strict routine of walks and early bedtimes for the sake of his health. From 1755 to 1770, he was a Privatdozent (a lecturer funded by collecting fees from those who attended his lectures). He was a popular lecturer and, as his career matured, his philosophical writings sold well.

Context of Kant's ethics

In order to understand Kant's ethical thinking, we need to consider the intellectual context in which his thoughts developed. Kant wrote towards the end of the formative years of the 'European Enlightenment', sometimes called the 'Age of Reason'. Kant was one of the last, and probably the greatest, thinkers of the Enlightenment.

The Enlightenment developed radical ideas about the rights of the individual and democracy which led to the French and American Revolutions. Two key themes of the Enlightenment were a focus on the individual and on **reason**. Significant figures in the Enlightenment included:

Reason:
The ability to work out correct ethical decisions, with which every human is born. This is a key concept in Kantian Ethics.

● *Isaac Newton and John Locke*, who emphasised the importance of rational and scientific explanations for natural phenomena. Newton's universal laws of motion were to shape Kant's desire to uncover similar laws in Moral Philosophy.
● *David Hume and Voltaire*, who showed scepticism about inherited tradition and authorities in politics, religion and the universities.
● *Jean-Jacques Rousseau and Thomas Paine*, who put forward revolutionary ideas opposing the status quo and emphasised reason and autonomy rather than the **heteronomy** (law of the other) of monarchy, Church and aristocracy.
● *Francis Hutcheson and Thomas Reid*, who proposed a moderate, 'common-sense' approach to developing society's values.

Newton's influence

Kant saw in Newton an example of how reason had transformed physics and astronomy. Newton's mind had not only brought order to our perception of the natural world, he had offered a new vision or model of seeing in which universal laws were discoverable in nature under the light of reason. As the poet Alexander Pope (1688–1744) wrote, 'Nature, and Nature's laws lay hid in the Night. God said, Let Newton be! and all was Light.' Kant saw the moral law as knowable by a priori reasoning about maxims that would be universalisable in a manner analogous to the laws of nature. His mother was well educated and taught him about nature (bears and wolves lived around Königsberg)

Isaac Newton (1643–1727)

and the stars. For his tombstone, Kant's friends selected the quotation 'Two things fill the mind with ever new and increasing admiration and awe, the more often and steadily we reflect upon them: the starry heavens above me and the moral law within me.' Though his mother died when he was thirteen, he says of her: 'I will never forget my mother, for she implanted and nurtured in me the first germ of goodness; she opened my heart to the impressions of nature; she awakened and furthered my concepts, and her doctrines have had a continual and beneficial influence in my life.'

The influence of Jean-Jacques Rousseau on Kant's ethics

Kant's belief that humans are responsible for their actions and could do otherwise than they do is not provable – he terms it instead a postulate of practical reasoning (without freedom, we cannot reasonably be held responsible). Some scholars think he gets this first from Rousseau, who wrote *The Social Contract* (which argues that political freedom is possible only when a people are governed by their collective general will, not by external authorities such as the monarchy or the Church). Rousseau gives Kant an anti-elitist respect for the common man.

Jean-Jacques Rousseau (1712–78)
A political philosopher whose *Social Contract* (1762) saw liberty and equality as promoting a spirit of fraternity – a kind of commonwealth of ends. It includes the famous phrase 'man is born free; and everywhere he is in chains', which expressed the *Zeitgeist* of the French Revolution and many revolutionary movements since then. Kant initially supported the French Revolution but soon became troubled by the bloodshed and injustices. Nonetheless, he supported republican government and saw that historical progress often came about through violent and unjust actions such as war. Kant's emphasis on freedom and reason draws on Rousseau's republicanism and reputation as a liberator who supported individual freedom.

> **To research:**
> Find out more about the Enlightenment and how it affected philosophy, politics, literature and culture.

Kant's emphasis on the universalisability of ethics draws on both Newton and Rousseau. Kant wished to universalise moral judgements in a manner analogous to Newton's three universal laws. Yet his Kingdom of Ends is, in some senses, an extension of Rousseau's social contract.

Kant's works on morality

Kant wrote several books on morality. The main ones are:

- *Groundwork of the Metaphysics of Morals* published in 1785
- *Critique of Practical Reason* published in 1788
- *The Metaphysics of Morals* published in 1797

Deontology vs teleology

Deontology:
The idea, central to Kant's ethics, that there should be universally applicable rules, which are true without exception and not dependent upon the consequences of actions

The term '**deontology**' comes from the Greek word '*deon*', which means 'duty'. Examples of deontological ethics include that of natural law, divine command ethics, and Kantian ethics. This differs from 'teleological' ways of thinking and decision-making. In the latter, we look at the world around us, searching for evidence of how things are. This evidence is gathered from our five senses, so we see, or hear, or touch things, and learn from doing this that things exist. For example, if we want to know whether it is sunny today, we would look out of the window to check. If we wanted to know the temperature at which water boils, we would heat some water up and measure the temperature when it started to bubble. In teleological thinking, therefore, we 'know' things by experiencing them.

For Kant, this teleological way of learning was fraught with difficulties. We know that sometimes we get things wrong, because we can be mistaken about what we have seen or heard. Think of a trial in a criminal court; sometimes two witnesses will give conflicting evidence about what they have seen. This leads to conflict and might have serious consequences for the defendant. It is quite common to read about 'miscarriages of justice', when someone has been convicted wrongly, based on faulty evidence provided by a witness.

In his book *The Critique of Pure Reason* (1781), Kant argues for the existence of a priori knowledge. This is a kind of knowledge that does not depend on our experience of the world. He links a priori knowledge with our ability to reason, to think rationally and logically. The purpose of the *Critique* was to examine whether human reason is capable of achieving a priori knowledge, and, if so, how and to what extent. He wanted to avoid the pitfalls of teleological thinking, so that our knowledge of the world, and our moral decision-making, would be on a firm basis and could not be faulted. He makes the distinction between a priori and a posteriori knowledge. A priori knowledge is the knowledge we gain from our ability to reason, and a posteriori knowledge is what we learn through our experience of the world.

Kant believed that the ability to reason is innate in human beings, and is a distinctive and necessary characteristic of being a human. It exists more or less equally in every person. Humans' ability to reason and think objectively (not merely from one's own point of view, or one's preferences and wishes) is one of the important things that sets them apart from all other creatures. According to Kant, humans have an intrinsic dignity because of their ability to reason. This ability thus has a unifying function: because all humans have the ability to reason, they should all come to the same conclusion about any moral problem, as there is only one correct answer – i.e. the rational conclusion.

For example, if one person argues rationally and logically to a particular conclusion – say, that telling the truth is the correct thing to do – then all other people, going through the argument and thinking rationally, will come to the same conclusion. The important thing here is that reason dictates that their answers are the same. Kant says that this principle holds for all moral problems. If I reach the conclusion that a particular action is correct (using my powers of reason), then all rational people would arrive at the same conclusion.

We may put this principle in a slightly different way. Kant believed that human beings are made up of two different aspects. Their desires, urges, and appetites link them to the beasts, but their capacity to reason objectively according to the moral law, made them more like the angels and God. He makes a distinction between the 'phenomenal' world and the 'noumenal' world. The phenomenal world is that of the physical, instinctive (non-rational) self, while the noumenal world is that of the higher, rational being. As will be clear, if a person is to be a moral being, he/she must act in accordance with this higher, rational, noumenal self. This is because the noumenal self is objective and rational. Acting according to the rational, noumenal self is to have freedom and autonomy; acting according to the phenomenal self is to be a slave to base instincts, and therefore against reason. This is to lower oneself to the status of a creature, to be non-human. Paradoxically, when human reason conforms to the moral law, it is free (self-willed) and autonomous (self-governing). When it is controlled by desires/passions or by external rulers such as kings, it is dictated to by another law external to itself (heteronomy – *hetero* = different/other, *nomos* = law).

This conclusion about the rational, noumenal self leads Kant to say that:

- all moral laws must be universal – they must be obeyed by all people at all times
- the way to decide which laws are moral is to apply reason to them
- if reason is universal, then any law based on reason will be universal and therefore applicable to everyone.

In the *Groundwork of the Metaphysics of Morals*, Kant sketches what these moral rules are and how they are created by reason.

The Good Will:
Kant's term for
acting in accordance
with the moral law
and out of a motive
of duty rather than
for pleasure or to
achieve a desired
outcome. The Good
Will is intrinsically
good. Unlike other
goods such as
pleasure, wealth, or
health, the Good Will
cannot be used for
bad purposes; the
Good Will is good
without exception,
an honourable
motive even if the
consequences
do not turn out as
hoped.

The Good Will

Kant's aim in the *Groundwork of the Metaphysics of Morals* was to give an overview of Moral Philosophy, so that people could develop a clear understanding of how they should make moral decisions. He begins the *Groundwork* with these words: '*It is impossible to conceive of anything in the world, or even out of it, which can be called good without qualification, except a Good Will*' (Kant, *Groundwork*, Cambridge Texts in the History of Philosophy, ed. Mary Gregor, Cambridge University Press, 1997, p. 7).

As he is a deontologist, Kant says that the moral law, if it is to be unconditionally and universally obeyed, must be unconditionally and universally good. This good must be good in itself and the highest good. He calls this the *summum bonum*. He clarifies what he means by excluding some possibilities. The highest good cannot be anything that depends on the results or consequences it produces, because this would be teleological, not deontological. Many factors other than reason, and therefore outside of our control, might influence the results. The Good Will comes about when a person acts rationally and gets rid of his inclinations or wishes (as these would be contrary to rational decision-making). Kant also dispenses with the 'talents of the mind' like intelligence, wit and judgement. He rules out various 'qualities of temperament' like courage, perseverance and resolution. Eliminated also are the 'gifts of fortune' – power, wealth and honour, as well as the motive of happiness. None of these can produce the Good Will. He does not say that any of these characteristics are necessarily wrong. They may be admirable qualities for any individual to possess, but they are not a reliable guide to the intrinsic rightness of moral behaviour. Each of these characteristics is rejected by Kant because it is capable of making a situation morally worse. The Good Will must, for Kant, be intrinsically good, or 'good without qualification', i.e. it cannot be capable of reducing the moral worth of a situation.

Exercise

Make a list of each of the characteristics Kant rejects above, and then give an example of how they might make a situation morally worse. For example, an 'intelligent' blackmailer is more likely to succeed in extorting money from his victim.

The concept of the Good Will must assume that people are free to make rational and unconditioned moral choices. Without this prerequisite, there can, for Kant, be no morality, as morality assumes that an individual has the real ability to choose freely to do the right thing, or the wrong thing. If individuals do not have this freedom of decision-making, then they are not moral agents, just mere automatons.

Kant has shown by this point that it is not the consequences of an action that make it right, and that individuals must be able to make free decisions. What is of paramount importance for Kant in terms of the Good Will is having the right intention. The person's motive for performing any moral action is of the utmost importance, not the consequences. He says: 'A good will is not good because of what it effects or accomplishes . . . It is good through its willing alone – that is, good in itself.' For example, if someone avoids running a child over with her car, and the car then crashes into a house, that person would not be thought of as acting wrongly. Although there were unfortunate consequences to her action, her motive for saving the child was correct. We would think of that person as being brave and doing 'the right' thing. Her action was motivated for the right reason – to save the life of the child. The fact that she put her own life in danger did not occur to her; the fact that she might be praised as a brave person afterwards did not occur to her; she wanted to stop the child from being run over. For Kant, this would be an example of the Good Will in action.

God, freedom and the afterlife: three assumptions of practical reasoning necessary to the *summum bonum*

> . . .practical reason is based on a duty to make the Summum Bonum the object of my will so as to promote it with all my strength. In doing so, I must presuppose its possibility and also its conditions, which are God, freedom, and immortality.
>
> (Kant, *Critique of Pure Reason*)

Clumsy with his hands, Kant was not cut out to follow his father into the harness-making business, but he did learn from him the importance of hard work and truth-telling. He records an incident from his childhood in which his father became involved in a heated labour dispute between the harness-makers' guild (which his father represented) and the saddle-makers' guild. Kant observed that his father conducted himself among other ill-tempered and self-interested people with forbearance, love and honesty towards the opposing party and the incident left its mark on him. In disputes like this, it is tempting to give up the hope that happiness and virtue ought to correspond, and to fight fire with fire, being as mean-spirited and pragmatic as those who deal unfairly with you. He acknowledged that 'a virtuous disposition is just as likely to increase the pain of this life' (*Lectures on Ethics*, Collins, 27:303).

Kant wants to iron out contradictions in our practical reasoning about the moral law. Firstly, we feel a duty to seek the highest good, yet a perfect alignment between virtue and happiness is unachievable in this lifetime and there is little point in aiming at an end goal that is unachievable. So, to keep faith with it, we must assume **the existence of an afterlife**. Even after death, we can progress and perfect our virtue to fulfil completely the demands of the moral law.

Secondly, we must postulate or assume **the existence of God**. In Kant's moral argument, he argues that the moral life requires belief in the real possibility of the highest good: that a moral law originates from a moral lawgiver. This is an important point to grasp. In saying that happiness is proportioned to duty, Kant is not urging us to be moral in order to earn some happiness external to virtue. Rather, the end goal of the *summum bonum* is that happiness be in proportionate to perfection, so virtue or duty is its own reward. So to aim for this end goal, we must believe this to be possible, and it would only be so if there exists 'a higher, moral most holy, and omnipotent being who alone can unite the two elements of this good' (*Religion Within the Limits of Reason Alone*, 6:6–7). The characteristics of this 'head of the kingdom of ends' perfectly align virtue and happiness, and this being is 'a cause of all nature, distinct from nature which contains the ground of the exact coincidence of happiness with morality' (*Lectures on Ethics*, 27:302). God, with unlimited power and benevolence, understands the moral law and governs in accordance with it.

God's existence must be postulated to make the moral law meaningful, but Kant doesn't believe that reason can prove God's existence. This is because, firstly, we are sensible beings in a phenomenal world and can only take 'weak glances' into 'the realm of the supersensible' or the noumenal realm. Secondly, in the providence of God, it is best that speculative reason is unable to prove his existence, or else we might lose our freedom to act out of duty to the moral law, and conform to it out of hope or fear, given that 'God and eternity with their awful majesty would stand unceasingly before our eyes' (quotations from *Kant's Critique of Practical Reason*, 5:147).

A third postulate of practical reasoning is **freedom**. In *Religion Within the Limits of Reason Alone* (6:50, p. 94), Kant writes, 'For if the moral law commands that we *ought* to be better human beings now, it inescapably follows that we must be *capable* of being better human beings.' If doing our duty is to be meaningful, we must suppose that we are sufficiently free and responsible to obey the commands of the moral law. We would not feel the sense of duty and obligation if it were impossible to fulfil it. You do not feel responsible for causing the Syrian refugee crisis, because there was nothing you could have done to prevent it. But suppose you came across a Syrian refugee of school age in your neighbourhood. They cannot afford books or clothes, and they ask you for help. Then you sense a duty to help because you are free and capable of responding.

With our freedom, we may well ask, 'Why should I conform to the demands of the moral law?' Kant's answer is to say that the autonomous (self-governing) rational person can see that to fail to do so would be to be contradictory in their reasoning. They could make a **contradiction in conception**, like saying 'Everyone should just take and keep whatever they want of anyone else's.' This thought is contradictory, because the very concepts of ownership and theft would disappear as concepts if such a state of affairs were universalised. As Kant says, 'Some actions are so constituted that their consequences cannot even be thought without contradiction as a universal law of nature.' An example of a **contradiction in nature** would be a lying promise. Each time I lie to borrow money, I erode the trust that allows me to borrow. This is a practical contradiction between willing: (a) that I be able to borrow money on a false promise when needed; and (b) that this be universalised, thereby ending all loans.

Duty

Kant says that acting according to the Good Will, i.e. unselfishly, is the same as acting according to 'duty'. He gives an example to illustrate what he means by duty.

> It certainly accords with duty that a grocer should not overcharge his inexperienced customer; and where there is much competition a sensible shop-keeper refrains from so doing and keeps to a fixed and general price for everybody so that a child can buy from

him just as well as anyone else. Thus people are served honestly; but this is not nearly enough to justify us in believing that the shopkeeper has acted in this way from duty or from principles of fair dealing; his interest required him to do so. We cannot assume him to have in addition an immediate inclination towards his customers, leading him, as it were out of love, to give no man preference over another in the matter of price. Thus the action was neither from duty nor from immediate inclination, but solely from purposes of self-interest.

(I. Kant, *Groundwork to the Metaphysics of Morals*, ed. Mary Gregor, Cambridge University Press 1997 p. 63)

Kant is here explaining that the grocer is not acting according to duty. He is merely acting according to his own selfish interests. Keeping prices the same for all customers is good for business; if he charged different people different prices, he would get a bad reputation and would not be trusted by customers, and could easily find himself out of business. It might be that the grocer is honest by inclination, but this, says Kant, is not the Good Will in action. The grocer may gain pleasure from treating customers honestly, but he is not due any praise for something that comes naturally to him. It is merely a coincidence that his action is the same as the Good Will, but he has a selfish motive in performing it – to do what he enjoys. It may be that he would treat his customers differently if his circumstances changed – if perhaps he no longer enjoyed treating them fairly, or his business was in financial trouble, etc. So this is not an example of the Good Will.

QUICK QUESTION
Why ought the grocer to be honest? Out of duty, self-interest (he's after customer loyalty and repeat business) or inclination that results from training in virtue?

If a person is to do the Good Will, they must be acting in accord with duty. This means that in disregard of personal motive they do things because it is their duty, rather than because they will gain something for themselves from it, whether it is personal pleasure, a sense of importance, praise from others, or whatever other reason. Shedding all personal motives allows those acting from the Good Will to act in accordance with reason, so that the noumenal self is in control; the good person's only motive in doing the right thing is their awareness that they are doing it out of their sense of duty and for no other reason. They act morally because it is the right thing to do.

The Categorical Imperative

According to Kant, being a moral person has to do with acting according to duty. This duty is universal, because reason is universal. This means that acting morally (according to the Good Will) is something 'good-in-itself', rather than merely instrumentally good, or good because of the consequences it brings. It is at this point that Kant introduces the principle of the **Categorical Imperative**.

An imperative is a command, something that you ought to do. There are two kinds of imperative: the hypothetical, and the categorical.

A hypothetical imperative takes the form 'If x, then y'. For example, 'If you want to achieve an A* grade in your RS A Level, then you must work very hard.' Here, the result (gaining an A* grade) is dependent upon the means (working very hard). If, however, you do not want to gain an A* grade in RS, the command is not relevant

Categorical Imperative:
This is Kant's test for knowing whether a proposed action is good or not. He discusses three main versions of the Categorical Imperative.

for you. Of course, for Kant, it is clear that the hypothetical imperative is not the imperative of morality. 'Working very hard' is not seen as a good thing in itself, it is merely a means to an end, and it is not universally applicable. He rejects the hypothetical imperative because it is only an instrumental good, not an intrinsic good.

A categorical imperative takes the form 'Do x' (or 'Do not do x'). For example, 'Tell the truth' and 'Respect your teachers' are examples of categorical imperatives. The Categorical Imperative is a command which is 'good-in-itself'. It is universal, as it applies to everyone; it is unconditional, as it is not dependent upon circumstances or situations. The Categorical Imperative would be followed by any rational person; it is an end in itself, not a means to an end. For Kant, the Categorical Imperative is the 'imperative of morality'. Moral duties are followed for the sake of duty alone, not because of any ancillary gain. As Peter Vardy notes, 'Categorical imperatives are arrived at through practical reason and they are understood as a basis for action' (Vardy, *The Puzzle of Ethics*, 1996, p. 68).

Hypothetical Imperatives are conditional on situations or feelings. Such feelings can be fickle in turning an 'If X' (e.g., if you want to save a cute panda, but not an ugly bird like a rare bearded vulture) into a 'Then Y' (then you need to give generously to a conservation project to save it). We might see Kant as a closet consequentialist who seeks the greatest good by universalising rules, but this would be a mistake. Michael Sandel points out that Mill saw Kant's test of whether he could universalise

Mill vs Kant

the principle behind his actions as 'making a consequentialist argument after all' (*Justice*, Penguin, 2010). For Mill, rules (even universal ones like the Categorical Imperative) were good insofar as they were useful in maximising welfare. Sandel shows that Mill misunderstood Kant's thinking on this point. Kant's purpose in universalising the principles behind actions was to scrutinise motives and distinguish those who acted out of Good Will from those who acted out of self-interest in making exceptions to rules; unlike Mill, his aim was not to optimise outcomes. Mill's position is neatly illustrated in Zac Brown's cartoon.

Kant wrote about the Categorical Imperative in different books, over a number of years and using different wording. He expresses the Categorical Imperative in three major formulations. In each, he is attempting to establish a test for showing whether our maxims can become universal moral principles. He does this because he wants our moral thinking to be as certain as the rules underlying mathematics and logic. To establish universally binding moral principles would mean for Kant that everyone must obey them, and that they will be acting in accordance with reason and moral rules will be incapable of contradiction.

Formula of the law of nature: 'So act that the maxim of your will could always hold at the same time as a principle establishing universal law'

Kant gives four examples to explain how the Categorical Imperative works.

Suicide

A person feels so full of despair about his quality of life that he contemplates committing suicide. He still has his powers of reason, however, and asks himself whether committing suicide would be contrary to his duty to himself. Could his maxim count as a universal law of nature? His maxim is: 'From self-love I make it my principle to shorten my life when continuing it would lead to more evil than pleasure.' Kant says that we can see immediately that this would lead to a contradiction – life is a fundamental principle in nature, so any action that would take it away would be against nature. Therefore, Kant argues that suicide is always morally wrong.

Borrowing money

A man needs to borrow money, but knows that he will not be able to pay it back. He also knows that no one will lend him money unless they think he will repay it. Should he ask to borrow money and lie about his intention and ability to pay it back? His maxim would be: 'When I believe myself to be in need of money I shall borrow it and promise to repay it, even though I know this will never happen.' Kant asks again what would happen if this became a universal law. It is clear that this could never become a universal law as, if everyone made promises that they had no intention of keeping, the whole institution of promise-keeping would be meaningless. No one would believe anyone who promised to do anything, and, in Kant's words, 'would laugh at all such expressions of vain pretences'.

Talent

Another person has a talent that could be useful in a number of different contexts. However, this person has a comfortable life and he prefers to give himself over to pleasurable pursuits rather than cultivating his talent. He still asks himself whether this could be a universal law, so that everyone should live for pleasure and neglect their natural gifts. He concludes that it *is* consistent with reason and duty for all people to do this, and devote their lives to 'idleness, amusement, procreation – in a word, to enjoyment'. However, Kant says, this person cannot possibly *will* that this should become a universal law, because, as a rational being, he necessarily wills that all the capacities in him should be developed, because they serve him and are given to him for all sorts of possible purposes.

Selfishness

Everything is going well in life for someone, but he sees that other people have to struggle to survive. He could help them without much difficulty or hardship to himself. Should he do this? He considers the maxim: 'Let each person be as happy as heaven wills or as he can make himself; I shall take nothing from him nor even envy him; only I do not care to contribute anything to his welfare or to his assistance in need.' According to Kant, this maxim could be applied universally, because there is nothing logically inconsistent in it. However, for Kant, we could not possibly *will* that this ought to become a universal law. This is because it might backfire on us, as, if we needed help at some point in our lives, no one would help us.

These four examples show that Kant understands the Categorical Imperative in two different ways. First, he understands the morality of actions as being decided by whether they are self-contradictory according to reason and logic. The first two scenarios are examples of what Kant calls *contradictions in the law of nature.* These are rules that do not make logical sense – they contradict themselves if applied to all people. Examples of such a contradiction would be 'Open the door but do not open the door', or 'Hold this but do not hold it.' These commands simply do not make sense. For Kant, committing suicide and failure to keep promises are self-contradictory if they are applied to all people all the time.

The final two scenarios are different; they are not logically self-contradictory, but what Kant calls *contradictions in the will.* No rational person would wish these laws to be universally applicable, because they are unacceptable. They are unacceptable because no one could possibly want to have a situation where they were in need but no one would help them. Holding that people should be selfish is counter to what we would want if we needed help ourselves. In this case, the contradiction lies in making universal a rule that might later be used against us.

Formula of the end in itself: 'Act in such a way that you always treat humanity, whether in your own person or in the person of any other, never simply as a means, but always at the same time as an end

This is known as the 'formula of the end in itself'. Kant argues that it is always morally wrong to treat people as a means to an end. They should be treated as 'ends in themselves', as having their own needs, desires and rights. It would be wrong, then, to become friends with someone simply because you could gain some benefit from that friendship. In this case, you would be treating them as a means to an end. All human beings, according to Kant, merely by being human, have certain rights, one of which is to be treated as equal to ourselves. Kant is here stating the important principle of the equality of every human being, irrespective of race, colour, class, gender, age or social status.

This principle runs counter to the Utilitarian principle of 'the greatest good of the greatest number'. If a law were enacted, or a decision made, that would benefit the majority of people in a community but where a minority were thereby disadvantaged, Kant would object to it on the basis of this second formulation of the Categorical Imperative.

Exercise

Find out about the Bakun Dam in Indonesia, which was instigated to produce hydro-electric power to benefit hundreds of thousands of people, but which required the flooding of a significant area which was home to 10,000 tribespeople and many indigenous animal and plant species. What would Kant have said about this plan?

Formula of the kingdom of ends: 'Act as if you were, through your maxims, a law-making member of a kingdom of ends'

Kant here describes a possible community where all the members have similar ideas about what is good. They make laws on the basis of making rational decisions which are consistent with the laws of logic. The laws made by this community will be accepted by everyone in it and, if there were any disputes, these would be resolved by using rational arguments. Kant was not enough of an idealist to believe that this could actually happen in practice, but he said that it was important to attempt to make it happen, as most humans are rational and want to live in harmony with others.

Strengths of Kant's ethics

1. Kant's system is logical and based on the use of the innate ability of all humans to reason.
2. Every human being, just by being human, has the ability to make valid and objective moral decisions.
3. The Categorical Imperative provides a clear and unambiguous method for testing the validity of proposed moral actions.
4. The Categorical Imperative produces moral rules that apply to everyone at all times, thus simplifying moral decision-making.
5. Kant says that the moral value of an action is based on the nature of the action itself, not on any of its potential consequences.
6. Kant's system does away with any special pleading or vested interests, as it is based not on feelings or emotions but on reason. Bias towards family members or national interests, therefore, is avoided.
7. Kant sees all humans as having value and dignity as they have the innate ability to reason. This means that things like paedophilia or the subjugation of women are automatically outlawed. In putting reason before desires, he emphasises the dignity of man compared with beasts.
8. All people should be treated equally, so that the view of a poor person is just as important as that of a rich one.
9. Kant's ethics is independent of any external authority, like God. It works simply on the basis that all people have the ability to reason.
10. It ensures that each individual takes part in moral decision-making by ensuring they are autonomous and free to make rational decisions.

Weaknesses of Kant's ethics

Conflicts of duty

The Existentialist philosopher Jean-Paul Sartre gives the example of a student of his during World War II who was faced with the dilemma of either going to war against the Nazis by joining the Free French fighters, or looking after his aged mother. Sartre writes:

> The Kantian ethic says, never regard another as a means, but always as an end. Very well; if I [the student] remain with my mother, I shall be regarding her as the end and not as a means; but by the same token I am in danger of treating as means those who are fighting on my behalf; and the converse is also true, that if I go to the aid of the combatants I shall be treating them as the end at the risk of treating my mother as a means.

Jean Paul Sartre (1905–80)
Sartre defined French Existentialist philosophy. He was a playwright, novelist and political theorist. In 1980, 50,000 people turned up at the funeral of a philosopher of radical freedom whose work had inspired students in the 1968 student uprising in Paris. He served as a meteorologist for the French Army in 1939 and was captured and imprisoned in 1940. On his release, he considered joining the Resistance but, being unable to decide between the Gaullists and the Communists, instead devoted his time to writing his diaries, *Being and Nothingness*, and his first play. He turned down a Nobel Prize for Literature in 1964, but he is perhaps most remembered for his 1945 lecture 'Existentialism and Humanism' which marked him out as a writer who brought optimism and hope to a post-war generation.

The problem for Sartre in this example, and the problem for many non-Kantians, concerns how helpful Kant's Categorical Imperative actually is when there is a conflict of duty. The conflict for Sartre's student is between the principles of 'caring for your mother' and 'fighting for justice'. Both principles are worthy, and both are universalisable, but the student cannot enact both at the same time.

The conflict of duties raises a significant problem for Kant's theory. To take a different example, if it is always wrong to tell a lie, and always right to keep promises, what should I do if I have to tell a lie in order to keep a promise? Consider what might happen if you have promised your friend that you will hide him from a potential murderer. Do you lie to the murderer when he turns up at your door asking for your friend? More recent followers of Kant agree that he did not give enough thought to this kind of situation, where principles could be in conflict with each other. Modern Kantians say that, because his theory does not help in this situation, we should probably make an exception to the general rule to overcome this difficulty.

'Immanuel Kant – ruining date night since 1785'

Universalisability

The English-born philosopher Alasdair MacIntyre has noted that it is possible to use Kant's idea of **universalisability** to justify anything: 'All I need to do is to characterise the proposed action in such a way that the maxim will permit me to do what I want while prohibiting others from doing what would nullify the action if universalised' (*A Short History of Ethics*, Routledge Classics, 2002, p. 126).

For example, consider the maxim: 'All people called Mark, living in Manchester and having a cat called Troy, should be given free access to concerts at the Bridgewater Hall.' This maxim could be universalised – it would not be self-contradictory – but it is clearly so specific as to apply to only one person. This is not what Kant had in mind with the principle of universalisability, and is therefore a problem for his ethical system. Some way needs to be found that limits the ability to universalise any maxim but allows valid principles to be formed, which can logically and coherently apply to all people.

> **Universalisability:** Refers to Kant's first version of the Categorical Imperative: what would happen if everyone were to do what is proposed? If a maxim is universalisable, without contradiction, it is the moral thing to do

Abstract nature

One of the real strengths of Kant's ethical theory is that it is powerfully argued, carefully presented and thoroughly abstract. The three formulations of the Categorical Imperative, for example, are very precisely and unambiguously stated. The level of abstraction, however, is also seen as a weakness of the theory. As we have seen above, Kant has concentrated on stating his theory in an abstract way but sometimes does not think through how the theory would actually work in practical situations. Many critics would say that the whole point of an ethical theory is to help with solving practical difficulties and dilemmas in real-life situations. If this is true, Kant's theory fails to deliver. Another way of putting this is that Kant's theory tells us the right *type* of action to do, but does not tell us *what* to do in particular situations.

Lack of humanity

Kant argued that people should perform moral actions because they have the *right intention*. People will be acting morally if they *intend* to do some good, by which he meant doing their duty. In the real world of practical morality, however, most people do not act from 'duty', but because they want to help someone else, perhaps because they feel sorry for them, or because an injustice has been done, or because they want to make things better for the person. That is, they act morally because of the *end* or *result* of their potential action, not because it is their duty to do it. People act out of emotion and a feeling for humanity, not out of (abstract) duty.

Hegel argued that Kant placed too low a value on the place of community in the moral life. The state is not just the total of individuals but an organic culture involving language, social practices and values. Its strength of wanting to universalise maxims can become a weakness if it totally ignores the special relationships that provide the very roots of our morality in terms of kinship-altruism or loyalties and duties that obligate us to, say, care for our children (or parents in later life).

Consequences

Almost all people perform any action, including moral actions, only after thinking about the consequences of that action. For example, in deciding whether I should help the old lady across the road, I would weigh up the pros and cons: Is it a dangerous place to cross? Might she fall on the way across? Will she reward me for helping? Will my friends laugh at me? . . . etc., etc. In a more serious example, would having an abortion be a 'good' thing for the pregnant fifteen-year-old? This would normally be approached by looking at the possible consequences, not by considering whether she would be acting according to duty – that is, according to a principle without thinking about what would happen if . . .?. Kant's theory goes against the way that human beings think and normally operate.

> **Exercise**
>
> Watch the film trailer for *The Remains of the Day* and consider the dutiful butler played by Anthony Hopkins. How does his unquestioning duty to his employer lead him to neglect other duties (to his own flourishing by not falling in love, to the protection of Jewish workers, and to his country in not questioning his Lordship's pact with the Nazis)? Is Kant's own strict and abstemious life after severe ill-health and as a bachelor shaping his moral austerity?

Freedom

In 1947, the English philosopher H. J. Paton in *The Categorical Imperative* (Hutchinson 1947), raised a serious objection to Kant's theory. Kant's ethical theory is founded on two ideas: (1) our innate ability to reason, with which we can build non-contradictory and universalisable principles; and (2) our freedom to agree to do our duty. Paton says: 'we have no independent insight into the alleged necessity for presupposing freedom. Kant is indeed ingenious and, I think, sound in suggesting that freedom . . . is a necessary presupposition of all thinking. This may serve as a defence of the presupposition . . . but it is not sufficient to justify this presupposition' (p. 244).

Many people in the world do not possess the freedom to make valid moral decisions, even if they have the rationality to do so. Thousands of people live under political regimes that take away the freedom of individuals to make decisions which disagree with the government. Many women live in societies where they are limited in doing what they want to do, in terms of either education, dress or personal ambition and freedom. Kant's theory does not recognise the severe limitations for many people on the practical possibilities of acting in accordance with his theory. For these people, Kant's theory is of little value.

On the other hand, the German philosopher Jürgen Habermas (1929–) argues that, in modern societies, nearly all reasoning is instrumental. This is to say that we nearly always think in terms of hypothetical imperatives – 'we think about how to achieve certain ends, while the ends in themselves are not subject to rational assessment (instrumental reason). Thus "reason" may tell me to build divided highways to enhance rapid movement of traffic, but it is not clear how it could tell me that a social organisation requiring such rapid movement is itself "reasonable"' (Norman Lillegard, *The Moral Domain*, Oxford University Press, 2010). So, according to Habermas, Kant provides a much-needed corrective in our times. The dominance of economic growth or technological progress is accepted as reasonable and policies are instruments in delivering these ends. Kant shows us a freer form of reasoning whereby we can stand back and question the dominance of such instrumental reasoning and ask what ends we ought to be pursuing. Is the accumulation of wealth the primary end goal of society? Is what we currently take to be reasonable growth environmentally sustainable? Are the elites who set the terms of the debate really thinking universally or more short-term and out of self-interest? Here, as impractical as Kant's Categorical way of thinking may appear, it could yet help us to recover our freedom to think outside of the acceptance that the way things are is the way they ought to be and always will be. We are given grounds to critique the worst aspects of instrumental reasoning in public life.

Limiting human characteristics

Following on from the previous criticism, another important point to make concerns the narrow focus of Kant's theory. He argues that the ability to reason is the sole characteristic that should be considered in making moral rules. In this, he was following in a lofty tradition reaching back to Plato, Aristotle and Descartes. Many philosophers, however, have taken issue with this view and argued that reason is not the most important human capability. The Scottish philosopher David Hume (much admired by Kant), for instance, said that reason should be less important than the emotions, needs and desires of an individual. He famously said: 'reason is and ought only to be the slave of the passions, and can never pretend to any other office than to serve and obey them'.

Many people, then, use other human characteristics to establish ways of acting morally. Virtue ethicists, for instance, look at a range of characteristics that humans have – courage, honesty, sense of justice, practical wisdom, understanding, among others. A further point, made by Alasdair MacIntyre in *After Virtue: A Study in Moral Theory* (2007), is that Kant not only uses only one human characteristic to determine his moral theory, but also assumes that this ability to reason is set at birth and does not develop as a person goes through life. Virtue ethicists, like Aristotle, argue that humans begin life as *potentially* good persons; they only become *actual* good persons by putting into practice the moral and intellectual virtues. People have to practise doing good things if they are eventually to become morally fulfilled people. Our ability to make the 'right' decisions in moral dilemmas, that is to say, is not innately part of our character; we have to develop this ability, through the practice of a number of qualities of mind and character. Just as a good musician needs to practise their instrument, often for years, before they become proficient, so a person who wants to be proficient at making moral decisions needs to practise using their qualities, throughout their lifetime. Kant was wrong, therefore, to assume that: (1) reason is the only relevant characteristic in making moral decisions; and (2) it is present and fully developed from the moment of birth, without the need for development.

1. Think of an example of a country where an individual's freedom to act morally is impossible or severely limited. What would Kant say about their moral duty in such cases?

2. Whilst a world where people break all their promises or always lie to avoid taxes would fail to work, what if this only happened rarely or infrequently? In cases where people did so, it would lower the general level of trust and increase the costs to honest citizens, but, as in our own world, a lack of universal goodness does not cause society to collapse. What would Kant say to this pragmatic defence?

3. One example of a Hypothetical Imperative is 'If you want to be successful in life, be generous to your friends', and one of a Categorical Imperative is 'Always tell the truth and never lie! This is your duty.' Think of one more example of each.

4. Would it be a contradiction of the will to say 'Look out for yourself and disregard the needs of others, and will that others leave you alone when you are in need'? How would Kant respond to this objection?

5. In his lectures on ethics, Kant comments on people as having the dignity of beings as ends in themselves. He writes, 'Everything has either a price or a dignity. If it has a price, something else can be put in its place as an equivalent; if it is exalted above all price and so admits of no equivalent, then it has a dignity.' Would this give Kant grounds to argue that prostitution (even where consent is given) ought to be made illegal?

6. Although Kant emphasises the law-like quality of the Categorical Imperative, he argues that only when we are not governed by heteronomy (ruled by another law, such as happiness, virtuous inclination or consequences) are we autonomous or truly free-thinking individuals. How does reason make us free according to Kant?

7. Kant seems to set up emotion as an obstacle to fulfilling the moral law. But could I feel that an action were both my duty and a privilege and source of happiness or fulfilment (such as caring for an elderly parent or, as a soldier, fighting for my country?) What would Kant say for and against this?

8. How, in Habermas' view, can Kant's Categorical Imperative prove more relevant to our times than ever?

Amendments to Kant's theory

The twentieth-century British intuitivist philosopher W. D. Ross was a critic of Kantian Ethics. He thought that, in boiling ethics down to universal rules or to the one motive of the Good Will, Kant had oversimplified the moral life. Kant mistakenly supposed the moral life to be a 'contest between one element which alone has worth [i.e. the Good Will] and a multitude of others which have none; the truth is rather that it is a struggle between the multiplicity of desires having various degrees of worth' (*Foundations of Ethics*, 1939, 206). Kant's idea that moral rules have 'absolute authority admitting of no exception' (*Foundations of Ethics*, 313) also neglects our intuition that a wide range of sometimes conflicting duties need to be taken into account. In his books *The Right and the Good* (1930), *Foundations of Ethics* (1939) and *Kant's Ethical Theory* (1954), Ross proposed that a better way of responding to the problem of conflicting duties is to explore 'prima facie' duties, which allow us to make exceptions. Prima facie means 'at first sight', and a **prima facie duty** is one that is conditional and allowing of exception. This kind of duty can always be overridden by a different duty if the occasion arises. So, for instance, the command to 'Always tell the truth' is a prima facie duty, which may take second place to a more important duty, such as 'Always keep your promises', if the situation demands this. If it is normally our duty to 'tell the truth', this should be the way we operate unless there is a more important and compelling duty in a particular instance.

Ross lists seven prima facie duties:

Prima facie duty: W. D. Ross' attempt to clarify a difficulty with Kant's theory. When there is a conflict of duty, Ross suggests that they are put in order of importance.

1.	Duties of fidelity or promise-keeping	I act in accordance with a promise I made previously
2.	Duties of reparation for harm done	I act to make amends for something I did wrong previously
3.	Duties of gratitude	I act to repay a debt of some kind
4.	Duties of justice	I act in order to gain an equal distribution of pleasure and happiness
5.	Duties of beneficence	I act so that others will benefit, particularly in terms of virtue, intelligence or pleasure
6.	Duties of self-improvement	I act in order to improve my own intelligence or virtue
7.	Duties of non-maleficence	I refrain from doing anyone else any harm

The first three of these duties have to do with past events; the others look to the future. Ross stresses the personal character of our duties, which all have to do with other individuals. He was also aware that this list was not complete or definitive. Ross anticipates that a person will use these seven duties in any order depending upon the situation. If someone regularly gives money to a charity for homeless people, for example, then the duty of beneficence would be appropriate, as they would be acting for the benefit of someone other than themselves.

Ross' idea of prima facie duties is not without difficulties and has not been accepted by all modern Kantian scholars. There are two important sticking points with his list of duties:

How do we know what a prima facie duty actually is?

Ross places emphasis on the role of intelligence in his list of duties, but why should we agree with this? Ross was an academic philosopher, who spent his time discussing issues and matters which were of little or no concern to people outside the university. Why should we not come up with a different list of prima facie duties, using (for example) developing musical ability, or driving a car, or knowing how to behave at a dinner party? His list can be considered to be rather arbitrary, and different people could come up with a quite different list of duties.

What happens when there is a conflict of interest?

Ross says little about what should happen when there is a conflict of interest. Surely, however, any moral system must be judged by whether it can successfully navigate through conflicting moral rules. Ross does not provide any guidance about how to prioritise his seven duties. He says that we would intuitively 'know' which rule to prioritise in a given situation, as we apply reason in specific circumstances. This is not very helpful, though, as different individuals could disagree and Ross' system would be useless.

Discussion Questions

1. Work through Ross' list of seven duties, giving an example for each one.
2. Ross is trying to deal with an issue that in his view, Kant leaves unresolved – what to do when duties conflict. In your view, do moral intuitions solve this problem? Is intuition something Kant would have accepted in his moral universe – is it a type of reasoning or quite apart from it?
3. Is Kant right to give greater moral respect to the dutiful worker who is tempted to steal from their employer but resists from a sense of duty to the moral law, than to one who is by nature honest and works to the very best of their ability out of loyalty to their boss and a sense of pride gained from their work?

Exercise

Read the following paragraph and then discuss whether you agree with the list of moral rules presented. Give reasons for agreeing or disagreeing.

One example of a philosopher who has produced a competing list of moral rules is the contemporary American philosopher Bernard Gert. Gert says in his book *Common Morality: Deciding What to Do* (2004) that morality can be summed up in a list of moral rules, and that each rule in his list is rationally accepted by everyone. He does not mean that all people will accept all the rules all the time, but that, if people were rational, they would accept his list of rules. His list is as follows: Do not kill; Do not cause pain; Do not disable; Do not deprive people of freedom; Do not deprive people of pleasure; Do not deceive; Keep your promises; Do not cheat; Obey the law; Do your duty.

FURTHER READING

Immanuel Kant *Groundwork of the Metaphysics of Morals*, ch. 2

O. O'Neill (2013). 'Kantian Approaches to Some Famine Problems', in R. Shafer-Landau (ed.) *Ethical Theory: An Anthology*. Wiley-Blackwell

L. Pojman (2012) *Discovering Right and Wrong*. Wadsworth

Roger Scruton (2001) *Kant: A Very Short Introduction*. Oxford University Press

Sally Sedgwick (2008) *Kant's Groundwork of the Metaphysics of Morals: An Introduction*. Cambridge University Press

Roger J. Sullivan (1994) *An Introduction to Kant's Ethics*. Cambridge University Press

Jennifer K. Uleman (2010) *An Introduction to Kant's Moral Philosophy*. Cambridge University Press

Thought Points

(1) Explain what Kant means by 'duty'.

(2) Explain the difference between 'hypothetical' and 'categorical' imperatives.

(3) Do you think that hypothetical imperatives are more valuable than categorical imperatives in making moral decisions?

(4) To what extent do you agree that doing one's duty is the most important idea in Kant's moral theory?

(5) 'There are more strengths than weaknesses in Kant's moral theory.' Do you agree?

(6) Explain the differences between the three versions of the Categorical Imperative in Kant's thought.

(7) Discuss the view that the universalization of maxims by Kant cannot be defended.

(8) 'Kant's theory is more useful in making moral decisions than Utilitarianism.' Discuss this statement.

SECTION III

APPLIED ETHICS

5 Euthanasia

In this chapter you will learn about key ideas, including

- sanctity of life
- quality of life
- voluntary euthanasia
- non-voluntary euthanasia
- You will understand how to apply the moral theories of Natural Law and Situation Ethics to euthanasia.
  - ○ You will be able to assess critically . . .
  - ○ whether or not the religious concept of sanctity of life has any meaning in 21st-century medical ethics
  - ○ whether or not a person should or can have complete autonomy over their own life and decisions made about it
  - ○ whether or not there is a moral difference between medical intervention to end a patient's life (commission) and medical non-intervention to end a patient's life (omission)

Introduction: definitions

Euthanasia:
Bringing about the death of a person in a painless and gentle way for their benefit. Sometimes called 'mercy killing'.

The term '**euthanasia**' (or 'mercy killing') comes from the Greek word *'eu'* meaning 'good' and *'thanatos'* meaning 'death', so it means 'to die well'. Essentially, euthanasia means to bring about the death of a person who no longer wants to live, but is not in a position to end their life by themselves. Usually, such a person is suffering from an incurable or degenerative disease. Key to the definition of euthanasia is the idea that bringing about the death of the person is for his or her benefit. However, as we shall see, there are exceptions to this brief definition.

The first recorded use of the word 'euthanasia' was by the Roman historian Suetonius in his *De Vita Caesarum – Divus Augustus* (*The Lives of the Caesars – The*

Divine Augustus), ch. 99, to describe the death of Augustus Caesar. However, Augustus' death, while termed 'a euthanasia', was not brought about by the actions of any other person – rather, it was meant literally as 'an easy death'. The term was first used in a medical context by the English philosopher and statesman Francis Bacon in the early seventeenth century, to refer to an easy, painless, happy death, during which it was a 'physician's responsibility to alleviate the "physical sufferings" of the body'.

A brief history of euthanasia

Euthanasia was widely practised in the ancient world. The Stoic philosopher Epictetus thought that both euthanasia and **suicide** were acceptable options for individuals who no longer believed that they had any quality of life. Plato, in the early dialogues the *Apology* and the *Crito*, has Socrates say that death is nothing bad, is nothing fearful, is preferable to incurable disease, and will be a great gain for an afflicted individual.

Suicide:
A person takes his/her own life voluntarily and intentionally

The physician Hippocrates lived around the same time as Plato, but almost nothing is known about him, except that he was of small stature. The 'Hippocratic Oath', which all doctors promise to uphold, was formulated many centuries after his death. His writings, on all aspects of medicine, only exist in fragments, and many later books on medicine were ascribed to Hippocrates. Over the centuries, Hippocrates has acquired the reputation of being the epitome of the ideal physician and is referred to as 'the father of medicine'. It is not known what he actually thought about euthanasia. He is quoted as having said 'I will give no deadly medicine to anyone if asked, nor suggest any such counsel.'

The early Christian Church was opposed to the killing of humans in every context. Infanticide was forbidden, on the grounds that every human being, regardless of his/her quality of life, contained an immortal soul given by God. Suicide was forbidden because one's life was given by God, and only God had the right to take it away. Also, in the medieval period, Natural Law argued against euthanasia because this went against the Primary Precept of self-preservation.

In more recent times, during and after the Enlightenment, many philosophers tentatively moved away from Christian moral norms and argued that the religious foundation of doctrines concerning euthanasia were no longer justified. Philosophers such as Immanuel Kant and Wilhelm Friedrich Hegel argued that human reason and individual conscience should be used as the primary source of moral decision-making.

Both Kant and Hegel believed that moral truths are known through the use of reason alone. Though they tackled euthanasia from a different angle from that of Christian thinkers, they ended up agreeing with religious views, arguing that suicide and euthanasia were immoral. A notable exception to this way of thinking was the great Scottish philosopher David Hume, who argued strongly that any individual has the right to end their life when he or she pleases. Hume mercilessly criticised the theological arguments on the **Sanctity of Life (SoL)**.

SoL:
Sanctity of (human) Life: the belief that human life is made in God's image and is therefore sacred.

In the nineteenth century, a much more secular approach to morality became popular, mainly thanks to the writings of Utilitarian philosophers like Jeremy Bentham and John Stuart Mill. Bentham and Mill formulated a deceptively simple question: does providing a painless death for people who are dying in pain increase or decrease human happiness? As the main aim of the Principle of Utility was to increase the amount or quality of human happiness and avoid pain, the Utilitarians argued in favour of euthanasia and suicide as being morally correct.

Mill said that an individual is sovereign over his own body and mind; where his own interests are concerned, there is no other authority. Therefore, if a person wants to die quickly rather than linger in pain, that is purely a personal matter, and the government should not interfere. In fact, Bentham actually requested euthanasia at the end of his life.

Several significant movements and developments progressed the discussion during the twentieth century. In 1920, German authors Alfred Hoche and Karl Binding published the book *Permitting the Destruction of Life Not Worthy of Life*. They argued that patients who ask for 'death assistance' should, under very carefully controlled conditions, be able to obtain it from a physician. This book paved the way for the programme of involuntary euthanasia under the Nazi regime. Beginning in 1939, Hitler initiated a widespread programme for the 'mercy killing' of the sick and disabled. Using the code name 'Aktion T4', this enforced euthanasia programme focused on newborn and very young children, but it quickly expanded to include older disabled children and adults. Ultimately, this was further extended to include any and all people who did not meet the Nazi definition of 'human', and led to the enforced death of millions of Jews and other non-Aryan peoples.

Other landmarks in the history of euthanasia include the following.

In 1935, the Euthanasia Society of England was formed to promote euthanasia. In 1942, Switzerland passed a law allowing terminally ill people to take their own lives. In 2000, three foreigners committed suicide in Zurich. In 2001, the number of death tourists travelling to Zurich rose to thirty-eight, plus twenty more in Bern. Most of the deaths occurred in an apartment rented by Dignitas, an organisation which promotes an individual's right to choose to die and campaigns for this right to be made legal in other countries. The number of people who travel to Switzerland is increasing year on year.

In 1995, Australia's Northern Territory approved a euthanasia bill. This came into effect in 1996 but was quickly overturned by the Australian Parliament in 1997.

Rising numbers of UK citizens travelling to the Swiss Dignitas Clinic have brought media pressure to bear on the Director of Public Prosecutions and parliamentary legislators to alter the law – or its interpretation – on assisted dying.

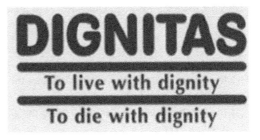

DIGNITAS
To live with dignity
To die with dignity

In 1998, the US state of Oregon legalised **assisted suicide**. Oregon remained the only US state to support any form of euthanasia until 2008, when the state of Washington also legalised assisted suicide.

In 1999, retired pathologist and advocate of **physician-assisted suicide** Dr Jack Kevorkian was sentenced to a 10- to 25-year prison term for second degree murder and giving a lethal injection to Thomas Youk, whose death was shown on CBS News' *60 Minutes* programme.

In 2000, the Netherlands legalised euthanasia, after tacitly accepting it for many years previously. Belgium followed suit in 2002.

> **Assisted suicide:**
> A deliberate act that causes death, undertaken by one person with the primary intention of ending the life of another person, in order to relieve the second person's suffering

---

Case study: Jack Kevorkian (1928–2011) – Dr Death, Jack the Dripper

My aim in helping the patient was not to cause death. My aim was to end suffering. It's got to be decriminalized.

Kevorkian worked for many years as a pathologist, but gained worldwide fame in the 1990s for his claim to have assisted at least 130 terminally or chronically ill patients to end their lives. These included people suffering from diseases such as cancer, arthritis, heart disease, emphysema and multiple sclerosis. He developed a 'suicide machine', which he called a 'Thanatron', to help people take their own lives. The first client to use this machine was Janet Adkins, a 53-year-old who suffered from Alzheimer's disease. (The machine was put up for auction in 2011, but withdrawn after it failed to reach the reserve price.) He was imprisoned in 1999 for second degree murder, after sending a videotape of himself euthanising a terminally ill man to the CBS *60 Minutes* programme.

Kevorkian was prophetic in calling for the creation of euthanasia clinics, which now exist in Switzerland. In 2009, the film *You Don't Know Jack*, was made, starring Al Pacino as Kevorkian. Kevorkian died in 2011 from a long-standing kidney complaint and pneumonia. Among his supporters, he was seen as a pioneering reformer, even a liberator from their suffering. Yet some of those who came to him for assisted dying were misdiagnosed and were not terminally ill. Had they been properly treated, they may well not have wanted to die. In the end, the courts deemed that he had progressed from assisted suicide to **active euthanasia**.

> **Physician-assisted suicide:**
> A qualified doctor prescribes a drug which assists a person to take their own life

> **Active euthanasia:**
> Someone (e.g. a relative or a doctor) brings about another person's death for the second person's benefit, at their request

---

Exercise

As you begin to consider the issue, list in descending order of importance, what you consider to be the most (1) and least (7) important issues in the euthanasia debate. You may exclude options but justify why these do not influence your judgement.

[_] Financial costs to the taxpayer of the treatment of a growing population of elderly patients.

[_] The quality of life a patient has – whether they consider their life to be a burden or a benefit to themselves.

[_] The Sanctity of Life – a commitment to the giftedness of life which no human being has the right to end.

[_] Whether doctor–patient trust is harmed by legalising euthanasia.

[_] The ability to implement an effective euthanasia policy that gives a choice to patients who are terminally ill, in pain, and looking for death with dignity.

[_] Ensuring that regulation of euthanasia can prevent unscrupulous doctors or next of kin from putting pressure on others who do not want to be a burden but would rather live.

[_] Avoidance of elderly people being made to feel a burden to their next of kin and sensing that the 'honourable' course of action is to seek physician-assisted suicide.

Ethical issues in euthanasia

Quality of Life (QoL)

One of the major ethical issues in the euthanasia debate concerns the 'quality' of a person's life, particularly at the end of their life. Decisions have to be made not only about the quantity of life a person has left to live, but also about its quality. We live in a society where we are used to people living long lives, and technology is capable of helping people to live longer, but, when they become irreversibly ill, the question has to be raised whether it is appropriate to keep them alive at all costs. Should those who suffer from severe dementia, debilitating physical illnesses and psychological conditions be kept alive until 'nature takes its course'? Or, given also that there is an ever-increasing number of people in the world and only a limited amount of resources, should individuals and medical professionals take a different approach and look to the quality of a person's life and take action to end a person's life when its quality diminishes to a point where it is considered to be not worth living any more?

Quality of Life (QoL):
Quality of Life: a key concept in deciding whether euthanasia is morally justified

The term **Quality of Life (QoL)** refers to a person's total wellbeing, including physical, emotional and social aspects of a person's life. In this sense, QoL is not uniquely an ethical term. In ethical and medical contexts, the term 'Health-Related Quality of Life (HRQoL)' is sometimes used. This focuses the debate on how an individual's wellbeing may be affected by *disease*, *disability* or a *disorder*. In the UK, however, and in most books and discussions on euthanasia, QoL is used in this more specific sense.

Quality Adjusted Life Years (QALY):
A method used by physicians to calculate the Quality of Life of a patient to estimate the number of valuable months or years a patient may live

The way that QoL is assessed is generally by means of a concept called **Quality Adjusted Life Years (QALY)**. This was set out by the National Institute for Health and Care Excellence (NICE). NICE uses an internationally recognised method of calculating an individual's QoL, considering factors such as the level of pain the person is in, their mobility and their general psychological state. They then look at available drugs to treat the person's condition and decide whether a certain drug will bring good value for money in the treatment of a patient. For example, one drug or treatment may help the patient live longer, but may also have serious side effects. A different drug or treatment may not help the patient to live longer, but may give them a better QoL for the time they are alive. The QALY method helps doctors to measure all the relevant factors so that they can compare different treatments for the same and different conditions. A QALY, therefore, gives an idea of how many extra months or years of life of a reasonable quality a person might gain as a result of treatment. Obviously, this is particularly important when considering treatments for chronic conditions, like cancer or Alzheimer's.

Once the doctors have used the QALY measurement to compare how much someone's life can be extended and/or improved with different treatments, they consider cost-effectiveness – that is, how much the drug or treatment costs per QALY. This is the cost of using the drugs to provide a year of the best quality of life available. Cost-effectiveness is expressed as '£ per QALY'. Each drug is considered on a case-by-case basis. Currently, if a treatment costs more than £20,000–30,000 per QALY, it would not be considered cost-effective. Although this appears to be simply a mathematical calculation for doctors to make, there will clearly be a personal response from the doctors and the patient and these will render any decision much more difficult to make and implement.

There are several ethical problems connected to the QoL:

- The question about QoL can appear to assume that an individual life can be quantified. This is particularly evident when the QALY system is used to determine the value of a person's remaining life. Many people would disagree with this kind of assessment.
- The decision about the value of a person's life is put in the hands of a doctor – this gives a great deal of power to that doctor: is this ethically justifiable?
- If such power is given to a doctor, this may change the nature of the doctor–patient relationship. People may not have confidence in their GP or specialist, and this might affect their treatment or state of mind.

> **Physician aid in dying:**
> A qualified doctor administers lethal medicine in order to assist a person who wishes to commit suicide

Sanctity of Life (SoL)

Most Christians are against euthanasia because they believe in the sanctity of human life. They argue that all life was created by God and that humans are made in the image of God. Life, therefore, is a gift from God and this makes humans unique among everything created by God. In Genesis 2:7, God breathes the breath of life into Adam. This implies that there is a special bond between God and humankind, something that is different from the rest of creation. The gift of life is precious, as it reflects something of the nature of God and that humans are made in God's image (Genesis 1:27). As Genesis 9:6 and Exodus 20:13 show, to take away someone's life is to commit murder, and, in a way, this takes away some part of God the creator.

As John Wyatt argues (2009, ch. 10), the idea that humans are made in the image of God has certain implications:

- it means that humans are dependent on God for their lives, because God is in control of every individual's life. See Job 10:8–12, 34:14f., and, especially, Jeremiah 10:23: 'A man's life is not his own; it is not for man to direct his steps.'
- it means that humans are in a relationship with God. Human beings live in relationship with other people (the poet John Donne said 'No man is an island') but they are also in a relationship with God.
- it means that each human life has a unique dignity. Because humans were created by God, this dignity is intrinsic, whether at the beginning or end of

life, whether in health or illness. Life is received as an entrusted gift, not a possession.

- it means that all human beings are equal, so women are equal to men, adults to children, healthy to sick, race to race, powerful to weak. This is because all humans are made of the same Godlike material. Proverbs 22:2 says: 'Rich and poor have this in common: the Lord is the maker of them all.'

These points are claimed to be sufficient reason to argue against euthanasia. In just the same way that murder is wrong because it cuts short the life of a human being, so euthanasia is wrong, even if the person's life is cut short by as little as a day. It is still the equivalent of murder.

The Sanctity of Life argument has clear implications for decisions about euthanasia:

- patients in a **Persistent Vegetative State**, although seriously incapacitated, are still living human beings, and they continue to have an intrinsic value and should be treated the same as anyone else. It would obviously be wrong to treat their lives as worthless and to conclude that they 'would be better off dead' – we ought to care even – perhaps especially – when we cannot cure.
- patients who are old or sick, and who are near the end of earthly life, have the same value as any other human being.
- people who have mental or physical handicaps have the same value as any other human being.

There are many arguments that disagree with the idea that life is sacred. These arguments tend to take the view that all humans have *autonomy* – that is, human beings have the power to make real decisions on their own, specifically about whether they wish to continue to live or to die. The term comes from the Greek words *'auto'* (self) and *'nomos'* (law). Autonomy, therefore, has to do with a person allowing himself to determine what happens to him. Such a person has the freedom to define the parameters that frame his or her life and can make real choices about the way their life is lived. So a person could freely choose to live a religious life, or not; to go into politics, or not; to live by a certain set of rules, or not; and so on. If that person uses her autonomy to choose to die at a time they want and in a way she wants, she would do so on the basis of her autonomy. For this person, then, euthanasia is a valid, freely chosen option at the end of her life. It is a tool for achieving the goal that she has chosen.

Stanley Hauerwas and narrative theology on death and dying

Theological ethicist Stanley Hauerwas has written several books and articles on medicine and care of the sick and dying. He thinks that, with the death of God, secular thought has shifted the burden of suffering from theodicy (justifying God in light of the problem of suffering) to anthropodicy (limiting or ending all evil and suffering that we humanly can). He is a narrative theologian and argues that every philosophy or way of life is 'storied' – it has a perspective and attitude to life. In facing death, modernity's perspective is to put its trust in being able to control the chaos of life rationally and in medical science. As modern people, we hope that 'we can get out of life alive' or take control of death so we can at all costs avoid dependency on others. Yet the fly in the ointment is, as Hauerwas puts it, that 'Sickness challenges our most cherished presumption that we are in control of our existence' (1990). We are mortal, and in Hauerwas' phrase, medicine at the end of life is not just biomedical science operating on faulty mechanisms/organisms, but 'a tragic moral art'. It needs a virtuous community to sustain it – who will have the hope of resurrection to give them the patience to be present in the face of suffering; in recognising that 'we are our bodies', subject to ageing and dying, this leads Christians to see their story in light of that of a God who died in the agony of crucifixion. Hauerwas argues that modernity's story of being able to tame and control nature makes it harder to face death than in pre-modern societies. Modern people want a quick and painless death. Yet, as writer Michael Ignatieff comments:

> As secular people . . . we no longer share a vision of the good death. Most other cultures, including many primitive ones whom we have subjugated to our reason and our technology, enfold their members in the art of dying as in the art of living. But we have left these awesome tasks of culture to private choice. Some of us face our deaths with a rosary, some with a curse, some in company, some alone. Some die bravely, to give courage to the living, while others die with no other audience than their lonely selves.
>
> (*The Needs of Strangers*, Chatto & Windus, 1984, quoted in Hauerwas 1990, p. 99)

Both the UK and US are increasingly elderly societies. In Hauerwas' view, modern culture is more individualistic than intergenerational. So if we view our lives in terms of time rather than as belonging to a wider story, the temptation is to increase longevity as far as possible. We lack what MacIntyre calls 'the unity of a narrative which links birth to life to death as a narrative beginning to middle to end' (1986).

Doctrine of Double Effect

The **Doctrine of Double Effect** (DDE) is where a doctor acts with good intentions (e.g. giving a drug to help a patient's condition) but where bad consequences arise (the drug harms or kills the patient). Some doctors sedate patients deliberately in order to keep them unconscious so that they do not suffer pain. The idea of the DDE was developed by Roman Catholic moral theologians in the sixteenth and seventeenth centuries.

According to this doctrine, it is morally permissible to perform an act that has both a good effect and a bad effect if all of the following conditions are met:

1. The act to be done must be good in itself or at least indifferent
2. The good effect must not be obtained by means of the bad effect
3. The bad effect must not be intended for itself, only permitted
4. There must be a proportionately grave reason for permitting the bad effect

The most important element here is the *intention* in the mind of the doctor in judging the moral correctness of his/her action, because of the Roman Catholic teaching that it is never permissible to 'intend' the death of an 'innocent person'. An innocent person is one who has not forfeited the right to life by the way he or she behaves, e.g. by threatening or taking the lives of others. The DDE is not, then, an example of

Doctrine of Double Effect: Where a doctor acts with good intentions (e.g. giving a drug to help a patient's condition) but where bad consequences arise (the drug harms the patient)

assisted suicide, which is defined as 'a deliberate act that causes death, undertaken by one person with the primary intention of ending the life of another person, in order to relieve the second person's suffering'.

Those who wish to legalise euthanasia claim that the DDE is really a covert way of practising euthanasia. Those who do not wish to see euthanasia legalised counter this claim by saying that the mere fact that some doctors use the DDE in this way does not make it morally right.

Exercise

Consider how the DDE works in the following example.

A patient has an aggressive form of cancer. The doctors who treat the patient know that her chances of survival beyond one year are virtually nil, but they agree with the patient that treatment will be given to extend her life as long as possible. They use chemotherapy drugs to treat the cancer, knowing that these will have painful side effects. These drugs eventually stop working and the cancer spreads. After a time, the patient refuses any more chemotherapy, is transferred to a hospice, where she is treated with increasing amounts of morphine, which have the effect of keeping her in deep sedation until she eventually dies from the cancer.

Passive euthanasia: A person (usually a doctor) allows another person to die painlessly by withdrawing treatment, which indirectly brings about that person's death

Involuntary euthanasia: A decision is made to end the life of a person, either without their knowledge or against their wishes

Non-voluntary euthanasia: A decision is made to end the life of a person who is not in a position to make that decision themselves

DNR status

A 'Do Not Resuscitate' order means that a doctor does not have to try to restart a patient's heart if it stops. It can be thought of as a form of **passive euthanasia**. The purpose of a DNR order is to stop unnecessary suffering for the patient. If a patient signs a DNR order, he is signalling to the doctor that, if his heart stops, then CPR (Cardio-Pulmonary Resuscitation) should not be attempted. This supersedes the default position which assumes that every patient with a severe heart problem consents to CPR, chest compressions, defibrillation, lung ventilation and injection of drugs and other similar treatments. DNR is a legal order which affects CPR only; it does not affect other medical treatments. Some doctors have suggested that the term 'DNR' should be replaced with 'AND' (Allow Natural Death), arguing that 'not resuscitating' is a negative action, whereas 'allowing death' is a more positive action. A DNR order is written evidence enabling a patient's wishes to be respected even after they can no longer express those wishes. This makes it more straightforward for the medical team managing the patient's care. A DNR is a type of advance directive.

A potential problem with DNR orders arises when there is insufficient discussion between the patient and the medical experts about what the patient wants. In 2011, it was reported (*Daily Telegraph*, 15 October) that DNR orders were routinely being made in elderly patients' notes without the knowledge of the patient or their relatives. An investigation into the practices at 100 English hospitals revealed that elderly patients were being left to die just because they were old and frail. One charity called this 'euthanasia by the back door'. The hospital involved subsequently made improvements to their practices concerning DNRs.

Other ethical problems with DNRs include the following.

- A patient may request that CPR be attempted, even if the doctors think there is a very remote chance that it would do any good. The medical team would have to respect this choice, but would wish to have an honest discussion with the patient beforehand.

- Doctors might decide that they will not inform a patient of a DNR order. For instance, if the patient is approaching death, or is not mentally competent, informing the patient would be of no value, or cause great upset. In this case, notes must be kept explaining the reasons why the patient was not informed.

- In an age when health authorities are forced to cut costs, it may be tempting to use DNRs as one method of keeping costs down. If a patient has a DNR order in his file, doctors do not have to spend valuable time in attempting to resuscitate a patient who will probably die anyway. In the *Guardian* in 2011, it was reported that: 'In an era when nearly seven in 10 people die in hospital – and most have "do not resuscitate" orders – there is increasing pressure for more mentally competent adult patients to help plan towards the end of their lives' (www.guardian.co.uk/society/2011/aug/26/do-not-resuscitate-medical-patient).

- Abuses of the British Medical Association (BMA) guidelines have been documented and cases have been found where a DNR order had been placed in a patient's file without their consent, or where junior doctors had written the order but not consulted with more senior medical staff.

Advance directives or living wills

An **advance directive**, formerly called a living will, is a way for an adult to make a statement about what they wish to happen to them if their medical or mental state deteriorates to such an extent that they can no longer function as they would wish to. A patient can refuse future life-prolonging treatment, in case he becomes unconscious, loses his mental capacity or cannot communicate his wishes. This would mean that he wishes to die rather than live in what he thinks of as an 'undignified' way, with no quality of life.

Advance directive: Also called a 'living will', in which a person states their wishes about dying before they become incapable of doing so

The BMA's guidance on advance directives is contained in *Withholding and Withdrawing Life-Prolonging Medical Treatment*. This gives medical professionals advice on the ethical, legal and clinical issues, and sets out safeguards for decision-making. It indicates how human rights legislation applies in this area. It also seeks to provide a coherent and comprehensive set of principles that apply to all decisions to withhold or withdraw life-prolonging treatment.

Advance directives are legally binding – although there are certain criteria to be met – and are covered by the Mental Capacity Act of 2005. The patient has to be very specific about the circumstances in which he does not want to be treated and which treatments he wishes to refuse and show that he is aware that such refusal of treatment will put his life at risk. His written statement has to be witnessed. The main benefit of an advance directive is that it puts the patient in control of what happens to him in certain situations or circumstances. By writing such a document, he can direct the medical staff as to how he wishes to be treated in these cases.

One ethical issue here is that, if the patient has written an advance directive some time previous to the occasion when it is needed, he may have changed his mind but not got around to updating the document. Medical staff would not necessarily know this and would have to treat him according to the wishes expressed in the document.

Case study: Terry Pratchett (1948–2015)

Terry Pratchett was a best-selling British author whose many children's novels, especially his Discworld series, and other books sold approximately 60 million copies around the world. In 2007, Pratchett was diagnosed with posterior cortical atrophy, a rare form of Alzheimer's disease. (See the announcement at www.pjsmprints.com/news/embuggerance.html). After that, he continued to write, but also spent his time campaigning for a cure for Alzheimer's disease. In 2012, Pratchett's controversial documentary, about a 71-year-old man suffering from Motor Neurone Disease, who travelled to Switzerland for assisted suicide, won an award at the Grierson British Documentary Awards, for best Documentary on a Contemporary Theme.

Pratchett also joined the organisation 'Dignity in Dying', a campaigning organisation with over 25,000 members in Britain, including many celebrities. They want to see greater choice regarding where individuals die, who is present and the care they receive in their final stages of life. As their website says, they campaign for change in the law on assisted dying for terminally ill, mentally competent adults: 'We do this by lobbying decision-makers, educating legal and healthcare professionals and empowering terminally ill people, and their loved ones, who are suffering under the current system to have their voices heard.'

Their partner charity, Compassion in Dying, undertakes research on end-of-life care, provides free advance directives and works to educate and empower people around their existing rights at the end of life. (See www.dignityindying.org.uk/about.html)

Pratchett said:

I endorse the work of Dignity in Dying because I believe passionately that any individual should have the right to choose, as far as it is possible, the time and the conditions of their death. Over the last hundred years we have learned to be extremely good at living. But sooner or later, and so often now it is later, everybody dies. I think it's time we learned to be as good at dying as we are at living.

(www.dignityindying.org.uk/about-us/patrons.html)

Discussion questions raised by the Dutch experience of euthanasia

Those in favour of legalising euthanasia have argued that the Netherlands provides a model example of a tolerant country where voluntary euthanasia works well. Yet questions have been raised in the *Independent* (14 May 2016) and the *Telegraph* (11 May 2016) about the Dutch system. Whereas just two people had themselves euthanised in 2010 for an 'insufferable' mental illness, this rose to 56 cases in 2015 (1 per cent of total). These non-terminally ill patients have mental health problems such as Post Traumatic Stress Disorder, clinical depression or even germ phobias. Opponents of euthanasia suggest that, when a country legalises it, attitudes become more blasé. Evidence of this may be seen in the statement by Dutch psychiatrist Paulan Starcke that psychiatrists are 'too hesitant' in agreeing to euthanasia in patients with psychiatric diseases, adding that children as young as 12 who ask to end their lives should be taken seriously. Cases of euthanasia for dementia rose from 25 in 2010 to 109 (2 per cent of the total) in 2016. Here, the question is whether someone who inserts a dementia clause in their living will, once demented, then experiences unbearable suffering. Overall cases of euthanasia in the Netherlands have risen 75 per cent from 3,136 in 2010 to 5,516 in 2016.

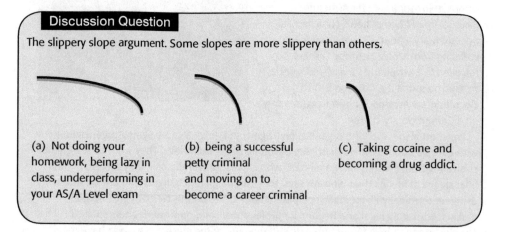

Discussion Question

The slippery slope argument. Some slopes are more slippery than others.

(a) Not doing your homework, being lazy in class, underperforming in your AS/A Level exam

(b) being a successful petty criminal and moving on to become a career criminal

(c) Taking cocaine and becoming a drug addict.

1) Do you think that legalising physician-assisted dying would lead inevitably to a slippery slope from:

   (a) a terminally ill patient making a competent and free decision to end their life with the assistance of a physician, to . . .

   (b) allowing the next of kin to terminate the life of a relative in a persistent vegetative state (non-voluntary euthanasia) when it is believed to be in the patient's best interest, to . . .

   (c) a non-terminally ill patient who is suffering from clinical depression, PTSD or trauma caused by abuse being allowed to end their life with the help of a physician rather than attempt suicide?

2) Is there evidence from the Dutch experience that such a slope is possible or even likely?

Discussion Questions

Is there any cause for alarm in these recent figures from the Netherlands? Do they represent a slippery slope?

Two other key areas of discussion in the specification are outlined for discussion below.

1) Sanctity of life vs Patient autonomy

For religious believers, the sanctity of life ethic is generally strong (e.g. Natural Law), but it is weaker or less absolute in Situation Ethics. Writing in 1 Corinthians 6:19–20, Paul says 'Do you not know that your bodies are temples of the Holy Spirit, who is in you, whom you have received from God? You are not your own; you were bought at a price. Therefore honour God with your bodies.' In the Bible, there are strong prohibitions against taking human life (Exodus 20:13), which is made in the image of God (Genesis 1:27).

By contrast, in *Rethinking Life and Death: The Collapse of Our Traditional Values* (Oxford University Press, 1995), Utilitarian philosopher Peter Singer sees the sanctity of human life as undergoing a Copernican revolution in liberal democratic societies around the world. Three of Singer's five new commandments relate to euthanasia:

(1) Recognize that the worth of human life varies; (2) Take responsibility for the consequences of our decisions (in end-of-life care); (3) Respect a person's desire to live or die.

Singer is a libertarian philosopher who emphasises patient autonomy, and, in chapter 7 of *Practical Ethics*, he addresses several scenarios in which the taking of human life may be deemed justifiable, including voluntary and non-voluntary euthanasia. Arguably, his position extends euthanasia beyond what John Stuart Mill would have thought safe. Whilst Mill's *Harm Principle* (in *On Liberty*) seems to give complete sovereignty to the individual except where it risks harm to others, his *Offence Principle* recognises that psychological harm may at times be comparable to physical harm. An example of this could be where patients choose to access physician-assisted suicide in cases where they judge their mental illness to be unbearable, and not because of a terminal condition. Extending patient autonomy to this degree could send shock waves through the mental healthcare system. Mill thought that individuals were generally the best judges of their own interests, offering the example of a person crossing a broken bridge. We may warn and urge them not to cross, but we ought not to prevent them judging the balance between the worth of their life and the risks of crossing / not crossing the bridge. Yet Mill saw exceptions to this, arguing that choices which completely deprived one of the capacity to make further choices should be prevented. Here he included selling oneself into slavery or killing oneself. These are self-defeating as exercising the choice ends all future choices. It is not freedom to alienate one's freedom from oneself. This is especially true when a mental health patient is not competent to judge the worth of their own life, deeming suicide preferable to living. In the UK, such patients might be sectioned under the Mental Health Act, and given support and treatment to recover from mental illness as they would a physical illness. The concern about giving patient autonomy in non-terminal cases of euthanasia is that for many, physician-assisted suicide in such cases is not judged to be a rational act, hence the concerns raised about the figures in the Netherlands.

The question raised above is how do we find a balance between patient autonomy or choice, and society's authority to regulate the degree to which this can be exercised?

---

2) Commission/active euthanasia vs Omission/passive euthanasia

The intentional termination of one human being's life at their request, by a doctor. Active and deliberate, non-therapeutic drugs are often employed, such as potassium chloride whose sole use is for ending life.	A patient's / their immediate family's decision not to use extraordinary means to prolong bodily life when there is irrefutable evidence that biological death is imminent.

In order to discuss this distinction, consider the following cases, deciding whether each is an example of commission or omission, and, in your view, whether it is ethically justifiable (YES), or not (NO).

	Commission/ Omission	Ethically justifiable?
A patient is in a Persistent Vegetative State and kept alive by means of a life-support system. They are unable to express their wishes, but their next of kin think that it is in their best interest to have their life-support systems withdrawn as their life is merely biological not biographical, more of a burden than a benefit to them.		
Someone who expressed in a living will a wish not to be resuscitated in the event of them having Alzheimer's disease, has a cardiac arrest. In line with their wishes, they are not resuscitated and consequently die.		
A patient who has late stage cancer refuses treatment in the form of chemotherapy. They are given all of the pain relief possible, and die within weeks where they might have lived for 6–12 months.		
A patient who is dying of throat cancer is given increasing dosages of diamorphine (medical heroin for severe pain management). Given their already precarious state of health, at high dosages, this drug hastens their death, though the intention of the physician in administering it remains that of alleviating their pain.		
A patient suffering from severe post-traumatic stress that is considered to be 'incurable' regards her life as unbearable and requests physician-assisted suicide in the Netherlands. She is granted it.		

Christian views on euthanasia

In the discussion of euthanasia, as with other issues in this course, religious views have had an important historical and contemporary influence on the debate. Here, we will look at Christian views, in which much of the justification for firmly held beliefs emanates from the Bible. In general, Christians are against euthanasia, mostly because of the Bible's statements on the Sanctity of Life. The most often-quoted passages, which are all used to argue against euthanasia, are listed briefly below.

- *Genesis 1:26–7* 'Let us make humans in our image'. Human beings were made in the image and likeness of God. This is taken to mean that human life is sacred and it is implied that, because God created life, only God has the right to take it away.
- *Exodus 20:13* The sixth commandment says simply, 'You shall not commit murder.' To perform any kind of euthanasia is taken to be equivalent to murder, and is therefore forbidden. Matthew 19:18 makes the same point.
- *Job 1:21* 'The Lord gave and the Lord has taken away.' The book of Job discusses the nature of suffering and justice. Job is afflicted with a great deal of suffering – the death of his wife and children, the ruin of his livestock and livelihood. Job, however, remains faithful to God and accepts that God is in control of the entire universe and that his suffering must have a purpose. By implication, therefore, for humans to perform euthanasia is wrong.
- *Psalm 31:15* 'My times are in your hand.' The Psalmist is talking to God and accepts that God knows everything and has a plan for each individual. Humans should not try to play God.
- *Ecclesiastes 3:1–2* 'To everything there is a season, and a time to every purpose under the heaven: A time to be born, and a time to die; a time to plant, and a time to pluck up that which is planted.'
- *Ecclesiastes 7:17* 'Do not be too wicked, and do not be a fool: why should you die before your time?'
- *Ecclesiastes 8:8* 'No man has power over the wind to contain it; so no one has power over the day of his death.'
- *1 Corinthians 3:16* 'You yourselves are God's temple.' St Paul reminds the Christian community in Corinth that they should abstain from immorality, and says that, because God created them, they should not do anything that would detract from their sacred origin.

Exercise

Look up the following biblical verses and work out what they have to contribute to the debate on euthanasia:

Numbers 16:22; 27:16
Ecclesiastes 3:21
Proverbs 31:6
Hebrews 9:27; 12:23
James 2:26

There are also some biblical passages which are used by those who wish to argue in favour of euthanasia from a Christian perspective:

- *Judges 9:50–5* The armour bearer of the Judge Abimelech assisted his master in dying. Abimelech had been waging war against the city of Thebez, but, when he was besieging a strong tower in the city, a woman from the city threw down a piece of a millstone which hit Abimelech on the head. To avoid the indignity of dying at the hands of a woman (!), Abimelech asked his armour bearer to thrust him through with his sword. The armour bearer did so.
- *I Samuel 31:4* Saul, Israel's first king, had been defeated in battle and was mortally wounded. This was a sign to him that he had sinned against God and that God was no longer protecting him. He asked his armour bearer to kill him. In this incident, the armour bearer refused to do what Saul asked, so Saul committed suicide.
- In *II Samuel 17:23*, King Ahitophel committed suicide by hanging after putting his affairs in order.
- In *I Kings 16:18*, Zimri was defeated in battle, retreated to his palace and committed suicide by setting it on fire.
- In *Matthew 27:5*, Judas Iscariot hanged himself because of the guilt he felt after betraying Jesus to the authorities. (NB: the account of what happened to Judas in Acts 1:18–20 is somewhat different.)

Some Christians use these passages to argue in favour of euthanasia, though Christian opponents will argue that none of these accounts is approved of by the biblical writers.

Other Christians will also take the teaching of Jesus on love as a general principle which they then use to justify euthanasia as the 'most loving thing' in a particular situation. For them, euthanasia may be the most compassionate response to the suffering of a family member or close friend.

The Church of England's position

The 2012 Falconer Commission on assisted dying called for a change in the law to allow terminally ill patients to end their own lives at home with the assistance of a doctor. The Church of England responded that there were several flaws in the Commission's report. The response reiterated the Church's continuing strong opposition to any change in the law or medical practice to make assisted suicide permissible or socially acceptable. Authored by the Bishop of Carlisle, the Right Reverend James Newcome, the response acknowledged that the issues were complex, but argued for the intrinsic value of human life, a value that underpins much of human rights legislation, criminal law and social cohesion. If this principle were to be disposed of, there would be nothing wrong with such things as infanticide or capital punishment, or not giving money on Red Nose Day to alleviate the suffering of children in this country and abroad. The Church continued to encourage the view that suffering must be met with compassion, commitment to high-quality services and effective medication.

In February 2012, the then Archbishop of Canterbury, Rowan Williams, argued that allowing assisted dying would put both vulnerable patients and doctors under threat. Drawing parallels with the growth of abortion, he warned that any change in the law would create a situation in which life would be 'legally declared not to be worth living'. He said that 'every life in every imaginable situation is infinitely precious in the sight of God'. In his view, a compassionate society will invest in high-quality **palliative care** rather than lethal doses of poison.

> **Palliative care:**
> Caring for a person with an incurable disease so that they maintain some QoL and are not in pain in the final stage of their life

The Roman Catholic Church's position

> Euthanasia is a grave violation of the law of God, since it is the deliberate and morally unacceptable killing of a human person . . . True compassion leads to sharing another's pain; it does not kill the person whose suffering we cannot bear.
>
> Pope John Paul II, papal encyclical *Evangelium Vitae* (*The Gospel of Life*, 1995)

The Roman Catholic Church regards euthanasia as morally wrong. It has always taught the absolute and unchanging value of the commandment 'You shall not kill', as euthanasia is a form of, and morally equivalent to, murder. Any law that might be passed allowing any form of euthanasia would be unjust and against the will of God.

The Roman Catholic Church believes in the intrinsic value of human life. The value of a human life does not depend on whether people are happy, bring happiness to others or are socially useful, in terms of the work they do or any other part of living in society. The mere fact that someone lives a healthy and happy life does not make them more valuable than someone who lives a life of suffering and illness: both hold the same value in the eyes of God, because they are both human, made in the image of God. A person who is dying should trust in the all-encompassing love of God and should die with dignity by letting themselves be loved unconditionally by God and their fellow humans.

If an individual has an illness that involves suffering and pain, then there are many effective pain-killers, which are perfectly legitimate to use, unless they are the cause of death. For example, if a patient is given enough morphine to remove the pain he is in, but it also directly causes his death, this is not morally acceptable.

The Roman Catholic Church teaches that human beings have free will, but their freedom does not extend to ending their own lives. Only God has the right to give and take life, so euthanasia and suicide are both unacceptable.

The *Catechism of the Catholic Church* clarifies when medical treatment can be refused or stopped: 'Discontinuing medical procedures that are burdensome, dangerous, extraordinary, or disproportionate to the expected outcome can be legitimate; it is the refusal of "over-zealous" treatment. Here one does not will to cause death; one's inability to impede it is merely accepted.'

Since it is morally wrong to commit suicide it is also morally wrong to help someone commit suicide.

Case study: Dame Cicely Saunders (1918–2005)

Many people see the hospice movement as a viable alternative to euthanasia because of the emphasis on compassion and care for the dying person and their family.

(You matter because you are you, and you matter to the last moment of your life.)

Credited with founding the modern hospice movement, Cicely Saunders was the leading figure in the campaign to establish hospices around the world. She became a nurse, then a doctor, and specialised in developing ways to control pain. She believed hospices were a positive alternative to euthanasia.

She founded St Christopher's Hospice, established to relieve the physical and emotional suffering of the dying. She won an international reputation for her work and influenced the way in which people in many countries thought about the process of dying. She believed that the last days of a person's life could be understood positively and be happy.

Dame Cicely was guided by her Christian faith and strongly opposed euthanasia. She had a clear view of the role of hospices. She saw dying as an opportunity to say 'thank you' and 'sorry' to family and friends. According to her, death was 'as natural as being born', just a stage in a person's life. The process of death should be life-affirming and free of pain.

Due to her pioneering work, there are about 220 hospices in the United Kingdom and more than 8,000 around the world. The UK hospice care sector supports at least 120,000 people with terminal and life-limiting conditions each year. This increases to around 360,000 people when their family members are included. According to the BBC, about 30 per cent of people dying in the UK receive help at some stage from hospices.

Cicely's work on the development of the hospice movement was recognised with many awards: she was made a DBE in 1980, and awarded the Order of Merit in 1989 (one of only a handful of women to receive this), and an honorary doctorate of medicine (the first woman to receive this in nearly a century). She won the highly acclaimed Templeton Prize in 1981, and in 2001 she was awarded the financially most valuable humanitarian award – the Conrad N. Hilton Humanitarian Prize, worth £700,000 – for her life's work caring for the dying.

Cicely Saunders died peacefully at St Christopher's Hospice in 2005.

Natural Law and euthanasia

The essential principle in Natural Law is that God has created everything for a purpose. This purpose can be discerned by humans when they use their reason and they can make judgements about how to act in particular cases. The most important of the *Primary Precepts* formulated by St Thomas Aquinas was the *preservation of life*. Natural Law is not consequentialist; it is deontological, which means that we should look at the nature of the act itself, not its possible consequences.

How do these views relate to euthanasia?

- Natural Law adherents believe in the Sanctity of Life (SoL). Since all life is God-given, and human life is more important than other life on earth, humans are in a special position in the created world and have a special connection with God. They are sacred. For anyone to take their own life, or help to take the life of anyone else, therefore, would be a sin not just against that person, but against God himself.

- The Primary Precept of the preservation of life clearly goes against any form of euthanasia. It does not matter whether the person is in great pain, or in a **PVS**, or being tortured, or whether there are millions of people involved. The principle of the preservation of life is virtually absolute. Omitting to fight off an inevitable death aggressively is justifiable. Deliberative killing (a sin of commission) is not.

- However, if a patient wants to stop having treatment for an illness, he/she may do so, according to Natural Law. This is because the proposed treatment may go beyond what is reasonable or necessary for existence. Such a treatment would be taking *extraordinary means* to preserve her life.

- The *Doctrine of Double Effect* (DDE) has been used to argue in favour of euthanasia in cases where treatment with effective powerful drugs to preserve someone's life has the unfortunate and unintended side effect of shortening the patient's life. This outcome is allowed under Natural Law as long as the death of the patient is *foreseen* but not *intended*.

- Modern Natural Law theorists Germain Grisez and Joseph Boyle argue that the concept of *personhood* is central in the euthanasia discussion. According to them, there is no difference between being bodily alive and being a person. For them, someone in a PVS is still a person. It would be immoral to kill an able-bodied person, so it would be immoral to let a PVS patient die. A PVS patient still retains his essential 'humanness'. Having a bodily life, like having friends and an appreciation of beauty, are 'goods in themselves', and these cannot be taken away arbitrarily. Euthanasia goes against the basic good of life and should therefore be forbidden.

> **Persistent Vegetative State (PVS):** Most of a person's brain functions are absent, but the body may still function (i.e. heartbeat, breathing)

Proportionalism (associated with thinkers like Bernard Hoose and Daniel Maguire) is a controversial revision of Natural Law that began in the late 1960s and was condemned by Pope John Paul II in two encyclicals (1993, 1995). Proportionalists still hold to the sanctity of human persons and consider intrinsic evils to be wrong. But, in taking a holistic view of principles, acts, intentions and consequences, they grant that there can be proportionally good reasons to make exceptions to well-established Secondary Precepts. In weighing goods or values against evils or disvalues, the likely consequences are considered. It is claimed that the roots of this view can be found in Aquinas' Just War theory, which incorporated 'proportional force' in warfare to justify killing in self-defence and when intended to bring about a greater good. Some proportionalists extend this logic to euthanasia in terminal cases. Daniel Maguire, for example, takes the revisionist view that, while euthanasia has been regarded as an intrinsically evil act in Natural Law, it is the lesser of two evils. Furthermore, as death is a pre-moral evil (one that, though it causes suffering, is not immoral), shortening the dying process is not an intrinsic evil. Life is a basic good, not an absolute one to be prolonged. When it has become burdensome to the point that it is agonising pain or biological life, but not personhood, that persists, it may be permissible to end it. The same could be true when a patient is in a persistent vegetative or semi-conscious state.

When artificial feeding offers no benefit, medicine can become cruel in extending it. Given the arsenal of medical technology with which death can be fought off, in terminal cases we find ourselves in a grey area between the futility of extending biological life and bringing life to a close for a good death. For Maguire, there is proportional reason to choose the lesser of two 'pre-moral' evils – extended terminal decline, or deliberately shortened death.

Discussion Question

Can you think of an example of euthanasia or physician-assisted dying which would satisfy all of the four conditions (see below) for an action to be permissible under the Doctrine of Double Effect?

1. The action is morally neutral or good.
2. The bad effect must not be the means by which the good effect is brought about.
3. The motive for the actions must be the bringing about of the good effect only.
4. There must be a proportionately grave reason for permitting the bad effect.

Criticisms of Natural Law on euthanasia

1. From the consequentialist stance of a Utilitarian or Situation ethicist, the following distinctions made by Natural Law are of little or no significance.

   (a) The distinction between using **ordinary means** of end-of-life care (such as nutrition and hydration which are required as part of the duty of care) and avoiding **extraordinary means** (such as more aggressive methods of feeding the patient, or drugs/surgery that would extend their life but are not morally required and may be futile and of no benefit to the patient, only extending the length of their dying process). In the consequentialist's view, to withdraw extraordinary means may be an acknowledgment that a patient is dying and expressing an unspoken but deliberate willingness to shorten burdensome suffering.

   (b) The distinction between **omission** (a medical non-intervention to end a patient's life, such as not resuscitating a terminally ill patient who has a heart attack) and **commission** (e.g. in Switzerland, a medical intervention to end a patient's life using potassium chloride to stop the heart). In the above examples, if one considers the consequences rather than the motive, the outcome is the same.

   (c) The **Doctrine of Double Effect** may be judged in Natural Law to aim at **one** good end (the alleviation of pain) while the secondary effect (hastening death) is judged to be **foreseeable** but **unintended**. Yet where Natural Law may judge increasing the dosage of morphine to be very different from deliberately ending a patient's life by using potassium chloride, consequentialists would see this as cloaking 'consequentialist views in the robe of an absolutist ethic' (Peter Singer's phrase from *Practical Ethics*, 1993, p. 211). Singer sees these distinctions as permitting mercy killing or passive euthanasia

(d) Without the motive or intention appearing to break the *synderesis* rule that good ought to be done and evil avoided.

Absolutist ethics
Moral standards are seen as unchanging and universal. Slavery and cannibalism did not become wrong at a certain period in history – they were always so. Divine Command and Kantian Ethics are examples of this stance and depend on principles not upon consequences.

2. Natural Law's absolutist principles can be cruel in failing to take account of patient choices and circumstances. Situation Ethics is often taken to be individualistic, but it honours the autonomous will of dying patients who have a right to refuse treatment, and have a right to govern their own bodies. As John Stuart Mill put it in *On Liberty* (1859), 'over himself, over his own body and mind, the individual is sovereign'. Joseph Fletcher championed this view as president of the Euthanasia Society of the United States. Law ought to recognise the right of the terminally ill person to end their life with the assistance of a physician, but Natural Law would have us deny the wish for euthanasia of thousands suffering a prolonged death.

3. A third point is that, with people 'dwindling' between life and death due to the quality of medical care available, Natural Law pays little attention to the fact that medicine is increasingly playing God in extending life well beyond what is 'natural'. Thomas Aquinas' thirteenth-century notion of what was natural may have made sense when little life-saving treatment could be given. In an era of transplant surgery, dialysis and life-support machines, defibrillators, simple antibiotics and wonder drugs, people survive where Aquinas' age would have seen them die of natural causes. So it is inconsistent to say that we ought not to play God in terminal care when it might be argued that we do so in much of modern medicine in any case.

4. Natural Law presumes that there is a moral law underpinning state laws prohibiting euthanasia; and that, without fixed principles, there will be a slippery slope to a society that pressurises the elderly into thinking of themselves as a burden and nudges them towards euthanasia. This is simply not the case in Holland, Switzerland and Belgium where adequate safeguards are in place to ensure against coercion or pressure.

5. The Primary Precept of the preservation of life condemns many (against their will) to suffer extreme suffering and loss of personal dignity. Their biographical life (a sense of a life worth living) may be over, though their biological one persists. In our secular democracy where many people hold to a quality- not a sanctity-of-life view, Natural Law and religious voices (e.g. bishops in the House of Lords) were speaking against and lobbying MPs as the Assisted Dying Bill was debated and rejected by parliament in 2015.

Situation Ethics and euthanasia

Joseph Fletcher served as president of the Euthanasia Society of America from 1974 to 1976. He argued that an individual who fell below the 40 IQ mark in a Stanford–Binet test was 'Questionably a person', and, below 20, would not meet the criteria to be a person ('Indicators of humanhood', Hastings Centre Report, 1972). Whilst this relates to those with an intellectual disability, it suggests that Fletcher would have been open to extending euthanasia from voluntary to non-voluntary cases where the doctors diagnosed a patient to be in a persistent vegetative state and the next of kin wished to withdraw the use of life-support systems. He also sought a liberalisation of the laws on euthanasia, writing:

> Doctors and laymen have asked lawmakers to legalize direct euthanasia, thus far unsuccessfully. While this writer's decision is in favor of the direct method, it may be necessary to settle temporarily for an intermediate step in the law . . . To bring this matter into the open practice of medicine would harmonize the civil law with medical morals, which must be concerned with the quality of life, not merely its quantity.
> (*Moral Responsibility: Situation Ethics at Work*, Westminster, 1967)

As a former professor of medical ethics at the University of Virginia, Fletcher knew of the suffering of the terminally ill and favoured **voluntary euthanasia** or physician-assisted dying. He also foresaw changing times ahead in both medicine and the law. The relativism, pragmatism and personalism of Situation Ethics' sanctity-of-life ethic centres on the patient as a person. The sanctity of life is not an absolute for Fletcher, though love is. He saw how modern medicine could render a patient's life more of a burden than a benefit to them with life-support systems and drugs that prolonged their dying rather than their welfare. Compassion or *agape*, exercised in a Christianised form of Act Utilitarianism, allowed patients to die with dignity and be relieved of their suffering. To care when you cannot cure can sometimes involve taking control of the dying process and hastening it, and, for Fletcher, this was conscionable.

A focus on alleviating suffering and not prolonging it, in the name of agapeic love leads to a treatment of each case on its merits. Patients are to have autonomy in making their own decision where they are competent to do so. In the case of non-voluntary euthanasia, a patient's next of kin make their decision in the best interest of their relative, and are not bound by an absolutist, legalistic ethic. Fletcher's Situation Ethics seeks to replace the legalist's love of law for the law of love or *agape*. Its only absolute is love, and it seeks a middle way between legalism and antinomianism (the rejection of law). Christian love is responsible, and it acts not from the sentimental and naive approach of the well-meaning but clueless, but with eyes open to the circumstances and consequences of a situation. It is pragmatic, able to cope with changing attitudes to euthanasia from patients and in society.

> **Voluntary euthanasia:**
> A person states their wish to die and a doctor brings this about

Strengths of Situation Ethics applied to euthanasia

- Pragmatism, relativism, positivism and personalism combine to offer a system which is **principled, but not rule-bound**. Patient autonomy and agapeic reasoning are central in cases where the here-and-now of the situation clashes with the always-and-everywhere principles. If a patient is in an irreversible dying process, Situationists may have fewer scruples about a drip that delivers only hydration, not nutrition, as long as the patient is free of pain and has consented.

- **Individual conscience, patient welfare and the right to decide** are central to Situationists. Agapeic reasoning doesn't arrive with a rulebook, but decides with all of the factors in play in an individual case. For the state or churches to impose a view on such a personal decision as one's own death goes against the personalism and relativism of situational judgements.
- Being more consequentialist, the end does justify the means in certain cases for Situationists. But they would see this as **rooted in the ethics of Jesus**, who said to the Pharisees (who enforced a strict interpretation of the law), 'If one of you has a child or an ox that falls into a well on the Sabbath day, will you not immediately pull it out?' (Luke 14:5), and he said of the two great commandments to love God and one's neighbour, 'All the law and the prophets hang on these two commandments' (Matthew 22:40).
- Rigidity in church ethics when the **wider society** changes its views can cause tensions. Situation Ethics welcomes the autonomy of the individual patient having the freedom to make their own decision. **Chaplains can support them in a loving and non-judgemental way**, given the flexibility of a Situationist approach. If the Church is to serve the wider society, as Fletcher argued, it must be less legalistic and absolutist.
- One benefit over Utilitarianism is that Situation Ethics **puts motives (of love/ *agape*) for actions alongside consequences**. Where Utilitarians judge actions on their usefulness in delivering favourable outcomes, Situationists balance motives and consequences. Where consequences are unpredictable, one can then fall back on having acted with the right motives.
- **Agapeic love motivates people** to perform self-sacrificial acts of loving kindness. When combined with a pragmatic mindset, Situationists can work well with a wide range of people and so allow religious values to work in a wider healthcare system and in public policy and law.

Weaknesses of Situation Ethics applied to euthanasia

- As legislators recognise, **framing a law to legalise euthanasia justly is difficult**. It can lead to a **slippery slope** where unscrupulous doctors and relatives coerce patients/relatives into thinking this is the 'honourable' thing to do 'so as not to be a burden'. It is all well and good for private individuals to act situationally, but lawmakers and judges need to establish firmer principles to govern with. So is Situation Ethics irresponsible in neglecting to see the bigger picture?
- **We need absolutes like the sanctity of human life**. Leaving it up to individuals to assess ethical judgements on a case-by-case basis presumes that they are fully self-aware and competent. Yet, precisely because euthanasia is an end-of-life decision, many patients are in and out of consciousness, or rely on the judgement of their next of kin, or doctors, Situation Ethics' stress on relativism raises questions. Can relatives always know the wishes of their loved one

regarding end-of-life care options / refusal of treatment? Ought the life and death judgement in cases of non-voluntary euthanasia be down to the wishes of the next of kin?

- Situation Ethics is **essentially a version of Act Utilitarianism**. Ethicist Neil Messer claims that [Fletcher] more or less lifts a secular philosophical theory off the shelf in order to spell out what might be understood by Christian love' (2006: pp. 81, 82; emphasis added). In this sense, it suffers from all of the weaknesses that Kantians and Rule Utilitarians might criticise Act Utilitarianism for, e.g. over-reliance on one's ability to predict the future outcome of a given situation, an arrogant disregard for the wisdom accumulated in rules, and a lack of integrity or consistency in decision-making.

- Paul writes in Romans 3:8, 'Why not say – as some slanderously claim that we say – "**Let us do evil that good may result**"? Their condemnation is just! [emphasis added]'. This is seen in Aquinas' *synderesis* principle that good should be done and evil avoided. Given also the commandment 'Do not kill' (Exodus 20:13), Situation Ethics seems to depart from mainstream Christian ethics in its disregard for the sanctity of life in the euthanasia debate.

- Situation Ethics is considered **too individualistic** and lacking in universal standards or consistent principles. Fletcher means well, but he is a product of the permissive society and its radical individualism more than a product of scripture and the Christian tradition.

- **Human nature is too self-interested** and there are unscrupulous doctors and relatives who could manipulate their loved ones into requesting euthanasia, so naively liberalising the law may actually lead to coercion of, rather than love towards, some elderly patients.

FURTHER READING

Paul Badham (2009) *Is There A Christian Case for Assisted Dying?* SPCK

Nigel Biggar (2004) *Aiming to Kill, The Ethics of Euthanasia and Suicide.* Darton Longman & Todd

Glover, J. (1977) *Causing Death and Saving Life.* Penguin Books

Stanley Hauerwas (1990) *Naming the Silence: God, Medicine and the Problem of Suffering.* Continuum Press

Richard Huxtable (2012) *Euthanasia: All that Matters.* Hodder & Stoughton

Sacred Congregation for the Doctrine of the Faith (5 May 1980) *Declaration on Euthanasia*

Peter Singer (1995) *Rethinking Life and Death: The Collapse of our Traditional Ethics.* Oxford University Press

Gail Tulloch (2010) *Euthanasia – Choice and Death.* Edinburgh University Press

Mary Warnock (2009) *Easeful Death: Is There a Case for Assisted Dying?* Oxford University Press

John Wyatt (2015) *Right To Die?* IVP

Thought Points

(1) Make a list of the main ethical issues in the euthanasia debate.

(2) Explain the strengths on Situation Ethics when discussing euthanasia.

(3) Explain the weaknesses of Utilitarianism when discussing euthanasia.

(4) Discuss the view that Natural Law theory has nothing positive to contribute to the euthanasia debate.

(5) Explain how some Proportionalists may use the Doctrine of Double Effect to defend voluntary euthanasia.

(6) To what extent do you agree that Situation Ethics offers the best approach to voluntary euthanasia.

6 Business Ethics

> ## LEARNING OUTCOMES
>
> In this chapter, you will critically examine the following key ideas:
> - Corporate Social Responsibility
> - Whistle blowing
> - Good ethics as good business
> - Globalization
> - Consumerism
>
> In addition, you will apply Kantian and Utilitarian thought to these areas of business ethics.
>
> You will also be able to evaluate critically Kantian and Utilitarian ethics as applied to issues raised by business ethics, including:
> - the application of Kantian ethics and utilitarianism to business ethics
> - whether or not the concept of Corporate Social Responsibility is nothing more than 'hypocritical window-dressing' covering the greed of a business intent on making profits
> - whether or not human beings can flourish in the context of capitalism and consumerism
> - whether globalization encourages or discourages the pursuit of good ethics as the foundation of good business

Introduction: business and its relationships

In this section, we will examine the series of relationships set out in the specification.

business	&	consumers
employers	&	employees
business	&	environment

Whilst we will deal initially with business ethics separately from the moral theories, you will be required to apply theory to it and the two will be integrated in the second half of this chapter.

Business and consumers

In the economics of supply and demand, ethical consumers who are informed, discerning, and have choice can exert influence through their purchasing or boycotting power. The Co-op's 2012 report estimates the **Ethical Consumer** Market (people deliberately making choices based on moral beliefs or values) to have risen from £13.5 billion in 1999 to £47.2 billion in 2012. Significantly, it appears to be recession-proof, growing by £10 billion over the five years of the economic crisis. Duncan Clark's *The Rough Guide to Ethical Shopping* (Rough Guides, 2004) sees consumers as voting with their money. For example, it offers websites which grade energy providers on their green credentials. The estimated UK retail sales of **Fair-trade** products rose 19 per cent in 2012 to £1.57 billion. Responsible tourism with carbon-neutral flights, sustainable fishing, organic and local farm produce, energy-efficient appliances, charity shops, hybrid cars and use of wind and solar power are all part of the Ethical Consumer Market. Sustainable Consumerism also assesses how basic needs can be met and quality of life improved without costing the earth in terms of waste, pollutants, and use of natural resources. The needs of future generations should not be put at risk. In its 2011 survey, the Co-op found that 50 per cent of consumers would avoid a product based on the ethical reputation of a firm (Co-op Ethical Consumer Markets Report, 2012). So consumers are not powerless and the free market listens carefully when they boycott goods causing 'brand damage' that hurts profits (e.g. over child labour in Uzbekistan or sanctions in Burma). Customers are stakeholders. Companies that are interested in longer-term survival and growth need to treat their customers well and provide quality and value in their goods and services. Indeed, Seth Godin, a leading business writer, goes as far as saying, in *Unleashing the Ideavirus* (Do You Zoom, 2000):

Renewable energy, like that harnessed by wind turbines, offers an example of sustainable energy

Ethical consumerism: The deliberate choice to purchase certain goods or services rather than others based upon moral beliefs and values

Fair-trade: A movement which seeks fair treatment for developing-world workers and producers in the supply chain. It seeks fair prices, living wages, safe conditions and rights for workers, together with greater transparency and justice in trade.

Marketing by interrupting people is not cost-effective anymore. You cannot afford to seek out people and send them unwanted marketing messages, in large groups, and hope that some will send you money. Instead, the future belongs to marketers who establish a foundation and process where interested people can market to each other. Ignite consumer networks and then get out of the way and let them talk.

Another aspect of consumer power is seen in shareholder advocacy at annual general meetings of corporations, from institutional investors like pension funds, socially responsible mutual funds, unions or faith-based investors' resolutions. These put pressure on boards to adopt 'corporate social responsibility' and act as 'Corporate citizens' engaging in philanthropic and green agendas. Since the launch of Friends Provident's ethical fund in 1985, the ethical investment sector in the UK has grown to over 100 products and is valued at over £11 billion in 2013. These may exclude investments in tobacco, arms, alcohol or oppressive regimes, or promote community projects or loans to marginalised groups and small businesses, as well as encouraging environmentally friendly and sustainable businesses, including the alternative energy sector.

The above paragraph may lead us to believe that consumer sovereignty is alive and well. The reality is that not all markets are fully competitive and, in many cases, consumers are misinformed, vulnerable, excluded, determined or ignorant when making their choices. Critics of big tobacco companies cite their targeting of developing-world countries where consumers are less informed about the link between cigarettes and cancer (in 2007, 37 per cent of all cigarettes were sold in China). Furthermore, such is the marketing power of big brands like Apple, Coca Cola and Microsoft that **globalization** can actually constrict choice as smaller competitors are put out of business and consumer tastes are moulded. Pricing can be deceptive, as in the sale of certain budget airline tickets, and can be fixed by a 'cartel' of companies or exclude the poor from vital resources (e.g. when some multinational drug companies were criticised for pricing HIV/AIDS/anti-malaria drugs out of reach of the sick and poor of developing countries). Drinks and fast-food companies selling high-sugar products targeted at children raise questions of the duty to inform, as well as the ethics of marketing to vulnerable customers. More aggressive advertising aimed at creating insecurity and dissatisfaction or manufacturing 'needs' out of 'wants' has created a consumer culture which is less transparent, informed, free and unpressured than we might believe.

Globalization: The interconnectedness of global finance, markets, institutions, business, technology, culture, politics, law and environment

Employers and employees

From the rise of trade unions and workers' rights in an era of exploitation in Victorian mills and mines, UK employment law has come a long way. Employers are obligated to uphold rights, such as the right to a healthy and safe working environment, to belong to a union, to have holidays and time off, a minimum wage, maternity and paternity leave. Employers should not discriminate on the basis of race, religion, gender or sexual orientation, though limited exemptions exist for faith groups (presently it is not compulsory to appoint female bishops, such issues being seen as a matter of religious liberty with faith groups being able to appoint leaders from practising members). Employers typically own business assets like buildings, stock, equipment, etc., but their employees are a different type of resource. Employees may part-own and operate the business and are often among the most costly aspects of its operations, requiring management and training, leadership, career development and pastoral care.

There are 'moral hazards' for both parties in contracts. Employees may have to move to a new location with all the upheaval this creates, and their need to earn a living makes them dependent to a degree on their employer. Employers may, for example, discover that an employee puts at risk the reputation of the company through their professional or personal conduct, or lose intellectual property if confidential information or planning is leaked. Kantians would see the employer as having a duty not to treat their employees as a means to an end, instead valuing them as **stakeholders** in the business. To only satisfy *shareholder* interests is to take a very short-term view (given that many shares are bought and sold for profit over short periods). Although some businesses create a short-term outlook with bonuses, employees are often more likely than shareholders to take a longer-term perspective and to value other goods alongside profit (such as excellence or quality in the goods or services the business provides). Virtue ethicists would emphasise the role of chief executives or senior managers in setting an agenda of Corporate Responsibility and mutual respect in the DNA of their business culture. 'Tone at the top' is a term that describes the board of directors and senior executives setting the tone or values culture for the company to prevent fraud or unethical practices such as bullying, tax evasion or other abuses of power. The belief is that this sets an agenda which permeates throughout the whole culture of the company. Virtue theorists could see this emphasis on character and training in virtue in terms of practices aimed at excellence that develop virtues internal to them, such as truth-telling, respect and justice.

> **Stakeholders:** Parties such as customers, local communities, government, suppliers, employees, civil society and shareholders who are affected by business practice and therefore have an interest or stake in it, making business more democratic and accountable

> **Triple bottom line:** In addition to the bottom line of *profit*, in 1994, John Elkington's SustainAbility consultancy suggested that successful businesses also have a *people* account (for social responsibility to stakeholders) and a *planet* account (for environmental responsibility)

Exercise

1. Have you ever avoided a company or purchase on ethical grounds? If so, why?
2. Investigate the issue of accountability in terms of company responsibilities to workers in the garment industry in Bangladesh. Fires and the collapse of buildings, together with workers not being paid a living wage, have raised questions about the ethics of supply chains.

Businesses and the environment

Tracking sustainable consumption – look up:

1. 'zerofootprint' to do an online calculation to measure and manage your carbon footprint;
2. National Geographic's Greendex system, which is an annual sustainable consumption index of actual consumer behaviour and material lifestyles across eighteen countries.

QUICK QUESTION

Why is pollution an example of a negative externality?

Externalities:
The consequences (negative or positive) of commercial and industrial activity for other parties (e.g. where true costs of production are dodged by the producer)

Businesses seek to maximise profit by externalising the wider social costs of their goods and services, so they do not have to be met by the producer or the consumer at the point of sale. At worst, this can be seen as a form of theft: those who benefit from stealing from those who will have to bear the costs. In *The Value of Nothing* (Portobello, 2011), Raj Patel gives the example of McDonalds. He cites one estimate that the cost of voluntarily offsetting the 2.66 billion pounds of CO_2 created in the making of 550 million Big Macs sold in the United States every year would be between $7.3 and $35.6 million.

A further external cost borne by the environment is seen in the forests cut down to graze beef cattle. The Centre for Science and the Environment in India estimates this raises the price of each Big Mac to $200 (cited in Patel 2011). This does not even take into account the $562 million saved by the US beef industry, which fattens its produce on government-subsidised corn (according to a Tufts University study). Nor does it take into account the social subsidy estimated at around $273 million p.a. in the form of Medicare, food stamps, and government payments to turn the poverty-line wages of employees into living wages. One further cost to add to the **externalities** bill comes in the form of obesity and heart disease resulting from 'excessive meat consumption', which is estimated at $30–60 billion per year in the US.

It is also important to consider the externalising of environmental costs to businesses at the macro level. World Bank estimates put the cost to China's environment at 8 per cent of its GDP (M. Bekoff, *The Emotional Lives of Animals*, 2004). As each business looks to lower its costs in production, packaging, marketing, labour and interest payments, etc., moving goods around the earth's surface by land, sea and air adds to greenhouse gases. Carbon offsetting (whereby, through using alternative energy sources or planting trees, the environmental costs are factored into the price) is rarely taken up (though U2's and Coldplay's tours aim to be carbon-neutral, with varying success). At the Rio Earth Summit in 1992, governments discussed measures to reduce carbon emissions. In *The No-Nonsense Guide to Globalization*, Wayne Ellwood proposes that the World Trade Organization should incorporate an agreement that 'requires all governments to stabilise greenhouse gas emissions at 1990 levels' and provides 'for customs inspection, seizure and disposal of goods that were produced in ways that violate that agreement' (*New Internationalist*, 2005, p. 122). He wishes to see regulation set limits to free trade policies that add to global warming or biodiversity loss. Yet the consensus seems to be that dealing with environmental crises should be the responsibility of other specialist bodies rather than being regulated in international trade agreements.

The Kyoto Protocol is 'an international agreement linked to the United Nations Framework Convention on Climate Change, which commits its Parties by setting internationally binding emission reduction targets' (UN). It was adopted in 2005 and revised in 2012. As countries such as China, the US and Russia have been reluctant to commit to binding reductions on carbon emissions, governmental action on climate change at an international level still has a long way to go. The year 2014 saw the introduction of the United Nations' Clean Development Mechanism which 'allows emission-reduction projects in developing countries to earn certified emission reduction (CER) credits, each equivalent to one tonne of CO2. These CERs can be traded to allow industrialised countries to meet a part of their emission reduction targets under the Kyoto Protocol.'

Individuals, corporations and events can also trade in CERs. Another UN initiative is its Global Compact, which is a bottom-up rather than a top-down approach. Working directly with companies, it offers them a platform to support and enact ten core values in areas of human rights, labour, the environment and anti-corruption.

Corporate Social Responsibility

> There is **one and only one** social responsibility of business – to use its resources and engage in activities designed to increase its profits so long as it stays within the rules of the game, which is to say, engages in open and free competition without deception or fraud.
>
> **(Milton Friedman, *The New York Times Magazine*, 13 September 1970)**

For a free market economist like Milton Friedman, we should not confuse business with philanthropy. This appears to be the view of more than half of business leaders according to a survey by *The Economist* in 2008, which found that they viewed Corporate Social Responsibility (CSR) as 'having a better brand reputation' – a form of window dressing in other words. Where CSR is undertaken in a lip-service fashion rather than being integral to a business organisation, it will be the first casualty of an economic downturn. Yet consumer and activist pressure, together with executive fears over brand damage can lead to a form of enlightened self-interest. For example, CSR can play a role in attracting the best graduate employees, and voluntarily keeping to codes of ethics can discourage government from over-regulation.

The European Commission defines CSR as 'A concept whereby companies integrate social and environmental concerns in their business operations and in their interaction with their stakeholders', thereby contributing to 'a better society and cleaner environment'.

> **Research task:** Choose two companies and look up their CSR / Sustainability / Corporate citizenship page on their website. Is their reasoning focused on the profit motive (good ethics is good business for shareholders), or does it make the case for the intrinsic value of ethics?

Four key elements of CSR

1. LEGAL – Keeping within the law by avoiding fraud, corruption, and health and safety breaches.
2. ECONOMIC – Behaving responsibly economically by paying fair wages and producing services or products that adhere to regulatory standards. In an anti-competitive manner, some companies have informally set prices between them, agreeing to avoid competition to inflate their profits. Other giants like Microsoft (fined €280.5 million in 2006) have abused their monopolistic position to disadvantage competitors.

When the UK government bailed out many banks in the 2008/9 collapse, the crisis uncovered how irresponsibly their executives had acted. What was termed 'casino

Corporate Social Responsibility: in this concept, business is seen as having an obligation to society that extends beyond its duty to its owners or shareholders, and beyond its legal and economic imperatives. It ought to protect society and minimise negative impacts that may arise from its operations (e.g. pollution, discrimination, dangerous products, misleading advertising); indeed, it should seek to improve the welfare of society. Businesses need to be economically viable and efficient in a competitive marketplace. But they also have discretion to act for the public benefit (e.g. through their wealth creation, sponsorship and philanthropy).

banking' clearly needed further regulation and banks are now required to have stronger cash reserves to give them greater robustness against future crises and bankruptcy. So wealth creation ensures that jobs and pensions are secure and that small and large investors can rely on companies having good financial foundations.

*The second two aspects of CSR go beyond regulatory requirements and reflect a sense that businesses are corporate citizens of society with a moral obligation to ensure public benefit. Society expects businesses to act **ethically** and desires that they act **philanthropically**.*

3. ETHICAL – Given that the turnover of multinationals can exceed the Gross Domestic Product of many nation states, they are powerful players with huge resources and influence. They are expected to reduce their greenhouse gas emissions and to audit properly developing world factories to which they have outsourced production. Where child labour and workplace safety standards can be flouted in other countries, companies are not expected to keep their relationships with unethical supply chains at arm's length in order to deny knowledge of wrongdoing. The use of bribes and prostitutes to secure contracts abroad, or of executive abuses of the expense account, may not be criminal, but when investigative journalists or activists uncover it, public distrust and brand damage result.

4. PHILANTHROPIC – Philanthropy may be translated from the Greek as 'Love of your fellow human'. Examples can be seen in a business's charitable contributions, its sponsorship of the arts or sport, or improvements it delivers for the lives of its employees or local communities. This element of CSR is sometimes seen as less important, and even as in conflict with the others. In a ruthlessly competitive market, a company may put jobs at risk and lose investors their money if it is too generous for its own good. What anti-capitalists may see as 'greed for profit' could be a prudent judgement about a business's economic survival.

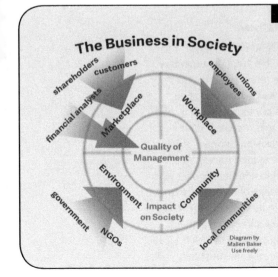

The Business in Society

Diagram by Mallen Baker
Use freely

Discussion Questions

1. Look at the diagram on business and society. Should businesses think of themselves as solely working for their shareholders' interests, or ought they to take into account the interests of multiple stakeholders as this diagram suggests?

    Stakeholders are groups who affect or can be affected by the organisation's actions, and range from employees to consumers, local communities, suppliers, local and national government.

2. The growth of multinational companies often sees a 'race to the bottom' which sees them relocate to 'low-cost' regions with lower levels of regulation on pollution, worker pay and tax. In what ways can multinationals who operate globally but have a large customer base in the UK be held accountable by consumers and activists in this country?

Case studies

1 Apple and the transition from leadership under Steve Jobs to Tim Cook

Steve Jobs has been immortalised in the 2015 film as a brilliant if flawed business innovator; under his leadership, questions were raised about the manufacturing of Apple products by Foxconn's factory in the town of Longhua, Shenzhen, China. Critics questioned the health and safety conditions of this 'sweatshop' of 200,000 workers. After eighteen attempted suicides there in 2010, and complaints of low earners on as little as £1.12 an hour and employees having to stand for excessively long shifts, new Apple CEO Tim Cook is receiving some acknowledgment from auditors for progress on this front. A member of the Fair Labour Association, Apple has increased its audits of labour practices and offered a greater level of transparency than in the Jobs era (In 2012 it published a list of all 156 suppliers in its supply chain for the first time). This said, as the market leader and a company that made a $13.4 billion profit for the first quarter of 2014, its competitors will be under pressure to follow its leadership in fair and living wages and the safety of its workers. The *Telegraph* mentioned reports in 2012 that Cook had sent an email to 60,000 employees saying that Apple 'care about every worker in its supply chain' and that, as it continued to 'dig deeper', it would 'undoubtedly find more issues' but never 'turn a blind eye'. It has acted swiftly against supply chain companies that fail to meet its guidelines, and if you are a sixteen-year-old girl in a developing country, a contract with a multinational company is likely to afford you more rights than those offered by state law. There are 8000 applications made every day to work at Taiwanese company Foxconn's 'military'-style factories employing 1 million people, so the alternatives must be even worse. Labour advocacy groups in China argue that Apple could share a little more of its spectacular profits with its workers, although this might inflate the low labour costs at the heart of the Apple business model. Tim Cook also hired the former head of the US Environmental Protection Agency, Lisa Jackson, as vice-president of Environment Policy and Social Initiatives. By 2014, 100 per cent of Apple operations in the US, and 87 per cent of its global operations were powered by renewable energy. Questioned in a Q&A about such environmental policies not necessarily being good for business, Cook said 'We do a lot of things for reasons besides the profit motive', adding that those who had a problem with that were free to sell their stock.

2 Nike and how consumer boycotts can make global corporations listen

The 1990s saw a global boycott campaign against Nike's perceived 'ignorance is bliss' approach to the pay and conditions of workers in its supply chain. In his 2004 documentary *Fahrenheit 9/11*, Michael Moore offered Nike CEO Phil Knight a free return ticket to visit the Indonesian factory where most of Nike's trainers are made and was astonished at his admission that he had never been there. *Life Magazine* published a photo in 1996 of a child stitching footballs with the Nike logo, and again, in 2006, the scene was repeated. With high demand in the lead-in to the 1998 World Cup, Saga Sports, a Pakistani supplier of Nike footballs, had ignored Nike's rules and sent out footballs to be made at local homes. At a cost of $100 million, they cancelled the contract with Saga and went to another supplier who guaranteed regulated factory production. This sent out a strong message of compliance to suppliers. Nike released the names and locations of manufacturers in its supply chain. It also withdrew from a low-cost supplier in Bangladesh that could not meet minimum standards for safe working conditions. This was prior to the Rana Plaza building collapse in which 1,130 died and 2,500 were injured, in a garment factory collapse that resulted from structural failure. So, in relative terms, Nike has made progress under pressure from boycotts and protests that threatened brand damage.

Nevertheless, Nike scores relatively low with ethicalconsumer.org (6/20 in October 2015 and equal with Apple), but higher than other competitors (Adidas scored 5.5/20). It prohibits child labour, forced labour and discrimination, whilst also limiting the working week of employees to 60 hours. Yet it does not agree to pay a living wage in many countries in which it manufactures, and certain of its workers may not earn enough to cover food, housing and healthcare for themselves and their families.

The whole business model of companies like Nike, Reebok and Gap is the outsourcing model using sub-contractors. They are marketing-driven firms who rechannelled the money saved by switching from US manufacturing to paying the considerably lower wages of workers in the developing world into product endorsement by elite athletes. They seek to 'transcendentalise' the brand as an aspirational identity or lifestyle. This said, Nike scores considerably better than Amazon, which achieves 2/20 on the ethical consumer assessment. This is for its tax avoidance, as it paid 0.3 per cent tax in the UK (£11.9 million on a £5.3 billion profit). Amazon also spends a lot of money globally lobbying government on tax, and is criticised for its lack of transparency on its environmental policy and supply chain management.

In 2002, Dita Sara was awarded the $50,000 Reebok Human Rights Award. It was offered to her because, in 1995, she was arrested and tortured by the Indonesian police after leading a strike of 5,000 workers who demanded more than $1 for working 8-hour days. She was released in 1999. Dita Sara refused the award. As she wrote:

> I have taken this award into a very deep consideration. We finally decide not to accept this. . . . In Indonesia, there are five Reebok companies; 80% of the workers are women. All companies are subcontracted, often by South Korean companies. . .. Since the workers can only get around $1.50 a day, they then have to live in a slum area, surrounded by poor and unhealthy conditions, especially for their children. At the same time, Reebok collected millions of dollars of profit every year, directly contributed by these workers. The low pay and exploitation of the workers of Indonesia, Mexico and Vietnam are the main reasons why we will not accept this award.

> No Human Rights Awards have been given out by Reebok since 2007.

3 BP, the Gulf of Mexico spill, and Stakeholder theory

Back in 1980, R. Edward Freeman wrote *Strategic Management: A Stakeholder Approach* (Cambridge University Press, 2010). He argued that the focus of management ought to broaden out from shareholders to stakeholders – any individual or group that had an interest in or was affected by an organisation's activity. Being proactive rather than reactive to social issues was not only good ethics, but good business.

Stakeholder theory included environmental stewardship and, in its glossy 2009 reports, BP talked the language of environmental sustainability – 'At BP we define sustainability as the capacity to endure as a group: by renewing assets; creating and delivering better products and services that meet the evolving needs of society; attracting successive generations of employees; *contributing to a sustainable environment*; and retaining the trust and support of our customers, shareholders and the communities in which we operate [emphasis added].'

Stakeholder theory is tested in balancing the profit motive with the competing costs of satisfying stakeholder interests – for example, investing finance or delaying production to

Greenwashing: When companies seek good public relations by making trivial and low-cost eco-friendly changes to products, services and processes that are merely for show. Brand damage concerns companies and boycotts or bad publicity that can have a big impact on their policies.

minimise environmental risks. In 2010, an explosion at the Deepwater Horizon oil rig in the Gulf of Mexico resulted in eleven deaths, and 4.2 million barrels of oil spilt over 87 days. BP was fined $18.7 billion to settle the legal actions. A Judge ruled that BP had been 'grossly negligent' in placing cutting drilling costs ahead of well safety in order to save time and money. With the benefit of hindsight, it is easy to judge, but given the heavy financial costs to BP, together with the brand damage, this is a case study in the importance of proactive rather than reactive thinking. In light of the losses to the seafood industry, and damage to the ocean in the Gulf of Mexico, the 'balancing of stakeholder and shareholder interests' has to be reassessed.

Exercise

List five ethical issues that the above case studies highlight for global corporations and their handling of CSR policy and supply chains.

Discussion Questions

1   Imagine you are talking with a conscience-free free market capitalist. He says that he admires Lidl for selling jeans at £5.99. He accepts that they're made in a Bangladesh factory where workers (mainly women) are paid at £48 a month (the Asia Floor Wage Alliance calculated in 2013 that a living wage in Bangladesh was £230 a month – figures from the *Guardian*, Gethin Chamberlain, Sunday 13 March 2016). Nonetheless, he argues that the job must pay better than alternatives, and that global markets and competition work – if they can undercut Tesco's equivalent jeans (£17.99), they'll bring in customers, and create jobs. He reassures you that, in the end, the labour market in Bangladesh will pay a fairer wage as demand increases and rival factories offer better wages / workers unite to demand fairer pay.

    How would you respond?

2   Why may a reactive rather than proactive approach to ethics prove to be more costly in the long term for businesses?

Whistle-blowing, or 'making a disclosure in the public interest' was established in UK legislation in 1998 (Public Interest Disclosure at Work Act) and 2013. Almost all employees have the right to provide information to a prescribed body or a journalist as to wrongdoing or illegal practices if it is in the public interest. They should not be treated unfairly, victimised or lose their job. This even applies to so called 'gagging clauses' or confidentiality settlement agreements made at the end of someone's employment. They are invalid in cases that include incidents such as:

● a criminal offence
● the breach of a legal obligation
● a miscarriage of justice
● a danger to the health and safety of any individual (e.g. a company is not honouring its legally required insurance)

Whistle-blowing: a practice in which employees who know their company to be engaged in activities that are illegal (e.g. fraud/corruption), to violate human rights, or to cause unnecessary harm inform the public or a government body. As long as they are acting in good faith and in the public interest, they are protected in law against retaliation.

- damage to the environment
- deliberate attempt to conceal any of the above.

Individuals can report information to their employers, or, if it relates to the conduct of senior managers themselves, to prescribed bodies in the sector of employment they are in. According to the *Guardian* (25 June 2013), the NHS has spent £2 million on 'gagging orders' from 2008 to 2013, and the BBC, £28 million to gag 500 of its departing staff. From 2013, there is a requirement that employees be allowed to report wrongdoing of the kind mentioned above if they reasonably believe their disclosure to be in the public interest. This was to insure against employees who didn't act in the spirit of the law by disclosing information that was purely private and not deemed to be in the public interest. They must act 'in good faith' and not for personal interest, or risk losing compensation or employment protection.

Discussion Question

Consider the following whistle-blowing case studies. Did the person act 'in good faith' and 'in the public interest' in your view?

Case studies

1 Geoffrey Wigand (1942–) and the tobacco industry

In 1996, the former vice-president of Research and Development at Brown and Williamson Tobacco Corp. (B&W), Geoffrey Wigand, appeared on the CBS programme *60 Minutes*, to whistle-blow on his former employers. Wigand was hired by B&W to make a cigarette that was less likely to cause disease and the build-up of pollutants like tar. The company spoke with him in his 1989 interview about reducing carcinogens and talked about making a safer cigarette that reduced the risks of cancer, heart disease and emphysema. Yet, as a Ph.D. research chemist, he discovered that B&W knew that tobacco was addictive. They ignored his research into less addictive cigarettes, and intentionally manipulated the amount of nicotine in cigarette smoke, 'impact boosting' through the delivery of additives like ammonia. This caused the nicotine to be more rapidly absorbed in the lungs and the brain and central nervous system. They also genetically engineered a tobacco plant named Y-1 which was twice as high in nicotine as regular tobacco, illegally exporting its seeds to be grown in Brazil, and then imported the tobacco harvested from them to the US. He also revealed that the company had known for thirty years that their tobacco products caused cancer and other diseases. Nevertheless, in 1994, a year after B&W sacked Wigand, its CEO lied to Congress when he said that he believed that nicotine was not addictive. Yet leaked documents, later in 1994, showed a memorandum from Addison Yeaman, the General Counsel of the legal department of B&W, which said 'we are in the business of selling nicotine, an addictive drug'. The Justice Department also uncovered evidence that the tobacco industry knew from its internal research (under the 'Harvard Project' led by Dr Gary Huber) that cigarette smoke caused emphysema in animals (rats and pigeons). After his findings, Huber had his research funding cut off and his lab shut down. He later learned that a Dr Price had found that emphysema was produced while exposing rats to the smoke of 500 cigarettes back in 1969. Asked why the industry would want to bury information that was of such public health interest, Huber said, 'From all I've seen it was to buy time. To buy time to pass the liability from the manufacturer to the consumer with the labels, to buy time to avoid regulation for greater profit. To buy time to diversify their markets overseas. To buy time to diversify their enormous profits into other industries. To buy time.' See www.pbs. org/wgbh/pages/frontline/shows/settlement/case/bergman.html for more information. Wigand's severance agreement with B&W led to a law suit for his public disclosures / breach of confidentiality. The personal consequences of his whistle-blowing included threats against his family, loss of income, and eventually a divorce. The lawsuit was dismissed as a condition of $368 billion settlement between the Attorneys General of forty States and the tobacco industry in 1997.

2 Sherron Watkins (1959–) and the Enron scandal

In 2001, Watkins was vice-president of Corporate Development at the Enron Corporation when she became aware of accounting irregularities and fraud in the company's financial reporting. As she looked at an Excel spreadsheet listing 200 assets which Enron wanted to sell to raise cash, she discovered that they were empty shell companies capitalised with a false promise of Enron stock. They hid the company's huge debts. She knew that this was deliberate accounting fraud. In August 2001, she alerted the CEO in an anonymous email (but not the US government), and after revealing herself as the source of the email, met with Enron Chairman Kenneth Lay to warn him that Enron needed to acknowledge its accounting tricks or face meltdown. She then sold thousands of dollars of shares. He promised to act on her advice and sack the auditors, but he simply began an internal inquiry that was not run by independent investigators and her warnings were ignored.

She has been criticised for not telling the US authorities (the Securities and Exchange Commission, a government auditing body which protects investors and maintains fair, orderly and efficient markets) about this in 2001. Enron, a group of electricity, gas, communications and paper companies launched in 1985 and which rose to be the seventh-largest company in the US (employing 20,000 staff and with a revenue of $111 billion in 2000), was to collapse and file for bankruptcy by the end of 2001, its shares being worthless. Its auditor, accountancy firm Arthur Anderson, was found guilty of illegally destroying documents, for which it lost its licence to audit, so the Enron scandal also caused its closure.

In 2002, Sherron Watkins testified about her role in the Enron case before the US House of Representatives and Senate. She was selected, along with two other 'whistle-blowers', as

Sherron Watkins

one of *Time* magazine's 'People of the Year' in 2002. The Enron scandal has gone down in US financial history as one of the most systematic cases of 'creative accountancy' and wilful corruption and fraud. Financial analysts in the firm acknowledged to Watkins that 'We're such a crooked company.'

Rather than seeing Watkins as a whistle-blower who alerted the authorities (the SEC), or reported fraud to the *Houston Chronicle*, some see Watkins as writing a memo to warn a bank robber that the police were on to them. It wasn't until her memo to the CEO came to light with the work of Congressional investigators that some in the media hailed her as 'Whistle-blower Sherron Watkins'. Reflecting on her role in the scandal, Watkins said, 'I think there were so many villains in the Enron story that I was made into a heroine, rightly or wrongly.' What she succeeded in doing was to start a chain of events in which it was provable who-knew-what-and-when, which helped investigators. She also raised the importance of whistle-blower legislation to protect employee rights if information was released 'in good faith' and 'in the public interest' from within companies where institutional bullying forced lower-ranking executives to collude with corruption. As Watkins commented on 21 June 2003 ('The Corporate Conscience') to the *Guardian*, 'I don't think Enron is that unusual. After all, we have a chief executive class which act like dictators of small Latin American countries.'

Discussion Questions

What does the Enron case and Sherron Watkins' role in it tell us about the culture of businesses and why might this make it difficult for honest executives to raise the alarm internally? Do you think Watkins emerges from this story as a hero, a villain, or something in between? Internal whistle-blowing (bringing wrongdoing to the attention of senior management) may be rare in corporate culture in which such reporters are seen to be snitches and disloyal do-gooders at best, or as acting in their personal interest at worst. How does whistle-blowing legislation that requires employers to brief employees of their rights seek to address this?

Retaliation against whistle-blowers can be subtle – being moved out of a role where malpractice is going on, and sidelined into another role in the company which is effectively a demotion, cutting down their hours, pay or future job prospects. Yet 2002 was termed the 'Year of the Whistle-blower' in the US, and it led there to the Sarbanes-Oxley Corporate Reform Act, which, for the first time, gave legal protections to whistle-blowers. Publicly traded companies were required to have a policy allowing employees to bring unethical and illegal practices to light and to train managers and executives on how to encourage openness. The Act made it illegal to 'discharge, demote, suspend, threaten, harass or in any manner discriminate against' whistle-blowers, with criminal penalties of up to 10 years for executives who retaliated against them. It brought in ethical policies and codes of conduct placing responsibility for unethical or illegal practice on the senior management.

Reasons against employees whistle-blowing	Reasons for employees whistle-blowing
• Being perceived as a disloyal 'snitch'.	• Legal protection against retaliation by employer.
• Misguided solidarity and a sense that to undermine one's employer puts at risk one's job or the value of one's shares in the company.	• Acting in good faith in the public interest is the right thing to do – one's duty.
• Fear of retaliation / alienation from peers / being overlooked for promotion.	• The examples of other whistle-blowers who are seen heroically or as fully justified.
• Belief that, for all their ethical policies, senior management dislike 'wets' who won't turn a blind eye to unethical company conduct.	• Integrity of character is more important than profit.
• Inaction by senior management on internal complaints creates a cynical culture in which employees 'hear no evil and see no evil'.	• The CEO and senior management are committed to a transparent culture and an honest, open-door policy on unethical conduct being reported.

The first decade of the new millennium saw massive corporate cover-ups which, when they came to light, led to the collapse of massive companies and big banks on which investors and pension funds depended, as well as many jobs. In your view, does the legislation in the US, the UK and many other countries on whistle-blowing make it less likely that this will occur again?

Kantian theory applied to business ethics

W. M. Evan and R. E. Freeman argue, in 'A Stakeholder Theory of the Modern Corporation: Kantian Capitalism" (in T. L. Beauchamp and N. E. Bowie (eds.), *Ethical Theory and Business*, 3rd edition, Prentice Hall, 1993, pp. 97–106), that Stakeholder theory is rooted in Kantian ethics. It gives consideration to employees, local communities and suppliers not merely as a means, but as an end in themselves. These people are free and autonomous rational beings, not merely tools of production, or income streams. The phrase 'Tone at the top' originates in accounting and refers to the ethical climate of a business as established by its directors and senior management. Its focus on the character of business leaders in the shaping of an organisational culture (polis) owes more to Aristotle and virtue ethics. If the tone set at the top is one of transparency, the rejection of fraud and the promotion of responsibilities towards the environment and stakeholders, it will filter down through the business. Kant's own father showed such character, acting with good will in heated disputes between saddle- and harness-makers' guilds, and the tests of this adherence to duty are the three formulations of Kant's Categorical Imperative. By contrast, Kant discusses the example of a grocer who might deal fairly with his customers out of enlightened self-interest rather than duty to the moral law. Competition and the desire for customer loyalty and repeat business are motives that fall below the moral standard of duty and the Categorical Imperative.

If we consider Kant's three formulations of the Categorical Imperative, they give a clear sense of how uncompromising his demands would be for Corporate Social Responsibility.

1 Act only according to that maxim by which you can at the same time will that it should become a universal moral law. Kant's awe at the starry heavens above and the moral law within is taken up by other scholars such as Emily Brady (*The Sublime in Modern Philosophy: Aesthetics, Ethics, and Nature*, Cambridge University Press, 2013). She attempts to save Kant from the charge of anthropocentrism by reading him as seeing the vastness, beauty and power of the natural world as awakening a sense of one's rational nature and moral vocation. Destroying habitats, species and natural resources, and over-hunting/- fishing all dehumanise this rational dignity of human beings in a failure to see the interplay of reason and awe at the sublime in nature. So Kantian ethics warns us against an unsustainable view of the environment as an infinite resource. As fossil fuels, rainforests and ecosystems are finite, this establishes duties of care that we owe to them.

'Earthrise' photo by astronaut on Apollo 8 – it has been described as one of the most influential environmental photos ever taken because it showed how finite earth's resources were

Although Kant appeared to give lesser importance to non-rational nature, modern Kantians emphasise his awe and reverence for nature and stress the importance of human stewardship of this. R. W. Hepburn (in *Wonder and Other Essays*, Edinburgh University Press, 1984) extends Kant's formula of the end in itself to the natural world. Kant's mother, Anna, took him for walks in the meadows and fields and taught him about the seasons, plants, animals (bears and wolves were common around Königsberg) and the sky, awakening a curiosity about and respect for the natural world. Although Kant was just thirteen years old when his mother died, her influence remained strong in him. As he wrote, 'I will never forget my mother, for she implanted and nurtured in me the first germ of goodness; she opened my heart to the impressions of nature; she awakened and furthered my concepts, and her doctrines have had a continual and beneficial influence in my life' (R. B. Jachmann, 'Über Immanuel Kant', 1804, p. 169, quoted in M. Kuehn, *Kant: A Biography*, Cambridge University Press, 2001, p. 31). So Hepburn thinks that Kant's sense of awe and wonder at the starry heavens above would reject an instrumental view of nature as purely for human ends. His second formulation of the Categorical Imperative would rule out exploitation of the environment and animals for short-term profits (e.g. the destruction of orangutan habitat in Borneo for palm oil production). Paul Taylor (*Respect for Nature: A Theory of Environmental Ethics*, Princeton University, 1986) is another Kantian who extends Kant's language of ends in themselves to assert the inherent worth of animals. Studies of how much of our genetic make-up we share with higher primates, and of chimps, elephants and dolphins, reveal in these animals a level of self-awareness and intelligence unknown in Kant's day. We ought therefore to revere nature as possessing an intrinsic good of its own, independent of human interests.

Our rational dignity and capacity to be moral agents lift humankind above nature, but it also gives us a special responsibility for it. Kant's emphasis on intrinsic worth and dignity and its connection with duties can extend to a non-anthropocentric ethic that is transferrable to animals in terms of their interests or 'will to live', or to the environment in terms of deep ecology or ecosystems.

Kant also calls us to attend to our duty to future generations. A carbon-neutral / 100 per cent renewable business model ought to be the goal of business, rather than one which degrades the environment of future generations. Take the example of a business executive who lives in the countryside and enjoys clean air, a beautiful landscape, and is conscientious in his local recycling, but whose business decisions increase pollution and deforestation. He is committing a contradiction of the will. Businesses and consumers ought not to will one thing for themselves, such as a high standard of living from company profits, while knowing that this is produced from the exploitation of workers in the developing world paid less than a living wage.

2 Act in such a way that you always treat humanity, whether in your own person or in the person of any other, never simply as a means, but always at the same time as an end. In a global age, Kant would say that companies could not deny responsibility for the poor pay and conditions of workers by outsourcing production to suppliers in developing countries and not disclosing their suppliers. If their profits are produced through the exploitation of the powerless and poor, this goes against his second formulation of the Categorical Imperative in treating others as a means to an end. This is especially the case with child labour, where both exploitation and the denial of an education are involved. If a business sells substandard goods or services that it charges a high price for, it again uses the customer as a means to an end.

3 Act as if you were, through your maxims, a law-making member of the common-wealth (or kingdom) of ends. Here, morality is rooted in the universal and a priori moral law and in our dignity as law-making (autonomous) members of the commonwealth or kingdom of ends. The word 'commonwealth' carries the sense that businesses take from this common store of wealth when they externalise environmental costs that result from their operations, or when they exploit workers who are not paid a living wage. To avoid tax by registering a company in a tax haven is, again, to take from the common wealth and not to pay one's fair share of costs. Businesses need educated and healthy workers, yet they are committing a contradiction by requiring this, yet not paying their share of the tax bill for schools and hospitals. Kant would applaud self-regulation that goes beyond the requirements of state law in the form of proactive CSR or stakeholder initiatives.

Kant reminds us that not every business judgement is down to the bottom line, and that there are lines that should not be crossed. As Kant showed in his examples, duty could be costly, e.g.

- – telling the truth when a tactical lie would seem more prudent;
- – dealing honestly with competitors who are less than fair;
- – keeping one's promises when this becomes very inconvenient or costly.

His rejection of the hypothetical imperative was on the basis that, when driven by desires and passions, humans were less than free and rational. He lived frugally, earning money from his students who were charged a fee for his lectures. When his father, a harness-maker, had died in 1746, Kant's uncle, a shoemaker, took him in, so he appreciated the challenges of making a living for skilled craft workers. Today's globalized, industrial-scale business world is an age away from Kant's experience, but still good will and duties matter. After a long period of de-regulation from the early 1980s onwards in the UK, US and elsewhere, the collapse of the banking sector in 2008 has led many countries to reassess regulations and safeguards. CSR regulations and Stakeholder theory are a recognition that, when giant corporations in the private sector fail on this scale, they can seriously damage whole economies. So businesses cannot act like psychopaths, ruthlessly exploiting others out of self-interest and without empathy and externalising costs and risks to society and government (as portrayed in the 2004 documentary *The Corporation* from the book by law professor Joel Bakan). Acting instrumentally for the bottom line of profit and disregarding people and planet, business leaders are tempted to compromise in the race to the bottom with conscience-free competitors. Yet principles matter and businesses have duties to their wider societies and the globe. Kant alerts us to the dignity of our reason, which measures worth in more than purely monetary terms.

Criticisms of Kantian ethics in business

1 **It is too abstract and purist**. It may work for cottage industries like harness-and shoe-makers, but in the globalized, industrialised world in which managers have to handle concrete problems according to the values of the firm, high-minded absolutes and universal principles do not prove to be practical. How does this decide local wage levels for workers in a company whose manufacturing is outsourced to China or Bangladesh?

2 Is it **imperialist** to think that moral norms are to be universalised? What may be considered a bribe in the UK may elsewhere be an integral part of a culture in which gifts reinforce business relationships. Norms and values are often relative to local cultures and business leaders need to be diplomatic rather than impose 'objective standards' on others.

3. Businesses need to make a profit to survive. Commercial logic is full of 'if. . .then' hypothetical imperatives and **lives or dies by how effectively it takes consequences into account** in cost–benefit strategising. Here, **Utilitarianism is more pragmatic** and recognises that, in times of austerity, philanthropic duties to stakeholders may need to take a back seat. Decision-makers need the flexibility to decide on strategy in a real-time context, and not have their hands tied by unbending rules. Where ethical practice has seen progress, it is through pragmatic, enlightened self-interest arguments made to business. Pragmatism is the art of the possible and Kant is not good at making the compromises that business leaders can agree to today.

4. Kantian ethics is action-based. With 'Tone at the top', there has been a revival of **character-based virtue** in business. Teaching courage, temperance, integrity, diligence, prudence, justice, perseverance and compassion in leaders requires there to be good role models and rigorous training. Kant seems to think of ethics more in terms of making the right calculations with good will, and more about doing than being.

5. Some **feminist ethicists** (e.g. Maier, 1997; Rabouin, 1997) are critical of Kant for his failure to prioritise healthy and harmonious relationships, social care and non-maleficence (do no harm) over fixed principles that are rooted in his autonomous rational male. It is precisely this rationalised and depersonalised ethic of Kant's which puts the human factor out of focus and neglects the more vulnerable.

6. **Kant seems to think that duties will never conflict**, but W. D. Ross recognises this as a problem in his notion of prima facie (self-evident) goods. It is far from clear that boardrooms and competing companies will agree on ethics. One firm's whistle-blower is another's disloyal rat. One company's successful negotiation is another's bribe. One company's philanthropic generosity could spell financial ruin if carried out by another. Many decision-makers in business face dilemmas

when laying staff off to keep a business viable, or ask what the shareholders will think if they do better – or worse – than government targets for renewable energy. These judgements are far from self-evident.

Utilitarianism and business ethics

Utilitarian ethics are consequentialist and take a prudent cost–benefit approach to weighing ethical decisions. Taking stock of likely consequences is a crucial part of business judgement. Given the scientific evidence for the impact of human industry on carbon fuel usage and the environment, the question is whether a Utilitarian mindset extends beyond the bottom line (profit) to the triple bottom line (profit, people, planet).

Bentham's focus on 'the greatest good of the greatest number' also encourages global responsibility. In an age in which multinationals often wield more power than nation states, Bentham's dictum of 'Every [person] to count for one and no one to count for more than one' serves to empower employees at the end of a supply chain in developing countries as well as stakeholders in a business (who could even include consumers boycotting its products for ethical reasons).

Bentham also focuses on sentience and extends ethical consideration to non-human animals. As he wrote: 'The question is not, Can they reason? nor, Can they talk? but, Can they suffer?' (*The Principles of Morals and Legislation*, W. Tait, 1838, ch. XIX, v). Continuing this tradition, Peter Singer's writing in books like *Animal Liberation* and *One World* expresses a desire for ethics to be less anthropocentric. Concern for animal welfare challenges the cruelty of the meat industry's factory-farming methods. He attacks 'speciesism' for being as ungrounded as racism in giving little or no value to the lives, interests and welfare of non-human animals. Rule Utilitarians may even go further and speak of animal welfare needing to be expressed in the language of rights. They would also advocate reforms in legislation, regulation and company policies that take account of the impact of businesses on the environment. Change requires movements, not just individuals making decisions on an ad hoc basis. Utilitarianism began as a social reform movement, Bentham and Mill both campaigning on prison reform. So it has, from the outset, had a practical and reformist mindset. Today, Peter Singer continues this activism, quoting with approval Marx's remark that 'The philosophers have only interpreted the world, in various ways. The point, however, is to change it' (*Theses on Feuerbach*).

John Stuart Mill would balance the liberties of individuals or companies against the harm principle. Law ought to intervene or regulate when significant harm is done to others, and environmental law and policy on carbon emissions reflect this. Critics claim the ends–means reasoning of Utilitarianism gives it a very shallow ecology, preserving the ground on which we stand for instrumental rather than intrinsic reasons. Yet part of Mill's recovery from his breakdown came through reading the Lakeland poets Wordsworth and Coleridge, so his qualitative emphasis on higher pleasures included an aesthetic appreciation of nature. Greedy consumerism and overconsumption would resemble the pleasures of the pig, and Mill would warn against undervaluing natural resources or the ecosystem in a purely qualitative cost–benefit analysis. Mill's harm principle expressed itself in his desire to see 'a law established interdicting altogether the employment of children' in a weekly publication of 1832. In his *Principles of Political Economy*, he also warned of the dangers to the environment, from unlimited growth. If people could be content with a 'stationary state' – i.e., they could constrain their habits of consumption – the earth would retain its pleasantness and the people be happier.

In his book *One World*, Peter Singer is critical of the role of global institutions like the International Monetary Fund and the World Trade Organization, which need serious reforms. In particular, he examines how they do not always act in the interests of the poor and marginalised, but take a macro-economic view hoping that wealth trickles down from the rich to the poor in an economy. Increased foreign aid budgets are needed (he states that annual US domestic spending on alcohol is $34 billion, compared to $14 billion spent annually by the US on foreign development aid). He is concerned about the environment (one atmosphere), and the US' failure under George Bush Sr to sign up to the Kyoto Treaty. As he writes in the book's preface, in 2003, 'The thesis of this book is that how well we come through the era of globalization (perhaps whether we come through it at all) will depend on how we respond ethically to the idea that we live in one world. For the rich nations not to take a global ethical viewpoint has long been seriously morally wrong. Now it is also, in the long term, a danger to security.' He pleads for the bottom billion who live in abject poverty. He is critical of global corporations for trading with dictatorial regimes.

Singer has, of late, moved away from the subjectivism of maximising people's preferences or interests/desires. He has, instead, taken up a more objectivist stance under the influence of the third great Utilitarian, Henry Sidgwick (1838–1900). In his 2014 book *The Point of View of the Universe: Sidgwick and Contemporary Ethics*, Singer outlines three moral claims that Sidgwick took to be self-evidently true:

- an axiom of Justice – 'Whatever action any of us judges to be right for himself, he implicitly judges to be right for all similar persons in similar circumstances';
- an axiom of Prudence – 'a smaller present good is not to be preferred to a greater future good';
- an axiom of Benevolence – 'each one is morally bound to regard the good of any other individual as much as his own, except in so far as he judges it to be less, when impartially viewed, or less certainly knowable or attainable by him'.

In today's globalized world, it is even more important that humans take the point of view of the universe, or an impartial, objectivist stance when considering their actions. Sidgwick reckoned that the 'profoundest problem of ethics' was the apparent rationality of both egoism and Utilitarianism. Reason alone cannot provide complete arguments for what we ought to do, but self-evident intuitions could supplement it.

Discussion Question

Do you consider justice, prudence and benevolence to be self-evident to any rational person?

Weaknesses of Utilitarianism in business ethics

1   Utilitarians may neglect the interests of future people. Generations yet to be born inherit the planet with its acid rain, desertification, lack of biodiversity, melting icecaps and global warming. If business is not reminded of its duty to future generations, if it only has to take the sentient into account, there is less grip for environmental arguments.

2   How do you weigh costs and benefits? Can the end justify the means in using an unethical supplier to keep a company afloat by lowering costs in order to save jobs? Is the lowering of a company's environmental or health and safety standards in a developing country in which it operates acceptable, even if it would be illegal in its country of origin? What if the suffering of the workers in a developing country is outweighed by the interests of thousands of pensioners dependent on pension funds?

3   The problem of injustice. If all that counts is the sum total (aggregate) happiness or the maximisation of preferences, and there are no objective rights and wrongs, or duties, then why not exploit the cheap labour of a relatively small number of factory workers to provide a high standard of living to a greater number of people?

4   With 'Tone at the top' recognising the importance of the values and character of business leaders, 'act'- rather than 'agent'-based ethics overlook the dynamic of power in business institutions. An institutional culture and character may mould young graduates in its image and shape their moral outlook and judgement. Neglectful of the virtues, Utilitarianism makes business ethics seem a simple matter of calculating consequences. Vision and virtue go together – an unjust employer may not see the health and safety of his employees as a priority, may show no empathy for exploited developing-world workers, and care nothing for the size of their company's carbon footprint as long as production costs are low and profits high.

Mill and Aristotle: Extension Reading

Mill's version of Bentham's theory was influenced by Aristotle and it is sometimes called eudaimonistic Utilitarianism from the Greek word 'eudaimonia', meaning human happiness or flourishing. In the discussion below, we examine the idea that good business decisions are good ethical decisions. Ethical integrity and practice in business are made more complex by the global marketplace, where a company's goods and services may be undercut by competitors or the supply chain may be hard to audit. Whilst companies may appear to be ethically sound in their public relations and marketing, Mill would ask how they contributed to the *polis* (the health and benefit of wider society). As Mill found, the ancient Greeks have much to teach us.

Steve Jobs, (1955–2011) Entrepreneur and co-founder of Apple Inc. and Pixar Animation Studios

Socrates and Aristotle believed in the unity of the virtues. Courage, justice, temperance, etc., were one. The pursuit of profit cannot be an end in itself, but part of a wider flourishing of character and society. To act virtuously is to have the wisdom and character to act in the right way at the right time to the right person for the right reason. When all of the virtues work together, values, priorities and principles become clear. Yet, like most people, business leaders exhibit some virtues, but lack others, and it's here that virtues can be vices when employed to the wrong ends (such as profit at all costs).

Take the example of Apple Computers. It has been challenged over the pay and conditions of workers in its supply chain. Critics say that the companies it outsources production to in China pay less than a living wage, use under-age labour and require excessive working hours. There are reports of oppressive management, environmental pollution, and even suicides reported at some plants. The founder of Apple Computers, Steve Jobs, said, 'I would trade all of my technology for an afternoon with Socrates.' If his wish had been granted, he may have got more than he bargained for. Plato called Socrates the gadfly, for just as a gadfly stings a horse into action, so Socrates stung the rich and powerful elites of Athens with his relentless questioning. Socrates may have applauded Steve Jobs for his pursuit of excellence in himself and in Apple and praised his company's contribution to people's efficiency and to paperless offices.

Yet Socrates may well have asked:
how the goals or purposes of Apple contribute to the wider flourishing of the world (Socrates called himself a citizen of the world);
how, if the workers in Apple's supply chain aren't flourishing in their lives, the company itself could be said to be flourishing;
why Apple had such huge cash reserves ($53.4 billion profit in 2014–15 and $215 billion in reserve as of January 2016) when there was so much preventable suffering in the world;
what, with Apple as the market leader, the leadership looks like in terms of the wages and conditions of factory workers;
whether, unless you possessed all of the virtues, you could truly be said to possess any of them.

Look up details of Apple's supplier responsibility (its term for CSR) and ask whether its ethics have changed from in Steve Job's day to under the leadership of Tim Cook (CEO) and Jeff Williams (COO) www.apple.com/uk/supplier-responsibility

FURTHER READING

Duncan Clark (2004) *The Rough Guide to Ethical Shopping* (Rough Guides). Penguin

Milton Friedman (13 Sept. 1970) 'The Social Responsibility of Business is to Increase its Profits'. *New York Times Magazine*

FTSE4Good. www.ftse.com/products/downloads/F4G-Index-Inclusion-Rules.pdf

Andrew Crane and Dirk Matten (2010) *Business Ethics: Managing Corporate Citizenship and Sustainability in the Age of Globalization*. Oxford University Press

Peter Singer (2004) *One World: The Ethics of Globalization* (The Terry Lectures). Yale University Press

Michael Sandel (2013) *What Money Can't Buy: The Moral Limits of Markets*. Penguin Books

Wanda Teays (2015) *Business Ethics Through Movies: A Case Study Approach*. Wiley-Blackwell

Thought Points

(1) Make a list of the main ethical issues in business.

(2) Explain how Utilitarianism approaches ethical issues in business.

(3) Discuss whether a Kantian approach to whistle-blowing is of more help than a Utilitarian approach.

(4) To what extent do you think that the ethical issues surrounding corporate Social Responsibility can be resolved by any ethical theory?

(5) 'Globalisation as caused more ethical problems than any other issue isn business.' Discuss this statement.

(6) How far do you agree that Corporate Social Responsibility is merely window-dressing covering the profit motive in business?

(7) Discuss the statement that 'businesses are entirely incompatible with Kantian ethics'.

SECTION IV

SIGNIFICANT IDEAS IN RELIGIOUS AND MORAL THOUGHT

LEARNING OUTCOMES

In this chapter, you will learn about key ideas including

- naturalism
- intuitionism
- emotivism

You will have the opportunity to discuss issues related to meta-ethics, including

- whether or not what is meant by the word 'good' is the defining question in the study of ethics
- whether or not ethical terms such as 'good', 'bad', 'right' and 'wrong':
  - ○ have an objective factual basis that makes them true or false in describing something
  - ○ reflect only what is in the mind of the person using such terms
  - ○ can be said to be meaningful or meaningless
- whether or not, from a common sense approach, people just know within themselves what is good, bad, right and wrong

In the following section, we will examine the nature of ethical language as illustrated in the meta-ethical theories of Naturalism, intuitionism and emotivism. By way of introduction, it is useful to understand two distinctions here.

(i) How meta-ethics differs from normative ethics

Meta-ethics focuses on the meaning and use of the language of ethics. We assume we ordinarily know what words like 'good', 'bad', 'right' and 'wrong' mean – but are these meanings universal or relative to time and place? Can their meanings be expressed in words or seen in terms of something in the natural world, or can they only be known intuitively? Are their meanings grounded in our attitudes, values, judgements, God (or some other metaphysical basis), reason, emotion, or something else? Are there any moral facts or claims that can be judged to be true or false? Meta-ethics is like the grammar of ethics and can appear both daunting and dry as dust. Yet clearer understandings and definitions of such questions and the meaning of moral language avoid confusion, misunderstanding or talking at cross-purposes in disputes. Meta-ethics wrestles with the very meaning of the moral language we use, and so precedes normative ethics, where value judgements, commands, and moral duties have their place.

Normative ethics is where ethics is in the mode of norms, or standards/rules to which our behaviour ought to conform. Depending on the theory, normative ethics can focus on a person's/group's intentions and character, or on their behaviour and the consequences of their actions. Such judgements can be specific, like 'You ought to revise harder for this week's biology test', or general, for example 'Torture is never justifiable.' They can relate to values like 'Honesty is a good policy', or to obligations like 'You ought to honour your parents.'

(ii) How cognitivism differs from non-cognitivism

Cognition refers to the mental process of knowing. **Cognitivists** believe that moral claims are a form of knowledge and can therefore be seen to be true or false. For cognitivists, there are moral facts, not merely opinions, and these can be true or false. Naturalism and intuitionism, as we shall see in the following chapters, are both cognitivist theories. Not all cognitivists are realists, however – error theorists, for example, believe that all moral statements are false, but are nevertheless cognitivist in the sense that they see moral statements as making knowledge which are capable of being falsified.

Non-cognitivists hold that moral truth claims cannot be known or demonstrated to be true or false. Emotivists take this view. Consider these two statements

1. 'Your room attracts mice because it has not been cleaned for weeks!' and
2. 'You ought to clean your room more often!'

The non-cognitivist sees the difference between them as being that:

> (1) is a truth claim that can be verified or falsified, whereas
> (2) is a moral claim or value judgement that cannot be verified or falsified.

Now, say a parent and a child were to argue over (2), the subjectivist would say they were each correct as long as they were speaking sincerely. All moral claims are relative, so each simply asserts their belief. Here, emotivists assert that there are no moral facts in the universe, only attitudes, feelings and desires. They also claim that moral statements are non-cognitive – rather than being knowable to reason, they are emotional expressions often aimed at commanding or urging others to feel the same. Moderate emotivism steps back a little from this position in attempting to distinguish between rational and irrational, informed and misinformed emotions, so here the parent may have the upper hand in arguing for (2).

Cognitivism: Moral judgements are not just feelings – they are making truth claims and so can be true or false (though it may be difficult to prove that the judgements of religion or relativism are true or false).

Non-cognitivism: The view that moral judgements are not true or false as they do not make truth claims. Instead they express emotions, preferences, commands or attitudes.

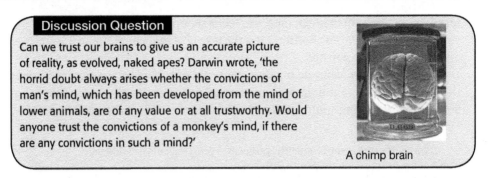

Discussion Question

Can we trust our brains to give us an accurate picture of reality, as evolved, naked apes? Darwin wrote, 'the horrid doubt always arises whether the convictions of man's mind, which has been developed from the mind of lower animals, are of any value or at all trustworthy. Would anyone trust the convictions of a monkey's mind, if there are any convictions in such a mind?'

A chimp brain

The fact–value gap

The eighteenth-century philosopher David Hume made a sharp distinction between facts and values that has been termed 'Hume's Guillotine' because it cuts through any connection between 'is' and 'ought' statements.

Take the following two examples of leaps between 'is' and 'ought' statements:

1 To leave lights and heaters on uses heat, and your gas and electricity use fossil fuels from a planet whose resources are finite. You ought to turn both off when not using them as it is wrong to be wasteful of energy.

2 Evolution is the competition for survival favouring the fittest, therefore we ought to promote the healthy, intelligent and strong in society, and seek to eliminate the weak.

David Hume (1711–76) was voted the second-greatest philosopher of all time by BBC Radio 4 *In Our Time* listeners. He is the key figure of the Scottish Enlightenment and a defining thinker in empiricism who sought to show how the mind is entirely furnished with its ideas from experience and sense impressions. Sceptical about miracles and religious testimony of them, he wanted to consign metaphysics to the flames and put his trust in the evidence that sense experience offered. In *An Enquiry Concerning the Principles of Morals*, Hume argues that the foundations of morality lie in human sentiment rather than reason. What motivates action in us is passion not reason. Hume roots morality not in a divine source, but in our feelings of sympathy and self-interest.

Statue of David Hume in Edinburgh

In his *A Treatise of Human Nature* (1738–40), Hume writes:

> In every system of morality, which I have hitherto met with, I have always remarked, that the author . . . makes observations concerning human affairs; when all of a sudden I am surprised to find, that instead of the usual . . . propositions, is, and is not, I meet with no proposition that is not connected with an ought, or an ought not. This change is imperceptible; but is however, of the last consequence. For as this ought, or ought not, expresses some new relation or affirmation, 'tis necessary that it should be observed and explained; and at the same time that a reason should be given; for what seems altogether inconceivable, how this new relation can be a deduction from others, which are entirely different from it.

(Quoted in Oderberg 2000)

1. Here Hume notes a drift from *factual* statements – for example, 'a human foetus is unborn and dependent upon its mother for life', or 'abortion is the deliberate

termination of a human pregnancy' – to *value* statements such as: 'Therefore you ought not to have an abortion – it is the taking of innocent human life and amounts to killing a person!'

Despite Hume's fact–value distinction, many philosophers have sought to bridge the gap between facts and values. One attempt to bridge the gap is set out by John Searle in the following argument (in *The Construction of Social Reality*, Penguin, 1996, p. 77):

> 1. Jones utters the words 'I hereby promise to pay you, Smith, 5 dollars.'
> 2. Jones promised to pay Smith 5 dollars.
> 3. Jones placed himself under (undertook) an obligation to pay Smith 5 dollars.
> 4. Jones is under an obligation to pay Smith 5 dollars.
> 5. Jones ought to pay Smith 5 dollars.

Searle argues that the gap between facts and values is bridged by 'institutional facts' as opposed to 'brute facts'. That is to say, social practice makes the descriptive statements tie in with the evaluative one. Here, the 'is' or factual statement in the community to which Jones and his debtor belong carries the force of a moral 'ought' or obligation. Schools and institutions are full of such codes of conduct and enforce sanctions on those who break them.

Many philosophers now argue that the fact–value gap was exaggerated in Hume and Moore. Facts and values are entangled in much of human behaviour – e.g. art, architecture, mathematics and science – so why should they not be in the practical rationality of moral thought? Pragmatists would argue that 'knowledge of facts presupposes knowledge of values'. For example, building a telescope or a microscope or designing an experiment presupposes that you value the knowledge that this instrument may possibly yield. As Hilary Putnam puts it, 'The logical positivist fact/value dichotomy was defended on the basis of a narrow scientistic picture of what a "fact" might be, just as the Humean ancestor of that distinction was defended on the basis of a narrow empiricist psychology of "ideas" and "impressions"' (Putnam, *Ethics Without Ontology*, Harvard University Press, new edition, 2004). In response to the economist Milton Friedman's claim that, over differences of value, 'men can ultimately only fight', what meta-ethical discussion deliberates over is the role of reason, emotion and knowledge in our moral judgements. Insofar as we are rational beings, moral deliberation can yield reasons to motivate us to act rationally. Perhaps this could be along the lines of Derek Parfit's formula in *On What Matters* (Oxford University Press, 2013) – 'Everyone ought to follow the principles whose universal acceptance everyone could rationally will and no-one could reasonably reject.'

Discussion Questions

1. Do you find Searle's attempt to bridge the gap between facts and values to be successful? Give reasons for your view.
2. What are the significant differences between the following two claims?
   (i) 'It is wrong to exploit the cheap labour of child factory workers and deny them an education.'
   (ii) 'Water boils at 100 degrees'.

Cognitivism	Moral judgements are not just feelings – they are making truth claims and so can be true or false (though it may be difficult to prove that the judgements of religion or relativism are true or false).
Non-cognitivism	The view that moral judgements are not true or false as they do not make truth claims. Instead they express emotions, preferences, commands or attitudes.
Egoism	The belief that individuals have a moral duty to optimise good consequences for themselves.
Emotivism	The view that any moral claim (e.g. 'Abortion is murder!') is essentially an *emotional* plea on the part of the one who expresses it for others to share such disapproval or adopt this feeling.
Ethical hedonism	The view that pleasure is intrinsically good and pain bad, so you ought to aim at maximising pleasure (note that this led the ancient Greek Epicurus to lead a life of moderation free of the highs and lows of excess).
Intuitionism	The view that 'good' and 'evil' are objective but indefinable. Basic moral truths are either self-evident or perceived similarly to how our senses experience the physical world.
Ethical Naturalism	This approach defines 'good' in terms of some natural property of the world, e.g. pleasure, human flourishing. A subjective naturalist might argue that moral statements are true in terms of the attitudes society approves of. An objectivist naturalist might argue that what is good is what will promote human flourishing in harmony with the resources of the planet.
Moral objectivism	The opposite of subjective ethics, this view holds that moral statements are true independently of what people think or feel.
Nihilism	In terms of ethics, Nihilists believe that objectivity is impossible. No moral truth claims exist, or if they do they're unknowable.
Prescriptivism	Moral statements are commands or imperatives, as opposed to descriptions. Moral terms are used to guide action and prescribe what people are to do in similar situations. An attempt to move on from emotivism and treat ethical reasoning as rational rather than a form of emotional manipulation, it sticks to 'ought' statements that one lives with consistently.
Moral realism	The view that claims are true in respect of how they correspond to the real world. Moral realists hold that moral statements can in principle be verified or falsified – there is an objective reality to them. This may, for example, derive from God's created moral order or commands, but not all realists are theists.

Naturalism

In this section, we will consider the belief that values can be defined in terms of some natural property in the world. This lends itself to a more objective view of ethics in which right or wrong may be evident in some natural state such as pain or pleasure.

Ethical Naturalists believe in two key things

1. Moral judgements can be true or false and make knowledge claims.
2. Moral facts are identifiable with / reducible to natural properties in the world (e.g. through the study of human psychology). There are a variety of observable states with which naturalists identify goodness, such as pleasure, human flourishing or the maximisation of human welfare. Naturalists believe in objective moral properties, but rather than locating the source of moral objectivity in a moral law revealed by God/gods (which would be Supernaturalism), they find its source in the natural world. Platonism and Judeo-Christian Ethics are ultimately both non-naturalistic in the sense that the moral order is rooted in a reality beyond and not reducible to features of the natural world (the realm of forms for Plato, or, for Judeo-Christian Ethics, the essential being of God who commands his creatures to 'Be holy even as I am holy').

Ethical Naturalists are moral realists (believing that ethical statements can be true or false). If 'good' were to be located in the maximisation of human welfare and minimisation of human pain, then it would be wrong to desire freedom, choice and a high standard of living for myself, but to achieve this through the 'slave labour' of workshops in Bangladesh or the Philippines that paid people below a living wage and made them work in unsafe factories for excessive hours in order for me to have cheaper clothes. So 'morally wrong' can be understood in terms of a property in the natural world (such as increasing human suffering). An ethical Naturalist who took this view could say: 'It is wrong for wealthy citizens of developed countries to think that they have no obligations to the global poor in how they use their power and resources.' Naturalists tend therefore, to replace the terms 'good' and 'evil', which have theological roots in divine command theory, with natural properties, as the Utilitarians do when they talk in terms of pleasure and pain. This generally assumes a Cognitivist view (that ethical sentences can express propositions which can be true or false). In the effective altruism movement, a great deal of attention is given to the best use of resources in countering preventable deaths and suffering. The website 'givewell.org', for example, sees 'good' in terms of lives saved and the reduction of suffering. It offers in-depth research to assess the impact of any given charity in these terms per dollar spent. In this way, using tools of accountancy, social science and data analysis, it seeks to measure the 'good' done and see moral facts as facts of nature.

Naturalists believe that moral terms such as 'good' and 'right' can be defined in terms of human nature or properties in the natural world that can be known by our mind or senses. They may be religious (grounded in the way God has made the world and the practical reasoning / goal orientation he has placed in his creatures, as in Natural Law theory). Equally, they may be secular, based upon what makes for a flourishing life or good consequences. The claim of Jeremy Bentham that nature has placed us under two sovereign masters, pleasure and pain, is a form of Naturalism.

What Naturalists share in common is their rejection of the view that we cannot prove moral judgements true or false – that they're just exclamations (as in emotivism). Instead, moral judgements are realist and can be proven true or false from within the natural world. As you can see, Naturalists disagree over which natural

Ethical Naturalism: This approach defines 'good' in terms of some natural property of the world, e.g. pleasure, human flourishing. A subjective naturalist might argue that moral statements are true in terms of the attitudes society approves of. An objectivist naturalist might argue that moral statements are true in terms of the attitudes society approves of. An objectivist naturalist might argue that what is good is what will promote human flourishing in harmony with the resources of the planet.

features of life are good. Cultural relativists, at one end, would define goodness in terms of society's values. At the other end of the spectrum, objectivist naturalists would locate the good in universal aspects of human identity, like reason or maximising choices and freedom, and minimising pain. What they have in common, however, is a commitment to defining morality in terms of natural features of the world.

F. H. Bradley (1846–1924) did much to promote one example of ethical Naturalism in the late nineteenth and early twentieth century. In his influential text *Ethical Studies* (1876), he offers a destructive critique of Utilitarianism's answer to the question 'Why be moral?' This is interesting, because it shows that it is by no means obvious which natural properties 'good' should be identified with. For Bradley, 'good is **not** the *maximisation of pleasurable and minimisation of painful consequences;* **rather**, it is human *self-realisation* that is the source of our motivation to be moral'. In part, he offers a psychological theory of moral maturation. By means of practical reasoning and deliberation, we move from childish appetites and egoism to the moral deliberation of seeing that our self-realisation is better

F. H. Bradley

achieved through making the world into a better place, or, as Bradley puts it, 'we have found our . . . function as an organ of the social organism'. Personal satisfaction is bound up with the creation of an interdependent society in which we each contribute in our particular station or role, and do our duty. We will ourselves to become the idealised self we hope to be. When we fall short of this, we feel disappointment at the moral gap between this ideal self and our actual self. In this process of growth, we develop a social self that takes into account the interests of others, as they are bound up with our own self-realisation.

This is a descriptive theory of ethics, and Bradley believes that our natural urge towards the realisation of our ideal selves (helped along by practices embedded in human institutions like the family/society, and language) is the end goal of ethics. It is not the pleasures of virtue alone that motivate us, but a sense of self-realisation that they help to achieve. So goodness is defined in terms of a property in the natural world – in Bradley's case, this is the satisfaction our practical reasoning finds in developing a mature self that lives up to its ideals and seeks for the same progress in the world around it. So, even among those who agree that goodness is to be defined in terms of a natural property, much debate remains as to which properties of goodness these might be.

Strengths of Naturalism

1   Moral virtues like justice and truthfulness are too serious to be reduced to a matter of taste and opinion. Naturalism's moral objectivism, i.e. its belief that

moral claims can be true or false, allows such claims to be discussed rationally. Although proof that moral facts are observable in the natural world can be elusive, basing our ethics on observations that can be evidenced and reasoned over offers a solid foundation for contesting controversial issues and resolving disputes.

2   Appealing to objective measures of pleasure and pain, rather than to preferences, is proving to gain more grip in persuading many young earners to give away 10 per cent of their income to the poorest, most vulnerable people in the world. The 'Effective Altruism' movement is data-driven and leans towards objectivity in its arguments. Peter Singer, a key thinker, has shifted from Preference Utilitarianism to Hedonic Utilitarianism because the subjectivity of preferences or choices seems curiously powerless to change people's behaviour on issues like environmental ethics or animal welfare. Naturalism can say to the rich young consumer who is a total egoist and spends exorbitantly on himself, while fully aware of the suffering of others, that his actions are ethically wrong as judged by an objective standard.

3   Rejecting Naturalism and believing that moral claims are nothing but opinions risks nihilism (literally, nothingness – no objective values or truths). This gives us little rational defence against tyranny and abuse where 'might makes right'. Affirming Naturalism can motivate protests against injustice or form a basis for natural rights. Seeing morality as subjective emotion can lead to cynicism and make citizens of democracies negligent in protecting the rights and privileges they presently enjoy.

Weaknesses of Naturalism

1   Naturalism typically reduces 'good' and 'evil', 'right' and 'wrong', to natural categories or psychological states such as pleasure and pain, or social approval and disapproval. *Principia Ethica* (1903) by G. E. Moore (1873–1958) advances the 'Open Question Argument' against Naturalism. A closed question is one which yields a 'yes' or 'no' answer, such as 'James is a bachelor, but is he male?' In this case, it is because maleness is intrinsically part of bachelordom. By contrast, to take any natural property and ask 'Is it good?' is to show that the two are not the same – this remains open to discussion and debate. Suppose a Naturalist says 'What is good (natural) is what maximises pleasure and minimises pain.' It would remain an open question to ask: 'Is what is pleasurable good?' It would be equally senseless (and circular) to ask 'Is pleasure pleasurable?' Robert Nozick's thought experiment using the 'experience machine' makes this point. If you could be hooked up to an experience machine that stimulated your brain with pleasurable experiences that were indistinguishable from real life, then what reason would there be to prefer real life to this? If, as an ethical naturalist, I identify pleasure as an intrinsic good, this could lead to absurd conclusions like good = maximising the number of pleasure machines available in the world. Similar problems arise when identifying goodness with natural properties.

2   If Hume is right, then 'ought' statements cannot be derived from 'is' statements. This fact–value gap cannot be bridged by drawing ethical conclusions from non-ethical premises. What kind of a social-science experiment would bridge the fact–value gap and move from description to prescription to show that humans ought or ought not to behave in certain ways? Moral norms may be a product of culture, they cannot be established with the objective certainty available in matters of science or logic.

3   Naturalists believe that moral knowledge can, in some sense, be observed in nature or human nature. Despite this, they find it difficult to convince sceptics. David Hume concluded that we just have to live with the limits of what humans can know and be certain about. Human nature will continue to emote and praise and blame – we cannot outrun our natures, but we need to exercise caution and focus our enquiry into matters of fact that we can empirically observe.

Discussion Questions

1. According to ethical Naturalists, what use might psychology be in discovering what goodness means?
2. How would you respond to the following statements?
   a Swimming underwater is unnatural, anything unnatural is wrong, therefore swimming underwater is wrong.
   b As there are no proofs in ethics, we may as well admit that any moral claim is just as subjective as any other.
   c If it makes you happy, it can't be that bad (Sheryl Crow).
   d Boxing and fox hunting just make me feel sick – of course they're immoral – anyone who needs an argument for why these are wrong is heartless.
   e All moral claims are relative to their time and place. Slavery and human sacrifice were right by the standards of some cultures in the past. Who are we to judge them by our standards?
3. Summarise the ethical Naturalism of Bradley in three bullet points.
4. What advantages may there be to bringing morality down to earth with Naturalism as opposed to rooting it in supernatural divine commands?
5. Without the belief that there are moral facts, or that one can make true or false moral judgements, is there any point arguing over morality?

Intuitionism:
The view that 'good' and 'evil' are objective but indefinable. Basic moral truths are either self-evident or perceived similarly to how our senses experience the physical world.

Intuitionism

In this section, we will consider the belief that 'good' cannot be defined.

This approach was developed by such thinkers as H. A. Prichard, G. E. Moore and W. D. Ross. We will look at this theory critically and evaluate its strengths and weaknesses.

Intuitionists are moral realists who believe that there are objective moral facts. In their view, moral knowledge is innately or intuitively known with the force of an 'ought' or duty to act. We have a special form of consciousness called intuition that accesses moral knowledge and gains emotional conviction. This leads to moral judgements and actions. Intuitionism describes a reaction against the Utilitarian view that there is one unifying principle that can guide our actions. There are many such principles (e.g. regarding when killing may be considered permissible, or how we ought to treat others in a relationship). These cannot be distilled into one unifying principle, but are self-evident to human reason or intellect, much like rules of logic or mathematical truths (like: prime numbers are those which are divisible by themselves and one). This is not to say that we cannot do things to improve the accuracy of our intuitions, for example by:

- seeking to be informed and consistent in our judgements
- consulting the intuitions of others as individual intuitions may be mistaken
- being aware of bias and self-interest, or seeking to be cool and calm in delivering moral judgements
- being aware that complex cases may have many different features and competing considerations, so we will need to rely on a range of intuitions and avoid reducing morality to narrow principles (like those of utility and justice).

In examining intuitionism, we will consider below several important thinkers who have come to define this position.

H. A. Prichard (1871–1947)

Moore saw moral thoughts as twofold: reason gathered the facts of the situation, whereas intuition decided what to do, providing the motive for action. He thought it mistaken to try to justify moral obligation by analysing it in terms of something else, such as pleasure or social approval – it was intuited directly, rather like how our five senses operate. Prichard's famous essay 'Does Moral Philosophy Rest on a Mistake?' (in the philosophy journal *Mind* in 1912) argued for common sense intuitions as opposed to reducing morality to a single principle. When conflicts arise between principles, we settle them by intuiting our primary duty or obligation in the given situation. Personal introspection accesses some standard sense of a moral law and acts on it, so its intuitions are not merely subjective opinions, but, rather, direct knowledge by rational insight.

G. E. Moore (1873–1958)

G. E. Moore's *Principia Ethica* agrees with Hume's fact–value gap, accepting that one cannot move from a descriptive statement like 'Torture causes physical and mental pain' to a moral statement like 'Torture is wrong!' If we define a value like goodness or justice in terms of a natural property X (where X = pleasure maximisation), in what is known as the 'Open Question Argument' (see also p. 160), Moore asks whether or not it makes sense to ask the question: 'Sure, this action maximises pleasure / people's choices, but is it right?' Naturalism's neat reduction of goodness to a natural property fails to work because these are two separate kinds of properties – facts and values. Defining one in terms of the other does nothing to bridge the gap between facts and values. It just leads to circular logic, as in saying 'The good is what is pleasurable because what is pleasurable is good.' Despite this, Moore still believes in objective moral knowledge, and how it is arrived at is clearly a problem for him. As he writes, 'If I am asked "What is good?", my answer is that good is good and that is the end of the matter. Or if I am asked "How is good to be defined?", my answer is that it cannot be defined and that is all I have to say about it' (Moore, *Principia Ethica*, 1903, p. 20). Moore defended a common sense view of 'good' as something which is self-evident to us, and known directly, rather than defined in terms of another property or description. Moore likes

G. E. Moore (1873–1958)

'goodness' to 'yellow'. Yellow may be defined in terms of reflecting light in a particular manner, but to someone blind from birth given such a definition, 'yellowness' would be pretty meaningless. In this sense, goodness is a simple, indefinable quality. Intuitivists claim that moral knowledge is just self-evidently true, such as the belief that all memories of the past are not fictional or that our sense experience of the world is not some *Matrix*-like conspiracy. That is to say, it is a basic belief that is not dependent upon some prior proof or justification. Intuitionists like Moore are not claiming that all moral dilemmas resolve themselves as self-evident intuitions guide us. Instead, there are some basic self-evident intuitions – such as the good of friendship or contemplating beauty – that give us moral knowledge (cognition), judgement and motivation to act.

Moore is often seen as a 'pluralist' Utilitarian due to his refusal to reduce goodness to one unifying principle such as maximising pleasure and minimising pain for the greatest good of the greatest number. Moore believed that we intuit the non-natural property of goodness but that it is then up to us, using the methods of science and practical reasoning, to figure out how to get the most right done. Goodness was simple and unanalysable. Yet this non-natural property of goodness could be intuited and (separately) be linked by reason to how we ought to act.

W. D. Ross (1877–1971)

Ross argued that there are real objective moral truths that are just as much a part of the fundamental nature of the universe as geometry or arithmetic. He saw these as simple rather than compound – i.e. they are not made up of smaller parts or definable with reference to anything other than moral truths. Our moral intuitions do not sort out every moral decision for us, but they do uncover basic moral truths whilst guiding and motivating our moral judgements and actions. In rejecting the one or two overriding principles in the Utilitarianism of Bentham and Mill, Ross set out seven self-evident duties or principles:

1. duties of fidelity, which are duties based on promises, explicit or implicit
2. duties of reparation, which rest on a previous wrongful act

3. duties of gratitude for past favours
4. duties of justice to upset distributions not in accordance with merit
5. duties of beneficence – that is, to do good for others
6. duties of non-maleficence – that is, to avoid doing harm to others
7. duties of self-improvement.

Where these self-evident duties conflict, we intuit one overriding 'actual duty'. We may also need later to make up for the duties we set aside. For example, after World War II which caused innocent civilian casualties, the Allies were duty-bound to invest in post-conflict nation-building to make up for the harm done, even though going to war was considered a duty in the first place. Ross does not see the list of prima facie duties as exhaustive, and particular situations may lead us to intuit different obligations. Yet the prima facie duty judged to be 'more incumbent than any other' will present itself. A few rules of thumb (which don't apply in every situation) are that avoiding doing harm generally takes priority in cases where it is in direct conflict with doing good for others (e.g. euthanising a patient to alleviate their pain). If my duty of justice causes me to break a promise (I promise to take my grandmother to the shops, but can't make it because I stop to help after a motor accident by giving my eyewitness testimony to police), I should still seek to make amends for this break in trust at some later time. Ross does not see disagreements over duties as a showstopper. We wouldn't reject our intuitive experience of beauty because of disagreements over which artists or art theories are best, so it would be unreasonable to discard our intuitive sense of right and wrong because of rival moral theories or differing judgements between individuals.

Discussion Questions

1. Do you agree with the idea that moral facts are self-evident to our intuitions, just as empirical facts are self-evident to our senses?
2. If you disagree with the idea of self-evident truths that are foundational and require no more basic supporting reasons, how do you know that:

   other people's minds exist?
   your memories of the past are reliable?

3. List one argument for and one against Ross' idea that conflicts between duties arise, but that an overriding duty presents itself as our duty.

Concluding note on Daniel Kahneman and the psychology of intuitions

Nobel Prize-winner Daniel Kahneman works in the cross-over between economics, psychology and philosophy. His research challenges the assumption in economics that people make rational choices. Intuitions about when and where to buy and sell, for example, can turn out to be made on limited knowledge of markets, or simply be driven by fear and greed. Kahneman shows that a gap often exists between our intuitive and our rational judgements. Generally speaking, our intuitions are automatic, quick, effortless, associative and emotionally charged. By contrast, our rational judgements are step-by-step, slow, effortful, conscious and flexible. The source of our subconscious intuitions may be reliable (e.g. experience, practice) or mistaken (e.g. emotionally charged with assumptions and bias), so it is important to make further rational investigation into their reliability.

He gives the example of a psychology experiment in hypnosis in which a subject is told 'I'll clap my hands and then you will get up and open the window.' When the subject wakes post-hypnosis, they are asked why they opened the window. They say 'Intuitively, I felt that the room felt warm.' In another experiment, subjects are asked to decide on the level of compensation for a robbery. Some are told that the victim was shot in the store he regularly shopped at; others, that he was shot in a store he had visited for the first time that day. As Kahneman puts it, 'because it is easier to imagine the counterfactual undoing of an unusual event than that of a regular occurrence' (Alex Voorhoeve, *Conversations on Ethics*, Oxford University Press, 2011), subjects awarded far higher compensation in the second case than in the first. Yet rational reflection should show us that the difference in the location of the shooting ought to present no significant factor in the amount of compensation. Yet, where philosophers get to compare multiple cases and identify significant factors, in everyday life people's intuitions are about one case at a time, and therefore intuitionism is too vague and non-cognitive a way of thinking about moral judgements. There needs to be a 'reflective equilibrium', whereby critical reviews and revisions of our intuitions are made by reasoning. According to Kahneman, we need our brain to work with both emotional processing (in the amygdala) and analytical processing (the prefrontal cortex).

Kahnemann thinks that certain moral theories gain motivational force when persuasive thinkers draw people's attention to certain intuitions (e.g. consequences), and away from other conflicting intuitions (e.g. the importance of rules and duties). We often seek to balance intuitions that draw us towards optimising consequences, fulfilling our duties, flourishing in our own lives, and acting impartially to treat others as we'd wish to be treated. So our intuitions are inconsistent and incoherent, and this is what it means to be human, and not some supercomputer calculating moral decisions.

Discussion Questions

1. Do you think that Kahnemann's insights strengthen or weaken the case for intuitionism? What reasons do you have for your view?
2. A Princeton University study in 2014 suggested feminine-named hurricanes caused 'significantly more deaths, apparently because they lead to lower perceived risk and consequently less preparedness'. Does this show that intuitions are often bound up with prejudices or mistaken subconscious beliefs, and therefore quite unreliable?

Strengths of intuitionism

1. It is morally realist, so it offers a sense of moral duty or a motive to act. This motivation to act in line with our moral intuitions fits with everyday common sense

morality. Faced with the fact–value gap, academic ethicists may scratch their heads to offer a watertight argument for why genocide or concentration camps are objectively and universally wrong. Nonetheless, there was and still is a deep and widely held belief and intuition in post-war Europe that they represent a crime against humanity.

2. If our consciousness of moral truths is successful, like our appreciation of beauty, we can trust it as realistic, and, without the need for divine commands, we can have a sense of there being duties and objective rights and wrongs.

Weaknesses of intuitionism

1. The argument from disagreement. Non-intuitionists can explain how disagreements arise in morality more easily than intuitionists. Each offers a different explanation as to why we should expect disagreements:

Relativists	Morality is a product of the different values of cultures.
Error theorists	Morality is a fairy tale – different people and cultures each invent their own fictional version.
Emotivists	Morality is a matter of individual taste and this varies widely.

Yet intuitionists see goodness as self-evident, in a manner analogous to mathematics or logic. Yet they vary greatly regarding what they take to be self-evident moral truths. Ethical disputes being so controversial, it seems unlikely that anything is quite so self-evident in ethics as the intuitivists claim. Unlike simple concepts like the primary colour yellow, 'goodness' is complex and not always self-evident. Believing or intuiting something to be true doesn't make it so. Clarity is crucial in settling ethical disputes, and relying on intuitions is a poor guide in disagreements.

2. Intuitionists like Thomas Reid (1710–96) responded to Hume's version of this attack by arguing that the mere fact that our native intuitions are reliable doesn't necessarily mean that we always use them reliably, or that we have no need of instruction, training, habit and exercise. He uses the analogy that, just because our limbs are healthy, this doesn't mean that we can dance, fence, ride or swim without training and practice. Reid's critics would argue that we can independently and objectively observe sense-based claims with science, whereas objective moral truths and intuitions cannot be verified or falsified, and therefore do not exist.

3. Our human moral intuitions can be seen as crafted by evolution or programmed by our social environment. Evolutionary Biologists like E. O. Wilson have seen our moral sense as a product of natural selection, cooperation giving evolutionary fitness to a group in promoting kin-altruism and cutting

down the 'free-rider problem' (how to deal with cheats who take from a group but don't give to it – see *On Human Nature*, Harvard University Press, 1978, and *Ants*, 1990). Reproductive success in ants and apes entails co-operation. Philosopher Michael Ruse argues that the causal explanation of evolution for our morality makes the idea of a human conscience or objective intuitions redundant. We have no need of a faculty of introspective perception when the origins of morality are evidently products of natural selection. The simplest explanation is best, and it lies in evolutionary biology, not in a mystical intuition of moral objectivity.

4. A similar account of origins intended to make objective intuitionism redundant, is set out by Freud and behaviourists like B. F. Skinner. They see many of our so-called 'intuitions' as products of parenting, schooling or other forms of cultural and social conditioning. Good Victorians 'intuitively' knew that children ought to be seen and not heard in polite company at meal times, or that marriage was a lifelong commitment. Propagandist states that vilify their enemies or scapegoat minorities set out to indoctrinate their 'moral' claims as 'self-evidently' true in the minds of their citizens. This makes it difficult for intuitionists to separate genuine from fake intuitions. Some intuitions once thought obvious, like the imperialist belief that slavery is justified because of the evident superiority of certain nations, are now regarded as absurd or intuitively immoral. D. D. Raphael (*Moral Philosophy*, Oxford University Press, 1994, p. 45) argues that it follows from this that some *single fundamental principle* is required to sustain intuitionism in cases where conflicting intuitions arise. Utilitarians offer the principles of utility and justice to settle disputes. Yet intuitionism can't find an easy way to arbitrate between conflicting intuitions.

5. Consider J. L. Mackie's argument from strangeness or 'queerness'. As he puts it, 'If there were objective values, then they would be entities or qualities or relations of a very strange sort, utterly different from anything else in the universe' (Mackie, *Ethics: Inventing Right and Wrong*, Penguin, 1977, p. 38). Moral truths as non-natural properties are just 'queer', in the sense of odd. They are claimed to exist, but in a non-physical, indefinable way. Perhaps a simpler explanation would be to go with the emotivists' suggestion that the origin of morality is in human emotions and that it is a by-product of the way we engage with the world as passional animals in it.

6. According to Hume, it is not beliefs that motivate us, but desires. Beliefs relate to facts (whether natural facts like the tides of the earth being affected by the moon, or non-natural facts such as those intuitionists claim we can have of morality). But the motivation to act comes from desire. The problem is that desires are subjective, so even if I grant that the intuitionist can intuit the moral knowledge that the pain of others should be avoided, this need not motivate me to act in line with it.

Emotivism

In this section, we will consider a distinction between the emotivism of A. J. Ayer and the moderated emotivism of C. L. Stevenson. We will also discuss emotivism critically and analyse its strengths and weaknesses.

> Most morality, thought Mma Ramotswe, was about doing the right thing because it had been identified as such by a long process of acceptance & observance. You simply could not create your own morality because your experience would never be enough to do so. What gives you the right to say you know better than your ancestors? Morality is for everybody, which means that the views of more than one person are needed to create it. That was what made modern morality, with its emphasis on individuals and the working out of an individual position, so weak. If you gave people the right to work out their own morality, then they would work out the version that was easiest for them and which allowed them to do what suited them for as much of the time as possible. That, in Mma Ramotswe's view, was simple selfishness, whatever grand name one gave to it.
>
> (Alexander McCall Smith, *Morality for Beautiful Girls*, Abacus, 2003)

What is it about modern morality that disturbs the Botswanan detective, Mma Ramotswe? Do you agree with her?

Emotivism is a form of ethics associated with the work of A. J. Ayer (1910–89) and C. L. Stevenson (1908–79). Before considering their view, we will look at the 'sentimentalism' of David Hume, whose fact–value distinction we mentioned earlier.

Hume believed that 'good' or 'bad' arose purely from human sentiments, or emotional reactions of praise or blame. As he put it:

> Take any action allow'd to be vicious: Wilful murder, for instance. Examine it in all its lights, and see if you can find that matter of fact . . . which you call vice . . . You will never find it, till you turn your reflexion into your own breast, and find a sentiment of disapprobation, which arises in you, toward this action. Here is a matter of fact; but 'tis the object of feeling, not reason.
>
> (Quoted in Oderberg 2000)

For Hume, it is in our wiring as humans to react emotionally and to judge on this basis; we cannot outrun our nature. He recognises, as a fact, that human beings will praise and blame and that this is the way their morality works. You may see the killing of a bird by a cat and the murder of a person by another, but it is not sight that distinguishes between killing and murder.

Hume was sceptical about the discovery of moral truths, asserting that 'Morality. . . is more properly felt than judg'd of'. He wrote that 'since vice and virtue are not discoverable merely by reason . . . it must be by means of . . . sentiment . . . that we are able to mark the difference' (Hume, *A Treatise of Human Nature*, Clarendon Press, 1960, p. 147). Hume sticks to the fact that nature orientates us to pursue pleasure and avoid pain. He is content to observe human nature rather than moralise about what we ought to do. Our emotions and desires motivate our actions, and reason has only an instrumental role to play in guiding them. As he asserts, 'both vice and virtue are equally artificial . . . 'Tis impossible therefore, that the character of natural and unnatural can ever, in any sense, mark the boundaries of vice and virtue.' Moral

Emotivism: The view that any moral claim (e.g. 'Abortion is murder!') is essentially an *emotional* plea on the part of the one who expresses it for others to share such disapproval or adopt this feeling

According to C. L. Stevenson, language is dynamic, influencing the attitudes and behaviour of others by magnetising them towards one's emotions. Statements like 'I forgive you', or 'There's the door!' are 'speech acts' that attempt to use words to perform an action.

judgement about vice and virtue does not move from 'is' to 'ought', but from cause (the usefulness of an action) to effect (our emotional approval).

As a young logical positivist, A. J. Ayer was deeply influenced by the work of Hume and that of the Vienna Circle (which met roughly around 1924–6). He boldly presented morality as meaningless, seeing it (as Hume did) as containing neither matters of fact nor ones of logic, and being neither verifiable nor falsifiable. Emotivism is sometimes caricatured as the 'Hurrah-Boo theory' of ethics. It holds that what may appear on the surface to be a reasoned moral argument is really an emotional appeal to share the positive or negative feelings of its advocate – 'They are calculated to provoke', in the words of the young A. J. Ayer who popularised Hume's scepticism about moral knowledge in his 1936 book *Language, Truth, and Logic*. Ayer believed Moore to be correct about the Naturalistic Fallacy, but thought his belief that we intuited moral knowledge to be nonsense. If I say to a cannibal 'It's appalling that you eat people!', what I'm really doing is asserting my disapproval and wanting him to begin to share my feelings. The logical implication of emotivism is that there need be no real disagreement between two contradictory propositions (e.g. 'Euthanasia is morally wrong' / 'Euthanasia ought to be legalised in the UK'). As a logical positivist, Ayer made the bold assertion that such statements were logically neither true nor false by definition and not empirically verified, but rather meaningless. As he wrote, 'The presence of an ethical symbol adds nothing to its content. Thus if I say to someone "You acted wrongly in stealing the money", I am not stating anything more than if I had simply stated, "You stole the money"' (Ayer, *Language, Truth, and Logic*, Gollancz, 1936, p. 67). There are, of course, facts involved in moral debate. In genetic engineering, there's a difference between research on stem cells from umbilical cords and on cells taken from aborted foetuses. When we dismiss moral statements as meaningless and pure emotion, this takes little account of how disagreements can relate to facts.

Stevenson moderated this view, observing that we may 'agree to disagree' on matters of taste, but with morality we seek to persuade others to share and adopt our feelings about an issue. 'Good', in such arguments, has tended to create some magnetism to an action in people's feelings. There was a dynamic or persuasive aspect to such talk. Whilst we could just view moral disputes as a form of propaganda war, Stevenson wanted to give a greater role to rational feelings (which may be distinguished from irrational ones) in his moderate emotivism. Informed and impartial feelings would be preferred to those of a fanatical Nazi blindly following the party line.

In *Ethics and Language*, C. L. Stevenson argued that disagreements amount to more than expressions of emotion in cases where our attitudes are based upon beliefs held within a social context. Words like 'good' or 'wrong' can be used descriptively ('a good pair of pliers' or 'the wrong screwdriver for the screw'), or dynamically ('a good character' or 'the wrong done to a victim'). Used dynamically in a social context in which an emotive meaning is conveyed, words seek to influence others. Hence Stevenson is open-minded about changing other people's minds using rational arguments and attitudes of praise or blame in a social context. Yet the problem is that most of our value judgements are emotive, gut reactions, and consequently immune to reasoning.

Stevenson's moderate emotivism argues that, to the extent that we can adopt the position of ideal and impartial observers and critically analyse the rationality of our beliefs, we can avoid arguments being propaganda wars that manipulate emotions. There are both cognitive and non-cognitive elements to beliefs in moral debate, and we can reason to the extent that we can unravel the one from the other. To the extent that our feelings can be informed and impartial, we can reason that this kind is preferable to those that are purely emotive. Yet Stevenson agreed with Hume that we are moved to action by desire, and that 'good' has an inescapably emotive sense in persuading and magnetising that would never be wholly rational.

Discussion Questions

1. Yossarian – 'From now on I'm thinking only of me.'
   Major Danby replied indulgently with a superior smile, 'But Yossarian, suppose everyone felt that way?'
   'Then I'd certainly be a fool to feel any other way, wouldn't I?'

   (Joseph Heller, *Catch 22*, Vintage Classics, 2004)

   Is there any flaw in Yossarian's logic here?

2. What, if anything, do the following uses of the term 'good' have in common?
   The Lord of the Rings is a good film
   Mother Teresa was a good person
   Eagles are good predators
   Luis Suarez is a good footballer
   God is good
   My lunch was good today
   That's a good smartphone you have there

3. The philosopher Philippa Foot, who studied at Oxford and worked as a government economist during World War II, reflected on her experience of returning to Oxford in 1945: 'in the face of the news of the concentration camps, I thought, "It just can't be the way Stevenson and Ayer say it is, that morality is just an expression of attitude"' (Voorhoeve, *Conversations on Ethics*, p. 91). Do you think that emotivism compares well with objectivist ethics as an 'argument that will stop them in their tracks when they come to take you away'?

4. Assume, for argument's sake, that morality is purely based upon human feelings and is non-cognitive. Does this give us enough to work with in building a stable society and a practical way of living in which humans can live peaceably and flourish together?

Strengths of emotivism

1. It avoids committing the Naturalistic Fallacy (the claim that right and wrong can be defined in terms of natural facts like pleasure and pain or social approval).
2. It reconceives how we think about ethics after accepting the fact–value distinction. As it is desires, not reasons, that move us to act, it offers a clear account of moral motivation that's free from non-natural properties that moral realists think are somehow built into the fabric of the universe, despite being imperceptible to our senses.

Survivors of a concentration camp demonstrate to General Eisenhower torture methods used on prisoners, 1945

3. In grounding ethics in emotion, it accounts for why moral disputes (say over abortion) are often interminable and filled with more heat than light. Emotivism cautions those who would negotiate between disputing parties that reason will have a more modest role given the emotional nature of the human animal in moralising. As a minimalist account of morality that does not go beyond the evidence, this is a strong candidate for the simplest and best explanation of what's going on in moral debate.

Weaknesses of emotivism

1. Reason may be a slave of the passions, but that doesn't mean we should exclude its role prematurely. It can ask of us that we be consistent, imaginative and informed. It can require that we apply logic to our sentences and arguments. It can ask of us that we live in accord with our claims and judgements on others (where we find ourselves in similar circumstances). Emotivism is too quick to give up on moral reasoning.

2. The US philosopher Brand Blanshard (1892–1987) offered a counterexample to challenge the emotivist. Consider a rabbit caught in a hunter's trap and dying painfully quite out of sight of humans. If right and wrong are merely human emotional reactions, then, in the absence of humans, this is neither wrong nor distressing, like the world before humans arrived on the planet. If humans do observe the rabbit's suffering and feel bad, the wrongness lasts for as long as their feelings do. If some hikers come upon it and eventually get bored of the rabbit and forget about it, its on-going pain and distress no longer count, according to the emotivist. Blanshard points out the absurdity, for the everyday man or woman in the street, of grounding right and wrong in something as fickle as our feelings.

3. If 'good' is defined in terms of emotions, then there is no need to universalise this

good and this is more likely to lead to ethical egoism. I might feel better about personal profit than about alleviating global poverty. I might feel like I would hate to be tortured myself, but happy about minimising my risk from terrorism by torturing those suspected of it. Morality as a matter of taste is wide open to persuasion by propaganda, when reason has been abandoned. But do our moral claims about right and wrong really boil down to trying to get someone to share our feelings (e.g. about nuclear weapons or capital punishment)? I may hate Marmite, but this is hardly analogous to hating torture or genocide.

4. If emotions are based upon beliefs or knowledge claims, then they can be reasoned over. For example, if a racist comes to see that their belief is mistaken, this may well change their conduct. But if morality is non-cognitive, then it is hard to see how moral progress can be possible. Were the abolition of the slave trade, voting rights for women, the Equal Pay Act and the establishment of legal rights for disabled people all due only to a change of emotions?

5. If the fact–value distinction can be shown to be mistaken, then emotivism is seen to be built on weak foundations.

Discussion Exercises

1. Having studied meta-ethics, explain why ethical Naturalism and intuitionism come under cognitivism, and emotivism under the label non-cognitivism, as set out in the diagram below:

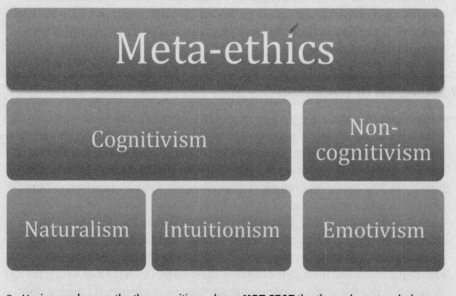

2. Having read up on the three positions above, **HOT SEAT** the three characters below (put them at the front of the class and question them). Ask them the following opening questions and then use the arguments against each view to attack their position. They can respond with supporting arguments. Alternatively, set up the room in a horseshoe of three sides with each side adopting a position and comparing and contrasting their view with that of the others.

	The Naturalist	The Intuitionist	The Emotivist
Do moral judgements express facts?	YES – moral facts can be discovered by observing something in the natural world (e.g. by using science or social science to observe human behaviour).	YES – but they are known intuitively rather than by observation. You just grasp or apprehend moral principles like 'don't harm innocent people without cause', 'tell the truth' and 'keep your promises' as self–evident.	NO (they are just expressions of desire / attitudes / tastes / emotions). Ethical language is non-cognitivist – statements cannot be true or false as they do not express propositions.
Are moral beliefs true in terms of some natural fact in the world?	YES – for example, minimising pain or maximising choices for sentient beings, or seeking greater levels of human equality globally.	NO – moral judgements cannot be reduced to some natural fact or natural science like psychology, anthropology, or sociology.	NO – they are merely expressive of feelings, perhaps with an attempt to get others to share them.
Can you be right or wrong about ethical judgements – their objectivity or realism?	YES – in respect of some natural property (e.g. human flourishing) the actualising of our potential means that modern-day slavery is objectively wrong.	YES – you have a native intuition for good and bad and can reflect on this to motivate you to act.	NO more than you can be right or wrong about your taste in ice cream.

FURTHER READING

A. J. Ayer (1936) *Language, Truth and Logic*. Victor Gollancz, ch. 6

Peter Baron (2014) *Meta-Ethics Study Guide*. PushMe Press

Andrew Fisher (2011) *Meta-ethics, An Introduction*. Acumen Publishing

Harry J. Gensler (2000) *Ethics: A Contemporary Introduction*. Routledge

J. L. Mackie (1977) *Ethics: Inventing Right and Wrong*. Penguin Books, part 1.3

Alex Miller (2003) *Contemporary Metaethics: An Introduction*. Polity

G. E. Moore (1903) *Principia Ethica*. Cambridge University Press, ch. II

David S. Oderberg (2000) *Moral Theory: A Non-Consequentialist Approach*. Wiley-Blackwell

Hugh LaFollette and Ingmar Persson (2013) *The Blackwell Guide to Ethical Theory*. Wiley-Blackwell

Thought Points

(1) Summarise the main points of Naturalism, Intuitionism and Emotivism.

(2) Discuss the extent to which ethical language is meaningful.

(3) Do you agree that 'ethical statements are no more than expressions of emotion'?

(4) Do you think it is possible to justify the claim that the word 'good' has objective meaning?

(5) To what extent do you agree that moral statements have objective meaning?

8 Conscience: Aquinas and Freud

Introduction

In democratic states, unions can strike, trainee doctors can refuse to take part in an abortion, and conscientious objectors can refuse military conscription. Freedom of conscience is enshrined in article 18 of the UN Declaration of Human Rights. Yet for all this talk of conscience, as the ethicist Paul Lehmann once observed, the modern history of the idea of conscience has led thinkers to either 'do the conscience over' or 'do the conscience in' (*Ethics in a Christian Context*, Westminster/John Knox Press, 2006). Some of the thinkers we will consider see it as a form of infantile neuroticism, the internalising of the moral codes of society. At the heart of the debate is the question of whether the conscience is innate to human nature or instilled in us from external authority figures such as parents, teachers or social structures (government, law, the media, etc.). The debate over the reliability of conscience in decision-making is bound up with questions over its nature.

"I've been getting annoying pangs of conscience when faced with ethical dilemmas. Got anything for that?"

Exercise

1. Research *The Awakening Conscience* by Holman Hunt at The Khan Academy. How does Hunt show us temptation and conscience in his symbolism?
2. What is meant by the terms 'prisoners of conscience' and 'conscientious objector'?
3. So-called 'whistle-blowers' in Industry and the military inform the public about malpractice or illegal activity. They are said to be acting 'in good conscience' in going against the interests of their employer. One such example is that of the research chemist Jeffrey Wigand, who witnessed against his employers in the tobacco industry. He claimed that they knowingly 'spiked' cigarettes to make them more addictive. He was played by Russell Crowe in the film *The Insider.* What do you think about whistle-blowers?
4. Consider the case of prosecutors at the Nuremberg trials after World War II. Some Nazi officers and commanders defended their atrocities and crimes against humanity by arguing that they were following orders. Some even argued that their consciences were so warped by their obedience to authority that they acted out of a false sense of duty. Does this undermine the value of conscience altogether?

QUICK QUESTION

Eric Liddell, Olympic 400m Gold Medalist, Paris, 1924. Liddell was a Scottish Presbyterian who would not run in his Olympic heat on the Sabbath day because of his obedience of the fourth commandment. The story of his achievements and beliefs is told in the film *Chariots of Fire.*

What makes people follow their conscience at great personal cost to themselves?

Conscience in the New Testament

Whilst the term 'conscience' derives from the Greek *'suneidesis'* (knowledge with/to know something about oneself) and is not found in the Old Testament, it underlies the Genesis story of Adam and Eve's disobedience and runs through biblical historical, prophetic and wisdom literature. In 2 Samuel 12, for example, the prophet Nathan confronts David with his adultery with Bathsheba and murder of her husband Uriah to cover his tracks. The classic confession of Psalm 51 is David's sorrowful response.

C. A. Pierce's classic 1955 study *Conscience in the New Testament* shows that Paul uses the word 'conscience' twenty times. Aside from his use, it only occurs in Hebrews and 1 Peter. He speaks of conscious awareness of righteousness (Romans 13:5), of conscience as a witness (Romans 2:15, 9:1; 2 Corinthians 1:12) which can accuse or defend, and of having a good and a pure conscience.

In Romans 2:14–15, he says that if 'the Gentiles [non-Jews], who do not have the law [of Moses], do by nature those things [the commandments] that are of the law . . . They show the work of the law . . . written in their hearts, their consciences bearing witness to them'. So he does believe in a universal faculty in human beings for making moral judgements. Nonetheless, the conscience can be misinformed (for example, when those of a 'weak' conscience wrongly believe that meat bought from public markets which is from sacrifices to idols is not unclean as these are not real gods). He also thinks that it can be trained by self-examination (1 Corinthians 11:28; Galatians 6:4) and by seeking the will of God (Romans 12:2). Its judgements should be tempered with love and peacefulness towards others (1 Corinthians 14:19). Pierce makes the point that 'Conscience is taken today as justifying, in advance [whereas] . . . in the New Testament . . . it refers only to the past and particular, and to the acts of a man's self alone'. It is 'the painful reaction of man's nature, as morally responsible, against infringements of its created limits' (Pierce 1955).

The conscience is part of a larger framework in Christian ethics, or what the philosopher Charles Taylor calls a 'moral ontology' (a sense of how the world *is*). That is to say that, in Christian thought, the study of man (*anthropology*) derives from the study of God (*theology*). For this reason, theologian John Webster argues that conscience 'ranks well after "prayer" or "following Jesus" in a Christian's moral framework (Webster, 'God and conscience', 2006). The theologian Karl Barth even wrote, in his *Ethics*, 'To have a conscience is no more or less than to have the Holy Spirit' (Wipf & Stock Publishers, 2013, p. 482). Indeed, Barth speaks of 'the secret energy of the Spirit' by which the conscience judges not by its own authority but through prayer and worship, aligned with the judgement of God. Conscience is not about individual freedom or being true to yourself for Barth, but about allowing one's love of God to shape the love of one's neighbour. As Paul puts it in 1 Corinthians 2:16, we are to allow the mind of Christ to be formed in us so that we grow in the art of moral discernment.

WE WERE KIND OF HOPING TO LET OUR *CONSCIENCE* BE OUR GUIDE.

The New Testament mentions the word we translate as 'conscience' thirty-two times (*Strong's Concordance*, 1985) but also uses the word 'heart' (*kardia*) for the seat of the emotions and moral awareness many more times in both Old and New Testaments. In a similar vein, St Paul talks of consciences becoming weak, seared or defiled with habitual disobedience of divine commands. As he writes, 'I do not understand my own actions. For I do not do what I want, but I do the very thing I hate . . . I can will what is right, but I cannot do it. For I do not do the good I want, but the evil I do not want, is what I do' (Romans 7:15, 18). For Paul, a healthy conscience is not so much about internal moral auditing, as uncovering those secret sins that honest self-knowledge and the Holy Spirit show up. Different consciences need not all agree, given the distinct circumstances in which individuals find themselves. Nonetheless, 'my conscience permits me to commit adultery' would be an example of self-justification, not conscience at work.

Aquinas' Theological Approach to the Conscience

For Aquinas, conscience is 'the mind of man making moral judgements', or 'the application of knowledge to some action', the inner faculty of moral reasoning that stems from our comprehension of the eternal moral law that God has established in his created order. Aquinas distinguishes *synderesis* from *conscientia*.

St Thomas Aquinas
(1225–74)

Five key terms

Synderesis: according to Aquinas, this is our natural disposition towards doing good and avoiding evil. It is a tendency towards the good which is implanted in us ultimately by God. Reference to this faculty or innate moral intuition in humankind can be seen in Paul's letter to the Romans (2:14–15).

Conscientia: Aquinas thinks that humans use their reason to make moral decisions. We have to train ourselves to recognise our conscience. *Conscientia* moves our will to act in practical ethical decisions and judgements.

Ratio: reason – having been made in God's image, we are rational creatures subject to the Natural Law or the design of the universe which includes a moral order in virtue of humans made in the divine image. We have a natural inclination towards our proper act or purpose. Humanity comes to know its *telos* and the principles of Natural Law through both theoretical reason (*intellectus*) and a practical reason (*synderesis*).

Vincible ignorance: lack of knowledge for which a person is responsible, perhaps through negligence or because they wilfully avoid it (in a 'hear no evil, see no evil' sense). Such ignorance could also be because of a lack of intellect, the matter being obscure, or, for Aquinas, because children and non-Christians had not yet had the chance to hear the message of Christianity or received the theological virtues of faith, hope and love.

Invincible ignorance: lack of knowledge which a person is not responsible for or could not prevent, as it was not wilful or voluntary ignorance and so is not seen as their fault.

Aquinas argues that acting against conscience is always wrong and, at the same time, that acting according to it cannot be sinful. As he writes in *Summa Theologica*, 'Every

> **Synderesis:**
> According to Aquinas, this is our inner knowledge of and natural disposition towards doing good and avoiding evil – 'that good should be done and evil avoided' – a natural disposition of humans to understand the first principles of morality instinctively.

> **Conscientia:**
> Aquinas thinks that humans use their reason to make moral decisions. We have to train ourselves to recognise our conscience.

judgement of conscience, be it right or wrong, be it about things evil in themselves or morally indifferent, is obligatory, in such wise that he who acts against his conscience always sins.' Yet this raises the difficult question of what happens when our conscience is mistaken over the facts of a case or prejudiced by self-interest. There are cases in which people do evil acts in obedience to their consciences, or they do the right thing and yet feel the pang of a guilty conscience. When British volunteers answered Lord Kitchener's call to arms in World War I, most did so with a sense of obeying their consciences. In contrast, Huckleberry Finn (in Mark Twain's novel) is troubled with a bad conscience when he fails to give up Jim, the runaway slave. His conscience tells him that he is breaking the law, but his feeling of sympathy for his travelling companion overrules it.

Here, Aquinas would argue that the individual has a responsibility to inform the conscience and seek to know right from wrong. The individual's faulty conscience could be dulled by habitual failure to listen; it could be misinformed or misled. He sees that the conscience can be mistaken. This can be knowingly so (vincible error) or unknowingly so (invincible error). Moral judgements can be faulty and we have a capacity for self-deception. We may also lack all of the facts of a given dilemma. For this reason, Catholic moral theology came to distinguish between *material sin* (where conscience is in error) and *formal sin* (where the voice of conscience is known and disobeyed). We are at fault when we could have taken more trouble to be informed before making our moral judgement (as in the case of some-

one who doesn't ask too many questions about why goods they are purchasing are so cheap in case they might discover them to be stolen, produced by exploited workers, or avoiding tax).

Our ignorance can be either voluntary (vincible) or involuntary (invincible). Where it is involuntary, we are not responsible. Take Aquinas' example of two cases:

- someone believes their conscience to be telling them to commit adultery;
- a man mistakenly thinks it good to sleep with what he takes to be his wife in his own bed when it is in fact her identical twin sister.

In the second case, the erroneous judgement is involuntary and therefore excusable, whereas in the first case, the person ought to have known that this was morally wrong as it goes against Primary Precepts and the moral law. They are therefore morally responsible for their actions.

Yet an erring or immature conscience grows through practical wisdom gained by experience, reasoning and listening to the Church's teaching and scripture. We have a high regard for the individual conscience in the modern secular world, yet, for theologian Michael Banner, authenticity and 'being true to yourself' are the precise opposite of what Aquinas means by the conscience. We have a duty to inform it, to train it through habit and experience in the virtue of prudence, to be wary of being misled, and to listen to the voice of the eternal moral law within us.

Freud's Psychological Approach to Conscience

The psychoanalyst Sigmund Freud (1856–1939) wrote that:

Sigmund Freud 1856–1939

The philosopher Kant once declared that nothing proved to him the greatness of God more convincingly than the starry heavens and the moral conscience within us. The stars are unquestionably superb, but where conscience is concerned God has been guilty of an uneven and careless piece of work, for a great many men have only a very limited share of it or scarcely enough to be worth mentioning . . . the critical voice of the superego is silent, the ego is re-instated, and enjoys once more the rights of man.

(Freud, *New Introductory Lectures on Psycho-analysis*, Leonard & Virginia Woolf, 1933, p. 88)

For Freud, the conscience was not an internal rational faculty, but an emotional imprint formed by early childhood development. Deep-seated feelings of guilt about 'taboo' acts or thoughts can be impossible to uproot in adulthood without the aid of psychoanalysis. The child internalises authority figures that imprint upon its emotional make-up through conditioning (by reward and punishment of behaviour). In Freud's understanding of the self, a tension existed between

The Super-Ego	The **Super-Ego** represses desires, is fearful of authority, and constantly warns of punishment. It contradicts the Id and works on internalised laws from parents and society. As Freud put it, 'It has long been our contention that "dread of society" is the essence of what is called conscience' (*Group Psychology and the Analysis of the Ego*, Boni and Liveright, 1922, ch. 2).
The Ego	This is the focal point that balances out pleasure and reality. It adjudicates between the conflicting voices of the Super-Ego and Id over instinctual drives (such as for food, water, sex, self-preservation and loving relationships). Following the 'reality principle', it mediates between the demands of the Id and the demands of social interaction.

The pleasure principle: This is the Id's desire for instant gratification. Unchecked drives for food, sex, aggression and sleep are immediate and primal. Reality is not taken into account as the immature Ego pursues desires which are fantasies rather than realities as they take no account of how others will react, often leading to painful conclusions. The Id is pleasure-seeking and indulges the biological and psychological needs of the immature Ego in an impulsive and uncritical manner.

The Id	The Id wants to give full release to unchecked lust, anger, greed, etc. Unchecked, it would be self-indulgent and self-destructive, entirely desire driven without recourse to reason. It follows instinctive impulses and operates according to the 'pleasure principle', wanting instant gratification.

In this scheme of things, the conscience is the Super-Ego, doing the work of censoring, reprimanding and warning of the need to keep ourselves in check as our parents once did for us. In Freud's version of the self, the moral role of conscience is replaced by the Ego, an internal psychoanalyst who, in the mature psyche, maintains an uneasy truce between the aggressive warring interests of the Super-Ego and the Id. We alone must take responsibility for this balancing act to become fully integrated selves. For Freud it is infantile of us to seek a father figure in God or his implanted conscience to lift the burden of decision-making from us.

Freud believed that, while the Super-Ego remains necessary, repressed instincts can result in psychological illnesses. He believed that too much attention to the Super-Ego's unbending and judgemental voice would lead to unhealthy repression and neurosis (a mild to severe mental illness with symptoms such as irrational anxiety, stress, depression and a guilt complex). Through his psychoanalysis and exploration of the unconscious, he sought to get patients to express their repressed desires. As Keith Ward (1998) writes, 'Freud sometimes wrote as though all supposed reasons for acting were no more than rationalisations of primitive drives to sex, aggression, or power, and as though all "moral" conduct was a disguised form of self-interest.'

Perhaps Freud's mentally ill patients (for many of whom religion was part and parcel of their neurosis and phobia) led him to see only their imprisonment in a neurotic and joyless obsession with moral restrictions and rules. Freud's disciple Jung, who later broke with his thought, came to see a more positive role for religious experience.

As early as 1907, Freud saw conscience as a form of consciousness, writing in a paper on 'Obsessive Actions and Religious Practices', that 'Conscience is the internal perception of the rejection of a particular wish operating in us.' Again in *Totem and Taboo* (1912–13), he saw the conscience as an inhibition in us against breaking a taboo (an external or societal prohibition). He is not always consistent in his description of conscience, at times seeing its work done prior to an act that breaks a taboo, while seeing guilt as being subsequent to the act. Elsewhere, he sees conscience as observing the act and castigating the Ego for the act that has been committed, largely without reason and due to the internalisation of external critical authority.

In Freud's assessment, the method of psychoanalysis had shown that the more moral a person is, the more they check and repress their desires, and paradoxically, the more harshly restraining becomes their Super-ego. In *The Ego and the Id* (W. W. Norton and Co., Inc., 1961, p. 51), Freud writes: 'Psycho-analysis has been reproached time after time with ignoring the higher, moral, supra-rational side of human nature . . . but now that we have embarked on the analysis of the ego we can give an answer . . . here we have that higher nature, in this ego-ideal or super-ego, the representative of our relation to our parents. When we were little children we knew these higher natures, we admired them and feared them; and later we took them into ourselves.' When Freud refers to the Super-ego, he is talking about the experience of the feeling of guilt, repression, or anxiety internalised in childhood. 'The super-ego', he writes, '– the conscience at work in the ego may . . . become harsh, cruel, inexorable against the ego which is in its charge. Kant's Categorical Imperative is thus the direct heir to the Oedipus Complex' (Sigmund Freud, *The Economic Problem of Masochism*, Hogarth Press, 1924, p. 169). Freud regularly treated his Vienna patients for obsessional or neurotic thoughts and behaviour. Today, his theory of psychoanalysis is seen as largely pseudo-scientific, given its lack of systematic and rather localised form of research. What it did reveal was the iceberg of submerged desires, aggressions and repressed impulses that lay beneath the surface of our conscious, rational minds. Freud sees us separating our conscience off from our Ego and setting the two against one another. The conscience is one part of the origin of the Super-ego, alongside repression, aggressive instincts and the Oedipus complex (the first stage of normal sexual development when a child's emotional and erotic attachment is to its parent of the opposite sex, which causes hate, anxiety and fear towards the parent of the same sex). In resolving this incestuous tension, Freud concluded that boys develop their Super-ego in order to overcome their unconscious fear of castration. In partly identifying with the father and repressing the Id impulses, the 'reality principle' takes shape (the recognition of the need to restrain instinctual desires and reckon with the reality of society's code of acceptable behaviour). The problem is that, while the Super-ego internalises the punishment and prevention role that parents once held, 'their loving care is not taken up and continued by it' (*The New Introductory Lectures*, W. W. Norton & Company, 1933, pp. 89–90).

With the help of psychoanalysis, the Ego can harmonise the internalised threats and fears of the Super-ego with the instinctual impulses of the Id. The mature Ego can act independently of the Super-ego and accept reality rather than the pleasure principle of the Id. In *Civilization and its Discontents* (W. W. Norton, 1930), Freud sets out tensions between primal individual desires for sex and aggression as opposed to the welfare of society, which requires conformity to laws. Law courts and punishments are internalised to restrain these powerful instinctive drives. As he writes, 'Conscience and morality have arisen through the overcoming, the desexualisation, of the Oedipus Complex' (*The Economic Problem of Masochism*, p. 169). In 'sublimation', these socially unacceptable impulses, desires and energies are deflected into scientific, artistic, sporting and social activity. Freud saw this as a mature defence mechanism, or the rechannelling of anti-social instincts into drivers of civilisation.

Yet Freud is no moral philosopher, and his use of the term 'conscience' is ambiguous. He blurs moral feelings such as those of the mature Ego's conscience with non-moral feelings like the anxiety and fear of punishment of the Super-ego. Therapy aims to release patients from the Super-ego's repressive, anxiety-laden and neurotic conscience. Yet this journey is to a mature and responsible Ego that takes account of social reality and shows a greater capacity for virtues like love and trust. Freud also tends to think of conformity to social norms as insincere, yet as the Ego sets aside the pleasure principle in acknowledging the greater good of others and society/civilisation, it can surely be both prudent and sincere. It is certainly more rational and free to bring unconscious anxiety and unacknowledged guilt into the conscious mind through therapy, and thereby to gain some measure of rational control over one's behaviour. Here, the philosopher David H. Jones challenges 'Freud's tendency to *reduce* morality to what he calls the operation of the super-ego; that is, his tendency to claim that morality is *nothing but* the psychological phenomena which he describes and purports to explain' ('Freud's Theory of Moral Conscience', *Philosophy*, 41, 155 (Jan. 1966), p. 57). He judges that Freud fails to offer a clear distinction between a good and bad conscience, due to his lack of a proper distinction between 'moral feelings of shame, guilt and remorse on the one hand, and security feelings such as anxiety, fear, and dread on the other' (ibid.).

The following table compares and contrasts Aquinas and Freud on several key aspects of the debate over conscience as set out in the specification.

Discussion Question

With another student, choose a theme below and make a 2-minute presentation on Aquinas' and Freud's views on it. Then debate this theme for a further 5 minutes with another student.

	Aquinas	**Freud**
Guilt	It is always wrong knowingly to disobey one's conscience, even though it may be mistaken. Paul, in his letter to the Romans (ch. 14), warns his readers about those of 'weak' conscience who refuse to eat meat that is likely to have been offered to idols. He says that those of 'strong' conscience should not cause those of a weak (overactive) conscience to stumble by suggesting that they're being overly scrupulous (e.g. by arguing that the man-made idols have no spiritual power to pollute meat). Guilt results from *synderesis* and *conscientia* warning our will about the Natural Law. Conscience is the exercise of reason and moral judgement, and ought not to be ignored.	In our childhood development, we internalise the prohibitions of parents and teachers who enforce social customs and taboos. A repressive force, the Super-ego can hamper the individual's development in anxiety, neurosis or damaging phobias. Freud saw the conscience as a 'guilt complex' inscribed in early childhood by parents and enforced by reward or punishment. A catharsis (cleansing) of neurotic fears and the discharging of repressed desires was possible through psychoanalysis and hypnosis. On the one hand, 'The Super-ego can be thought of as a type of conscience that punishes misbehaviour with feelings of guilt. For example, for having extra-marital affairs' (Arthur S. Reber, *The Penguin Dictionary of Psychology*, 1985). Indeed, one function of guilt is control of the human instinct for aggression and sex; the Super-ego keeps the Id in check. More problematically, it is not rational self-government by the adult self, but repressed, unconscious guilt internalised by the child which can be paralysing and lead to abnormal behaviour.

	Aquinas	Freud
God	Behind human law and conscience lies the Natural Law, itself rooted in the eternal law of the creator God who has providentially ordered the world and given us rational and moral faculties. Human beings, made in God's image, have, despite the Fall, an inclination to do good and avoid evil, and varying degrees of practical wisdom / moral rationality. Nature is goal-orientated and the theological virtues of faith, hope and love transpose the cardinal virtues of courage, wisdom, justice and temperance onto a higher level, more able to fulfil or actualise the true nature of human beings. So prayer, worship and contemplation of the beatific vision of the being of God are important in the moral life. Aquinas taught that 'grace perfects nature' – that our desire for God makes us more, not less, natural.	Freud, Ludwig Feuerbach and Karl Marx are sometimes referred to collectively as 'the masters of suspicion', and Freud has done much to establish the popular suspicion that religion is wish fulfilment and that the language of sin is the repression of primal instincts in line with society's values and taboos. Sex and Death are primordial in our consciousness, and Freud's *Totem and Taboo* examined the projection of human fears and desires in our inner life onto the external world. Taking Darwin's idea of primitive horde – in which early humans lived in large groups like the great apes, with young rivals challenging the dominant male – Freud suggested that, after killing their father and taking the females for themselves, the collective guilt of the sons was dealt with by means of a totemic replacement of the father figure, who was ritually worshipped. In *Totem and Taboo*, Freud sees religion as a modern form of animism. Whereas the scientific mind accepts the reality of the world's chaos and tries to overcome it through observation and careful planning, the animistic or religious mind seeks, through religious or totemic rituals, to order and control it. Superstition and the spiritual are often linked to taboo, suggesting to Freud that this was a mythical way for us to cope with our repressed guilt (e.g. the killing of the father figure in the Oedipal complex, which was the true origin of original sin for Freud). Our unconscious still reflects such beliefs today, hence, in Freud's assessment, the success of Christian Mass, in which the sacrifice of the son assuages the anger of the Father. In later works, Freud saw religion as an illusion or wish-fulfillment deriving from our infantile helplessness and longing for a father figure in the midst of life's fears, dangers and suffering. In Freud's assessment, projecting these fears onto God was illusory and only contributed to his patients' anxiety and obsessional delusions.

	Aquinas	**Freud**
Reason	Aquinas read enough of Augustine's *Confessions* to believe that human reason was impaired by the Fall of Adam and Eve. Humans have sinful desires and these draw us away from real to apparent goods or even to wilful wrongdoing. Again, in following Augustine's idea of evil as the absence (privation) of good, Aquinas believes that humans cannot be motivated by evil as evil is merely the absence of good rather than a separate and opposite category itself. Despite our fallenness, human beings have innate faculties of moral reason and inclination within us. Unlike other creatures, humans possess intellect and free will. We are drawn towards the actualisation of our nature and the final desire of our souls, which is seen in the diverse goods in the world, and, ultimately, in a desire for our creator God himself. Aquinas offers a positive role for reason in moral decision-making. We need to discipline our desires and train ourselves in virtue, but an omniscient God has endowed our nature with a rational mind and will.	Freud is, in an important sense, a successor to Hume, who wrote that 'reason is, and ought only to be the slave of the passions' (*Treatise of Human Nature* (1739–40), II.3.3 415). Hume saw the human will or motivation arising from emotions not reasons. Freud takes this idea deeper with his examination of the subconscious and repressed memories or traumas. He shows how the Ego mediates between powerful drives for pleasure and sex from the Id, and internalised parental voices of approval and disapproval from the Super-ego. The Id is irrational and out of touch with reality, purely seeking pleasure. The Ego is our closest hope of a rational self, seeking to harmonise the external world, the Super-ego, and the Id. In doing so, it 'breaks out in anxiety – realistic anxiety regarding the external world, moral anxiety regarding the super-ego, and neurotic anxiety regarding the strength of the passions in the id' (Freud, *The New Introductory Lectures*, pp. 110–11).
Subconscious	Aquinas recognises, in his reading of Paul's letters in the New Testament and in Augustine's *Confessions*, the human capacity for self-deception. The problem of 'self-opacity' or transparency was one Aquinas was familiar with, and he saw certain things to be self-evident or intuitively known, such as our moral agency – we act and have a moral sense of responsibility in doing so. We sense ourselves as having intentions (interior acts), and conscious thoughts. When we wilfully disobey our conscience or pursue apparent goods, our self-deceit deprives us of actualising our potential. To 'know thyself' was the beginning of wisdom for Aristotle and for Aquinas, and attention to one's thinking and the	Sublimation is where sexual or aggressive energy (from the libido) is channelled away from destructive actions and into more creative or socially acceptable activities such as sport or work. Freud's psychoanalytic method centred around uncovering the subconscious drives and repressed desires of his patients in order to help them gain more self-awareness and rational control over their phobias and anxieties. Freud's theory asserts that, like an iceberg whose main bulk remains concealed beneath the surface, our primitive urges, fantasies, desires, repressed memories, conflicts and anxieties are concealed in our subconscious mind. Only in unlocking this through introspection helped by psychoanalysis can we find a harmonious balance in our mature selves, and autonomy.

	Aquinas	Freud
	practice of virtue was crucial in the moral life, together with a sense of oneself as a compound of both body (senses, appetites, physical desires) and non-material intellect and soul. This is a very different account of the subconscious self from that of Freud, and it is one in which reason has the upper hand over the desires and passions (as with Plato's analogy of the charioteer representing intellect or reason, and the two horses, the moral impulse or positive passions, and the irrational passions and appetites). Modern Thomists, e.g. Anthony Kenny and Fergus Kerr (working in the tradition of Aquinas' thought), seek to revive and develop Aquinas' insights in understanding anthropology and psychology.	Freud was influenced by biologist Jean-Baptiste Lamarck (1744–1829) who believed that characteristics acquired during an organism's lifetime could be passed on to its offspring. Neuroses inherited during childhood would often be handed down in the parenting of a new generation. Whilst he may not have had access to DNA or the human genome, Freud did grasp the importance of survival and reproduction in human psychology and biology. The idea of psychological traits or neuroses internalised in the years of infancy to early childhood seemed evident in Freud's studies. Here, parenting and schooling instilled and reinforced behavioural patterns that could shape the relationship between the Super-ego, the Ego and the Id for life.
Environment e.g. culture, genes, education	Writing in the thirteenth century, Aquinas was quite unaware of genetics. Influenced as he was by Aristotle, Aquinas saw the importance of the *polis* in shaping character. His view of education was holistic, training dispositions of character and mind. He studied and taught at several major European schools or medieval universities including Naples, Paris, Cologne and Rome. Several Aquinas scholars today (e.g. John Finnis) accept the fact–value gap and place more weight on his practical reasoning, and on the bodily as well as spiritual dimensions of his thought. They would see Freud as too reductionistic about the origins of the conscience and reject his materialist account of the self in favour of an idea of the self as body, mind and soul. Whilst accepting that the conscience develops over time from immaturity in childhood, they would reject the idea that it can be reduced to the programming of one's environment.	

Evaluating Aquinas on the conscience

(a) The developmental psychology of thinkers like Jean Piaget (1896–1980) and Lawrence Kohlberg (1927–87) found experimental evidence that **abstract moral reasoning developed in stages of cognitive development** during childhood. If this is true, then the claim that the moral law is an innate faculty of doing good and avoiding evil may be called into question. Morality may be behaviourally trained into us through stimulus–response conditioning from social interactions with parents and teachers.

(b) Writing in the thirteenth century, Aquinas was quite unaware of the role of **genetics and evolutionary psychology** in the development of the human mind. Where conscience is viewed as evidence of a moral faculty placed by God in the creature that bears his image, it may be argued that it has an altogether more earthly origin in the reciprocal altruism of kinship groups, in which co-operation and survival / reproductive advantage go hand in hand.

(c) Even Aquinas acknowledges that the **conscience can be weak or mistaken**. Yet if it is **subjective**, a product of culture or particular parental values, it can be problematic, as in Huckleberry's Finn's conscience about helping a runaway slave. Freud treated religious patients who were paralysed by neurotic guilt generated by their internalised parental Super-ego. This harsh and obsessive type of conscience immobilised these individuals with irrational anxiety and fear.

(d) As theologian John Webster (1955–) argues, for Christians, the role of individual conscience comes after scripture, reason, prayer and the Holy Spirit. Protestant ethicists are wary of putting too much stock in individual conscience given the fallenness of human nature and our capacity for self-deception.

Evaluating Freud on the conscience

For Freud, the conscience represents infantile fears and fantasies. It emerges in the psychosexual development of early childhood. Freudian psychoanalysis and therapy have been widely criticised and rejected by mainstream psychologists and philosophers alike. Among these criticisms are the following.

(a) Karl Popper presented Freudianism as a perfect example of **pseudo-science that was unfalsifiable**. Unlike the behaviouralist psychologists such as John B. Watson, or B. F. Skinner, who made the experimental method central to their studies, Freud's sample of case studies was too small to be representative or methodical, and his claims seem more anecdotal than scientific. Added to this, rejection of the theory could be seen as a repression of traumatic subconscious memories, a strategy which simply verifies Freudianism in a circular manner. Falsifiability and prediction are tests of the scientific method, and neither are present in Freud's theory. Neurosis and depression can result from genetics or a wide variety of causes, such as PTSD or injury. To link this back to sexual trauma and religious obsession is at best an oversimplification on Freud's part.

(b) Freud is very much a creature of his time, with *Totem and Taboo* (1913) following in the tradition of Tylor's *Primitive Culture* (1871) and Frazer's *The Golden Bough* (1890), in believing that the study of 'primitive peoples' would unlock primal human traits. **Discredited among contemporary anthropologists**, this approach, like much of Freud's thought, goes well beyond any empirical evidence. Equally, the claim that the Oedipus complex is universal doesn't appear to fit with the fact that many cultures lack a male deity, or have a mother goddess whose male consort plays only a minor role. In philosopher Mikkel Borch-Jacobsen's assessment, Freud's approach was more akin to creative fiction than rigorous social science (both in his anthropology and in his psychology); in *Totem and Taboo*, he took 'the same method of interpretation [to history] that he used in the privacy of his office to "reconstruct" his patients' forgotten and repressed memories' (*The Freud Files: An Inquiry into the History of Psychoanalysis*, Cambridge University Press, 2012, pp. 179–80).

(c) Educational psychologists Karen Reivich and Andrew Shatte (*The Resilience Factor*, 2002, Broadway Books, p. 50) see Freud as **unduly pessimistic** about our ability to change ourselves radically, our personalities having largely been developed by the time we are five years of age. Pessimism itself is, of course, insufficient reason to reject his theory, but the basis of his method seems suspect. As a 29-year-old graduate of the University of Vienna's medical school, Freud undertook an internship in Paris with a French neurologist by the name of Jean-Marin Charcot who was using hypnotism in the treatment of hysteria. Without hypnosis, Charcot's patients found that their sicknesses (such as being functionally blind or paralysed) returned.

Perhaps a more reasonable default setting for human psychology would be the blank slate theory of empiricists like John Locke or Jean-Jacques Rousseau. Though his method of hypnotism and the 'talking cure' on the couch may seem antiquated today, Freud's most positive legacy may be to have unveiled to our conscious minds how much of our behaviour – our impulses, anxieties, motivations and fears – has been imprinted by experience on our subconscious. This could offer grounds for optimism as the stimuli and inputs into our conscious selves can, to some extent, be adjusted, or the ill-effects of the past, in some measure, unlearned, in what modern psychologists call 'cognitive behavioural therapy'. Here, as unconscious fears and irrational desires are brought within reach of our reflective self, we can gain a rational hold on our patterns of thought, and consciously alter our behaviour.

(d) **Karl Gustav Jung (1875–1961)** presents a more positive role for religion as the shared or collective unconscious of human minds (which he terms 'archetypes'). Freud saw the role of religion as oppressive and damaging to the personality, or, as he put it, the 'universal obsessional neurosis of humanity' (*The Future of an Illusion*). By contrast, Jung saw aspects of religious experience that were more positive and liberating for personal development, arguing that Freud had been too blinkered in his psychoanalytic approach by his preoccupation with his sick patients, whose anxiety was often rooted in their religious outlook/upbringing. **Jung was less obsessed with sexuality and**

focused more on libido in the sense of psychic energy. Even if we conclude that **religion** is entirely a product of human minds and perception, we can still see **an important and healthy role** for it in connecting the conscious and unconscious mind, and linking the individual and collective consciousness. Integration of these connected parts was indeed the goal of life, and God was the archetype of the deepest collective unconscious. In examining the symbols and images of this archetype, we can develop a persona, or self-identity in society, which integrates who we are at a deeper level than our outward role or job. Like the imagery of the Holy Trinity in Christianity, 'individuation' or self-identity arises as we integrate with the collective consciousness, individual self-knowledge maturing as we come to know more of the collective unconscious. The existence of God cannot be proven or disproven, and it is from the unconscious that we come to know/construct our view of God. Jung's thought diverged from that of Freud and gave a positive role to religious ritual and symbolism integral to human consciousness.

(e) **Eric Fromm (1900–80)** argued that it is **possible to reject the authoritarian conscience and to develop a mature 'humanistic' conscience** that reflects one's own considered values. In *Man for Himself: An Inquiry Into the Psychology of Ethics* (Routledge, 1947), Fromm saw the authoritarian conscience as a product of religious and political systems based on reward and punishment. Yet, unlike Freud, Fromm doesn't leave things here. Without faith in values and principles that guide their conduct, people become helpless prey for whatever authoritarian power gets a hold of them. Totalitarian states and religious cults overpower the conscience with guilt, or, as Fromm puts it, 'The most important symptom in the defeat of the fight for oneself is the guilty conscience. . .one has not succeeded in breaking out of the authoritarian net' (*Man for Himself*, p. 158). Yet guilt does not overpower the mature humanistic conscience, which has rational autonomy and

Eric Fromm (1900–80)

asserts its individual rights and freedoms and develops self-knowledge. Fromm agreed with Freud that: 'If faith cannot be reconciled with rational thinking, it has to be eliminated as an anachronistic remnant of earlier stages of culture and replaced by science dealing with facts and theories which are intelligible and can be validated.' Certainly, moral indignation in humans could quickly become destructive and 'permit envy or hate to be acted out under the guise of virtue', but where a healthy democracy encouraged individuals to think critically and to live in a way that encouraged individual freedom, this acted as a bulwark against tyranny in a religious or political form. So Freud may be guilty of throwing the baby out with the bathwater. Where Fromm went on to distinguish the humanistic (man's recall to himself) from the authoritarian conscience (external authority imposing its will upon the individual), Freud seems simply to dismiss the conscience as irretrievably bound up with religious neuroses.

Man for himself amounts to 'what man is, how he ought to live, and how the tremendous energies within man can be released and used productively. In analysing our behaviour, we can gain self-knowledge and, here, psychology and ethics interact. As Fromm wrote, 'The task of the moral philosopher-thinker is to support and strengthen the voice of human conscience, to recognize what is good or what is bad for people, whether they are good or bad for society in the period of evolution' (*Man for Himself*). So, rather than rejecting the conscience altogether, he wanted moral values that people owned for themselves and that empowered and gave a sense of meaning to their lives and society.

Exercise

Read the following extracts from two papal statements.

1. *What significant points are made about conscience in each statement?*
2. *How would the critics mentioned above begin to challenge this idea of conscience?*

In the depths of his conscience, man detects a law which he does not impose upon himself, but which holds him to obedience. Always summoning him to love good and avoid evil, the voice of conscience when necessary speaks to his heart: do this, shun that. For man has in his heart a law written by God; to obey it is the very dignity of man; according to it he will be judged. Conscience is the most secret core and sanctuary of a man. There he is alone with God, Whose voice echoes in his depths.

Vatican II, *Gaudium et Spes* (Joy and Hope), section 16

Certain currents of modern thought have gone so far as to exalt freedom to such an extent that it becomes an absolute, which would then be the source of values . . . The individual conscience is accorded the status of a supreme tribunal of moral judgement which hands down categorical and infallible decisions about good and evil. To the affirmation that one has a duty to follow one's conscience is unduly added the affirmation that one's moral judgement is true merely by the fact that it has its origin in the conscience. But in this way the inescapable claims of truth disappear, yielding their place to a criterion of sincerity, authenticity and 'being at peace with yourself.' . . . Conscience is no longer considered . . . an act of a person's intelligence, the function of which is to apply the universal knowledge of the good in a specific situation . . . Such an outlook is quite congenial to an individualistic ethic, wherein each individual is faced with his own truth, different from the truth of others.

Pope John Paul II, *Veritatis Splendor* (*The Splendour of Truth*; 1993), section 32

FURTHER READING

Thomas Aquinas, *Summa Theologica* I-I 79

Internet Encyclopaedia of Philosophy, 'Sigmund Freud', www.iep.utm.edu/freud

Sigmund Freud (1927) *The Ego and the Id*. Createspace

Eric Fromm (1947) *Man for Himself: An Inquiry into the Psychology of Ethics*. Routledge

Stephen Loxton (2014) Conscience (Ethics Study Guides). PushMe Press

Paul Strohm (2011) *Conscience: A Very Short Introduction* (Very Short Introductions). Oxford University Press

Keith Ward (1998) *In Defence of the Soul*. One World Publications, 'Conscience'

Thought Points

(1) Describe Aquinas' views on the conscience.

(2) Describe Freud's views on the conscience.

(3) Assess the claim that conscience is a reliable guide to making ethical decisions.

(4) Discuss the view that, after Freud, the idea that conscience is innate is no longer defensible.

(5) To what extent do you agree that it is not necessary to obey your conscience?

(6) Discuss whether conscience is intrinsically a religious idea.

(7) Do you agree that Freud's analysis of the conscience is more convincing than that of Aquinas?

(8) Evaluate the claim that Aquinas' view of the conscience is unhelpful for our psychological health in the light of Freud's theory.

SECTION V

DEVELOPMENTS IN ETHICAL THOUGHT

Sexual Ethics

In this chapter we will apply Natural Law, Situation Ethics, Kantian Ethics and Utilitarianism to ethical issues arising from

- pre-marital sex
- extra-marital sex
- homosexuality

We will also consider

- the influence of developments in religious beliefs and practices on debates about the morality, legality and tolerability of these areas of sexual ethics
- changing attitudes towards sexual ethics, including:
- whether or not religious beliefs and practices concerning sex and relationships have a continuing role in the area of sexual ethics
- the impact of secularism on secular ethics
- whether choices in the area of sexual behaviour should be entirely private and personal, or, instead, subject to societal norms and laws
- whether normative theories are useful in what they might say about sexual ethics.

Introduction: changing attitudes to sexual identity and practice

In 2013, the National Survey of Sexual Attitudes and Lifestyles (Natsal) published its results after interviewing 15,162 people resident in Britain during 2010–12. Among other issues, it looked at changing sexual attitudes and practices in British society.

Other figures below are from the Office for National Statistics (ONS) and from the British Social Attitudes survey by the National Centre for Social Research. Key findings from these three sources include:

- A significant minority of people (31% of males and 29% of females) are having sex before they are 16. Young people are sexually active at an earlier age than in previous generations.
- From 1990 to 2010, the number of sexual partners over the course of a life between 16–44 years has gone up (3.7–7.7 in women, 8.6–11.7 in men). The number of people in this age bracket and time period having same-sex partnerships has changed little for men (3.6%–4.8%), but risen for women (1.8%–7.9%).
- Since the 2013 Marriage (Same Sex Couples) Act, which came into effect in 2014, over 15,000 same-sex couples have been legally married (ONS figures).
- In 1990–1, roughly one in four men (and 28% of women) thought that same-sex partnerships were 'not wrong at all'; now the figure is around half.
- Not all attitudes are liberalising – there has been very little change in 30 years to the 84% in 2012 who disapproved of extra-marital sex (e.g. affairs or one-night stands). The majority of the public think that married people ought to be faithful to their partner.
- Between 1983 and 2010, the number of marriages per 1,000 unmarried men and women aged over 16 years has halved. Before 1983, 3 out of 10 people cohabited before marriage. Now it's closer to 8 out of 10 first-time married couples who live together first (E. Beaujouan and M. Bhrolchain, 'Cohabitation and Marriage in Britain since the 1970s', ESRC Centre for Population Change, University of Southampton, Autumn 2011).
- Between 1996 and 2012, the numbers of cohabiting couples increased from 1.5–2.9 million, and the number of children in these households doubled from 0.9 to 1.8 million (ONS).
- In 1983, 28% thought that pre-marital sex was 'always' or 'mostly' wrong, in 2013, the figure was 11%. The figure for those who consider sex before marriage to be 'not wrong at all' is up from 42% to 65%.
- Among Anglicans (members of the Church of England), the proportion that believes pre-marital sex to be wrong was 31% in 1983, falling to just 10% in 2012 (the corresponding figures for Roman Catholics are 32% down to 11%, and 11% down to 2% among those of no religion).

Discussion Questions

1) Which of the above findings do you find the most surprising, and why?
2) Why do you think that social attitudes towards sex are changing?
3) 'I don't think it's a good or a bad thing, people can do what they want' – a student interviewed on BBC's *Newsbeat* programme. Do you think that sexual behaviour is purely a subjective matter of personal choice between consenting adults? In your view, what responsibilities ought people to accept when entering into a sexual relationship?
4) In appealing for a decriminalisation of homosexual acts in 1967, Canadian Justice Minister Pierre Trudeau, wrote: 'there's no place for the state in the bedrooms of the nation'. How might a Natural Lawyer like Aquinas argue that, ethically (though not legally in a secular democracy), sexual behaviour is not just a private matter between consenting adults?
5) 'A couple who cannot marry legally or permanently but live together faithfully and honourably and responsibly, are living in virtue – in Christian love. In this kind of Christian sex ethic, the essential ingredients are caring and commitment. . . .. There is nothing against extramarital sex as such, in this ethic, and in some cases it is good' (*Sex and Morality: a Report presented to the British Council of Churches*, SCM Press Broadsheet, October 1966, pp. 39–40). Given the statistics above about changing attitudes to pre-marital sex and cohabitation, do you consider Situation Ethics to be more relevant for contemporary Christians than the ethics of Natural Law?
6) According to the Office for National Statistics, while religious marriages equalled civil marriages in the 1980s, 'By 2011, less than 30% of marriages were religious marriages – the lowest percentage on record.' With the number of people stating 'no religion' on their 2011 census being highest among those aged 20–24 and 40–44, this shows a downward trend in religious marriages. Evidence also suggests that it is becoming more socially acceptable for divorcees to have a religious ceremony (95 per cent of religious marriages were first marriages in 1966, whereas this was down to 82 per cent in 2011). This was due in part to the Divorce Reform Act which came into effect in the 1970s, making it easier for couples to remarry. What role do you think secularisation plays in the above statistics?

From the statistics above, it would appear that social attitudes towards marriage, cohabitation, divorce and homosexuality have changed over recent decades (with fairly constant attitudes towards extra-marital sex being the exception to this liberalising trend). Since the 1960s, there has also been a loosening of censorship around sexuality in the media and film, and the availability of pornography on the internet has contributed to what many see as a highly sexualised society which shortens childhood. The Huffington Post reported that, in 2012, police forces in England and Wales dealt with 5,000+ cases of child sexual abuse committed by other children (under 18s). From its research, the NSPCC is concerned that easy access to pornography normalises abusive, even violent, behaviour in relationships. Schools are more proactive in educating children about respect and consent and many universities are now running compulsory sexual consent classes.

Discussion Questions

1) In the sexual ethics debate, **paternalists** (arguing for an authority limiting the freedom of a group or individual, presumed to be for their own good) are opposed by **libertarians** (who argue that, as long as voluntary informed consent is given, sex is permissible). Limiting the discussion to adults, which side would Immanuel Kant be on, as regards sexual ethics, and why?

2) Evidently, images / portrayals of relationships and sex on the internet, film and TV have a significant influence on children. Why might this put limits on the view that sexual behaviour should be entirely private and personal? What limitations would each of the four theories set (Utilitarian, Situationist, Kantian and Natural Law) Is the least restrictive the most useful – why / why not?

Pre-marital sex

Christian perspectives

Case study: living together before marriage

In April 2011, shortly before Prince William married Kate Middleton, the Archbishop of York, Revd Dr John Sentamu, gave his backing to the couple having lived together before their marriage. He was reported as saying that 'many modern couples want to "test the milk before they buy the cow"'. He argued that the royal couple's public commitment to live their lives together would be more important than their past. Other Anglican clergy, on the traditionalist side of the Church, criticised the Archbishop for failing to reinforce biblical teaching that prohibits sex outside marriage (see *Daily Telegraph*, 29 April 2011, accessed online).

Do you think Dr Sentamu was correct in making this statement? Explain your reasons.

In Book II of his *Confessions*, Augustine writes that he 'ran wild in the shadowy jungle of erotic adventures' and that 'Clouds of muddy carnal concupiscence filled the air; the bubbling impulses of puberty befogged and obscured my heart; I could not tell the difference between lust and love.' Augustine saw sin as a deprivation, the absence of God's good created order (lust depriving love of its goodness). Whilst some commentators see his personal sexual guilt as the source of much negativity towards sexuality in subsequent Christian thought, he saw true sex as the expression of the whole person – the integration of body, heart and soul in a committed, lifelong devotion. It was this love between husband and wife that reflected the faithfulness of Christ's love for his bride the Church. As Paul writes in Ephesians 5:25–7, 'Husbands love your wives, as Christ loved the church and gave himself up for her.'

Conservative Protestant and Roman Catholic Christians see the Bible as being clear in its condemnation of pre-marital sex. They point to several quotations to justify this conclusion. 1 Corinthians 7:2 reads, 'Let each man have his own wife and each woman her own husband.' This statement comes towards the end of a long section in which St Paul criticises the Christians in Corinth for their

A traditional
engagement ring

failure to live up to God's laws – in particular, regarding sexual immorality. In 1 Corinthians 6, Paul makes the uncompromising statement: 'Make no mistake: no fornicator or idolator, no adulterer or sexual pervert . . . will possess the kingdom of God.' A few verses later, he says: 'The body is not for fornication . . . it is for the Lord' (v. 13). In v. 18, he says 'Every other sin one may commit is outside the body; but the fornicator sins against his own body.' A 'fornicator' is someone who has sexual intercourse with another unmarried person, and carries with it the sense of an illicit act. The eighteenth-century poet Robert Burns even writes a poem about himself called 'The fornicator', after having been sanctioned by his Presbyterian church (made to sit in the 'cutty stool' or 'fornicator's seat', separately from the congregation as an internal church discipline). Burns resented the public apology and humiliation required of him in church, the social or ecclesiastical sanctions of his day being a world away from today's social attitudes emphasising personal choice and freedom.

Yet this emphasis on individual freedom, according to Tim Keller (a prominent Christian leader, and co-author, with his wife Cathy, of a bestselling book on *The Meaning of Marriage*), leads to a 'consumer' rather than a 'covenantal' mindset. As he writes, 'our culture makes individual freedom, autonomy and fulfillment the very highest values, and thoughtful people know deep down that any love relationship at all means the loss of all three.' In place of a sacrificial love and covenantal commitment, the consumer mindset views relationships as a marketplace in which individuals are commodified. Intimacy consists of being known and loved, a commitment and promise to love beyond 'the frightening spells in which your feelings of love dry up'. The consumerist mindset sees relationships in terms of sexual chemistry or social climbing, whereas the covenantal mindset seeks friendship and commitment first.

One argument against cohabitation before marriage (7.5 million couples in the US cohabited in 2012 and this was up 1,500 per cent since 1960), is that cohabiting couples are more likely to split up than those who do not. Writing in the *New York Times*, clinical psychologist Dr Meg Jay attributes this to 'gender asymmetry' (women typically see cohabitation as a step towards marriage, whereas men view it as a way to test a relationship or postpone commitment). Cohabitation may, on the surface, appear to increase freedom, but marriage offers a stronger incentive to invest in a lasting relationship in which one has greater expectations and responsibilities. Several studies suggest that cohabiting couples are as likely to return to singleness as to enter marriage, the ONS figures for 2011 indicating that, after ten years of cohabiting, 50 per cent of couples married, 40 per cent split up, and 10 per cent continued to live together. Critics of sex before marriage more generally see it as leading to serial monogamy which can psychologically reduce commitment to marriage, or as leading to promiscuity in a 'hook up' culture, which has damaging personal and social consequences, such as increasing the numbers of children with fathers absent from their upbringing.

Natural Law and pre-marital sex

Aquinas taught that there were two functions of marriage: the 'generative' and the 'unitive'. The 'generative' or life-giving purpose is more important, as Natural Law is teleological. He argued that God created the universe in a particular way, and to go against that is a sin. This Natural Law argument has been upheld by successive Popes. For example, Pope Pius XI said:

> No reason, however grave, may be put forward by which anything which is intrinsically against nature may become conformable with nature and morally good. Since, therefore, the conjugal act is designed primarily by nature for the begetting of children, those who exercise it deliberately frustrate its natural power and purposely sin against nature and commit a deed which is shameful and intrinsically vicious.
>
> (*Casti Connubii* (Of Chaste Wedlock), December 1930)

Furthermore, the Catholic Church's Catechism teaches that chastity (refraining from sex outside of marriage) is the exercise of the virtue of temperance permeating the passions and appetites. Paragraph 2353 sees sex outside of marriage as 'gravely contrary to the dignity of persons and of human sexuality which is naturally ordered to the procreation of children'. Natural Law views the aim or purpose of sexual activity as reproduction, and several key thinkers, such as John Finnis and Robert George, have added marriage to the list of basic goods. The sexual nature of men and women is believed to be properly expressed in the commitment to life-long marriage. 'With my body I thee wed' is a phrase from the Anglican marriage service which refers to the wedded couple being 'united with one another in heart, body, and mind'. To treat your body as a mere instrument for pleasure, Robert George argues, leads to the disintegration of a person. As he puts it, 'Coitus is a unitary action in which the male and female literally become one organism . . . as a potential father and mother' (*In Defence of Natural Law*, Oxford University Press, 2001, p. 98). Sex is a metaphysical union of two people as 'one flesh' – we cannot compartmentalise off our bodies in casual sex, for as Genesis 2:24 puts it, 'Therefore a man shall leave his father and mother and be joined to his wife, and they shall become one flesh.' Aquinas distinguished between real and apparent goods, and when reason fails to control sexual desire, there can be a failure of *synderesis*, or reason thinking aright. Training in virtue, good role models and a strong community teach us right desire. The theological virtues of faith, hope and love also inform our conscience.

Situation Ethics and pre-marital sex

Joseph Fletcher's Situation Ethics is seen by its critics as a product of the permissive 1960s. Its pragmatism and relativism urge the Church to move with changing social attitudes and lifestyles. Perceiving Christian ethics to be strongly legalistic and prohibitive, Fletcher's proposition that Love is the only ruling norm relativises the absolute, but doesn't absolutise the relative. He seeks a middle way between legalism and antinomian permissiveness. Act agapeism looks at the facts of the situation without preconceived judgements, reading Augustine's dictum as the essence of Christian ethics: 'Love with care, and then, what you will, do.' This is an 'attitudinal ethic rather than a legal one' (Fletcher 1966, p. 79). Where erotic love focuses on desire and emotion, agapeic love is serving and self-sacrificial. Fletcher was concerned to be relevant to contemporary culture. As he wrote, 'The triple terrors of infection, conception, and detection, which once scared people into "Christian" sex relations (marital monopoly), have pretty well become obsolete through medicine and urbanism' (1966, p. 80). The church should not expect people to abide by an ideal standard that is not their own. As Fletcher asserted: 'we find nothing in the teachings of Jesus about the ethics of sex, except adultery and an absolute condemnation of divorce . . . He said nothing about . . . homosexuality, masturbation, fornication or pre-marital intercourse . . . Whether any form of sex (hetero, homo, or auto) is good or evil depends on whether love is fully served' (1966, p. 139). Legalism leads to hypocrisy and, in Fletcher's judgement, its roots in puritanism and romanticism need demythologising. We can have sex without love and sexless marriages. He goes as far as saying: 'if people do not believe it is wrong to have sex relations outside of marriage, it isn't, unless they hurt themselves, their partners, or others. This is of course, a very big "unless" and gives reason to many to abstain altogether except within the full mutual commitment of marriage' (1966, p. 140).

Fletcher endorses rule agapeism as long as rules are judged by their fulfillment of the law of love not the love of law. Here, they do not constrain love, so the situationist minister would avoid judgementalism in the pastoral care of a cohabiting couple. Indeed, where the relationship represents mutual loving commitment and care, is due to saving for a mortgage (weddings are expensive), or is the prudence of a trial marriage where divorce is common, it is the intentions of the couple that matter.

The idea that sex in a loving relationship outside of marriage might be more ethically acceptable than loveless sex in a marriage was controversial in Fletcher's day. Critics such as Yale Professor James M. Gustafson saw him as light on substance and method, and vague on the details of love and the specifics of how situations magically revealed the right thing to do. They dismissed his tactic of positioning himself as the balanced exponent of a middle way between legalism and antinomianism, arguing (as Paul Ramsey did) that 'no social morality ever was founded . . . upon a situational ethic'. Subjectivity and individualism can creep into Situation Ethics and the ideal of sacrificial 'neighbour love' can become self-deceptive in making exceptions to the rule as justified by the particularities of one's circumstances. In 1967, Peter Wagner attacked Fletcher's positivism – one of his four presuppositions. Fletcher wrote that, 'Christian ethics "posits" faith in God and reasons out what obedience to his commandment to love requires in any situation' (1966, p. 47). Faith, or the revelation of the law of love is absolute for Fletcher, but Wagner questioned his selectivity over other revealed commandments, such as 'do not steal', or 'do not commit adultery'.

Kantian perspectives and pre-marital sex

Kant was a lifelong bachelor and, in the opinion of his critics, had a negative view of human sexuality. In his view, sex and erotic behaviour were largely manifestations of the animal instincts, taking away our rational dignity. Sexual behaviour was only justified by the imperative of preserving the human race, within marriage. He wrote that 'Sexual love makes of the loved person an object of appetite; as soon as that appetite has been stilled; the person is cast aside as one casts away a lemon which has been sucked dry.' On this issue of pre-marital sex, he very clearly states in his *Lectures on Ethics* that, 'If a man and a woman have the will to enter on reciprocal enjoyment in accordance with their sexual nature, they must necessarily marry each other; and this necessity is in accordance with the juridical laws of pure reason.' He adds that, 'If I yield myself completely to another and obtain the person of the other in return, I win myself back . . . In this way the two persons become a unity of will.'

In the commitment of married life, partners begin to see each other as persons rather than as mere objects. Erotic love 'taken by itself . . . is a degradation of human nature', but it can be expressed with reciprocity in the monogamous, lifelong union of married life where it 'reestablishes the rational personality' (Kant, *Lectures on Ethics*, ed. J. B. Schneewind and P. Heath, Cambridge University Press, 2001, p. 163).

Kant's second formulation of the Categorical Imperative is that it is always wrong to treat people as a means to an end (i.e. to see people as only having instrumental value). He observed how prostitutes and concubines or mistresses were used as a means to an end, such exploitation most commonly being by men of women. As body and self are inseparable for Kant, when the man gave himself partially to his wife and a mistress, who each gave themselves exclusively to him, they were exploited and objectified 'into a thing' rather than being an end in themselves. As he puts it, 'the body is a part of the self. In its togetherness with the self it constitutes the person; a person cannot make of his person a thing.' Kant's attack here is, according to Roger Scruton, on fornication, or sex before marriage. Here Kant sees the other as being used as an 'object of appetite' rather than in the mutual covenant of marriage. Fornication falls short of the duties and responsibilities of the rational person (body and mind).

Utilitarian perspectives and pre-marital sex

> ### Discussion Questions
>
> In the preface to *Practical Ethics*, Peter Singer writes:
>
> > Even in the era of AIDS, sex raises no unique moral issues at all. Decisions about sex may involve considerations about honesty, concern for others, prudence, and so on, but . . . the moral issues raised by driving a car, both from an environmental and from a safety point of view, are much more serious than those raised by sex. Accordingly, this book contains no discussion of sexual morality. There are more important ethical issues to be considered.
>
> *Given the risks of sexually transmitted disease, sexual abuse, violence, trafficking, and the objectification and exploitation of women in pornography, do you agree or disagree with Singer? If you agree, why? If not, why not?*

John Stuart Mill married Harriet Taylor in 1851, two years after the death of her husband. He regarded her as his intellectual equal and the two were close friends for many years before being married, collaborating on several of Mill's books

As the surveys listed earlier in this chapter indicate, British people are increasingly accepting of the ethics of pre-marital sex and cohabitation. The secular, libertarian philosopher Bertrand Russell stood within the Utilitarian tradition. His view was that, although marriage was 'the best and most important relation that can exist between two human beings', contraception had altered the relation between sex and marriage. He asserted that, 'I should not hold it desirable that either a man or a woman should enter into the serious business of a marriage intended to lead to children without having had previous sexual experience.' Sexual ethics was, for Russell, about free and responsible choices for individuals. In his assessment, primal instincts had been repressed as 'sinful' by religious moralists, whereas the significant moral issues arose around betrayal, coercion, inequality, abuse or violence (Russell was among the first to campaign for marital rape to be recognised as a crime). He valued education, and virtues such as prudence, temperance, kindness, truthfulness and justice, but saw traditional morality as repressive and its moralism as frequently hypocritical. Russell's view typifies the Utilitarian emphasis on sexual freedom in relationships between consenting adults.

J. S. Mill was well known as a social reformer as well as a Utilitarian. When he was 17, he was arrested for distributing a pamphlet supporting contraception. He was influenced in this by the ideas of Thomas Malthus, an eminent economist and thinker, with whom Mill was closely acquainted. Mill was impressed by Malthus' theory of population (i.e. regarding the working class). Mill was convinced that population control was essential in improving the living conditions of the working class. He wanted them, along with everyone else, to be as happy as possible in their situation. He thought that the use of contraceptives would be more effective than legislation in controlling the population. With the UN projecting that the current global population of 7.2 billion is set to reach 9.6 billion by 2050, together with the immense human suffering caused by the spread of STDs, especially HIV/AIDS, the issue of contraception is very much on the agenda. Utilitarian critics of the Catholic Church, such as Peter Singer, argue that it could do much to decrease human suffering and death, as well as lower unsustainable population growth, if it promoted contraception and family planning across Africa and Latin America.

In his 1859 book *On Liberty* (J. S. Mill, *On Liberty and the Subjection of Women*. Penguin Classics, 2006), Mill wrote that freedom should be a matter of individual choice, and would not need the interference of the state, 'so long as we do not attempt to deprive others of theirs or impede their efforts to obtain it'. He was in favour of people having the freedom to experience sexual pleasure, except where this might result in social harm, for instance in the cases of rape or child molestation. He was also an activist in the promotion of the rights of women and, in this context, he campaigned for their right to use contraception.

The contemporary Utilitarian John Harris even goes as far as arguing (*The Value of Life*, Routledge, 1984) that sexual activity is less a moral issue than one of etiquette and manners. It may be objected that the risks of sexually transmitted disease, sexual abuse, violence, trafficking, and the objectification and exploitation of women in pornography, makes this a questionable claim. Yet Harris would respond that these issues are not unique to sexual ethics, but come under the areas of deceit, violence, coercion, exploitation and negligence. Clearly, the consequences of pre-marital sex in terms of unwanted pregnancy or promiscuity / sexually transmitted diseases, particularly when the interests of children are to be considered, call for responsible decision-making and the consequences to be taken into account. Cases of trafficking, exploitation, abuse or sexual violence are quite different and, on the grounds of Mill's Harm Principle (see the chapter on Utilitarianism), ought to be regulated by the courts and police. Health, honesty and liberty are concerns, but there is nothing intrinsically wrong with promiscuity or prostitution for Act Utilitarians. Rule Utilitarians would emphasise how societal happiness and welfare would be enhanced by a commitment to honesty and not cheating on your partner. Mill, a soft paternalist, would be more willing to regulate than Bentham – for example to protect minors against grooming and abuse, or to regulate prostitution to prevent criminal gangs and sex trafficking. His faith in education and freedom of choice is represented in school-level sex education and university consent classes today.

Discussion Question

Usefulness or utility is the measure of policies or rules, and Bentham, Mill and Singer would argue that the prohibitions of conventional morality have often been counterproductive with the young in the area of pre-marital sex. In 2016, the US Obama administration ceased all state funding (previously $10 million annually) for chastity campaigns, whose message is that it is best to wait for sex until marriage. 'Rigorous evaluation' by the US government suggests that such programmes increase teen pregnancy. Far more effective have been pregnancy prevention programmes which educate young people about responsible choices and the risks of sexually transmitted diseases, encourage the delay of sexual activity until they find a stable relationship, and promote contraception.

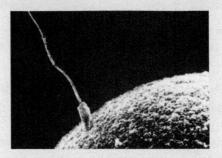

Sperm fertilising the ovum

How would a Utilitarian address US conservative Christians who believe that programmes teaching young people about contraception condone, even promote, sex outside of marriage?

Extra-marital sex

Extra-marital sex occurs when a married person engages voluntarily in sexual activity with someone other than the person to whom they are married. It is commonly known as 'adultery'. In the Old Testament, adultery is condemned as a very serious crime. It is specifically prohibited in the Ten Commandments (both versions: Exodus 20:14; Deuteronomy 5:18) and in the Holiness Code in Leviticus (18:20). Leviticus 20:10 states that those found guilty of adultery are to be put to death. In the New Testament, John 8:7 relates the story of a woman accused of adultery, in which Jesus says 'Let any one of you who is without sin be the first to throw a stone at her.' Commenting on this passage, Raymond E. Brown concludes that: 'The delicate balance between the justice of Jesus in not condoning the sin and his mercy in forgiving the sinner is one of the great gospel lessons' (*Gospel According to John*, p. 336).

St Paul condemns adulterers as sinful in 1 Corinthians 6:9–10, as part of a list of immoral people who will not inherit the kingdom of God. The basis of Paul's objection seems to be the same as that for pre-marital sex: that it is a sin against another

Still from Franco Zefirelli's 1977 TV mini-series Jesus of Nazareth with Jesus saying to the woman caught in the act of adultery, 'Where are your accusers now? Go and sin no more.'

person and God, and also that it is a defilement of one's own body (see 1 Corinthians 6:18). Many Christians condemn adultery because it breaks the bonds of marriage, which is a sacrament ordained by God. In Matthew 19:9, Jesus says that sexual unfaithfulness in marriage is the only exception for which divorce is allowed.

For most people, marriage entails public promises and binding, lifelong and monogamous commitment, together with the emotional bonding of a sexual relationship. Consequently, extra-marital sex breaks down this trust and ends many marriages. Some couples agree to an 'open' or 'polyamorous marriage' in which the couple raise a family together but consent to each other having sexual relationships. In countries such as Saudi Arabia, Pakistan and Somalia, adultery results in prosecution, with punishments including imprisonment, flogging and even the death penalty. South Korea decriminalised adultery only in 2015, and, perhaps surprisingly, in Idaho, Massachusetts, Michigan, Oklahoma and Wisconsin, adultery has never been decriminalised. This is due to the unpopularity that any politician might face for speaking out against it being a crime.

Natural Law and extra-marital sex

The contemporary Natural Lawyer, John Finnis (1940–), includes marriage in his list of basic goods (or, to use Aquinas' term, primary goods). In his understanding, marriage includes both sexual union (with the possibility of children to be raised) and companionship. For Finnis, marriage is more than a social institution; it combines the desire for friendship and sexual intimacy with reproduction (the papal encyclical, *Humanae Vitae* (1967) states that the latter two are inseparable). Germain Grisez (1929–) is another Natural Lawyer who sees marriage in the biblical sense of a one-flesh, unbreakable union. As he writes, 'Since they complete each other to become, as it were, one person, a man and a woman truly joined in marital communion cannot attempt to divide without severe trauma, analogous to, and in some respects even worse than, the loss of a substantial part of one's own body'

(*The Way of the Lord Jesus*, Franciscan Press, 1993, Vol. II, p. 577). Critics of this idea of a mystical one-flesh, unbreakable union point out that exclusive and life-long marriages succeed because the two partners work at them. A one-flesh union idea is no guarantee against well-intentioned couples having an affair, hating each other, living apart and then divorcing. For Aquinas, extra-marital sex broke both the law of God (the seventh commandment) and the promises made in the vows and sacrament of marriage. It also offended against nature, as the goal of sexual union was not only to reproduce, but to nurture and educate children in a stable and loving home, and extra-marital sex brought the risk of children being born out of wedlock. He also sees an inconsistency in the adulterer asking for faithfulness while being unfaithful. Adultery is therefore a mortal sin from which only a priest or perfect contrition can give absolution. The deliberate denial of one's conscience is a grave or mortal sin.

Situation Ethics and extra-marital sex

On the issue of divorce and sexual ethics, the Situation ethicist Joseph Fletcher's ethical tone is pragmatic and consequentialist:

> If . . . the emotional and spiritual welfare of the parents and children in a particular family could best be served by divorce, then wrong and cheapjack as divorce often is, love justifies a divorce . . . And this is the criteria for every form of behaviour, inside marriage or out of it, in sexual ethics or in any other field. For nothing else makes a thing right or wrong.
> (*Situation Ethics*, SCM Press, 1966, p. 133)

Intrinsic right and wrong are set aside in favour of doing the loving thing. Fletcher even offers the example of the sacrificial adultery of Mrs Bergmeier in a Ukranian POW camp in World War II. She wishes to be reunited with her family in Germany and learns that camp inmates can only be released if pregnant, for they are deported as a liability. After becoming pregnant by a friendly camp guard, nine months later she gives birth to 'Dietrich', who the family 'love more than all the rest' as it was he that enabled the family to be reunited.

Like so many of Fletcher's exceptional cases to prove the rule, Situationism is criticised because 'hard cases make bad law'. Fletcher has a habit of choosing atypical, even extreme, cases to make a point. Clearly, breaking marriage vows and any dishonesty in adultery is wrong, but the problem for critics is that the contextual relativism of Situationism can justify adultery, as in the aforementioned case. The liberal Catholic theologian and psychiatrist Jack Dominion took up Fletcher's relativism, going as far as claiming that: 'Adultery can be a one-night-stand far away from home with no threat to the relationship, or a serious involvement that puts the marriage in great danger. Like premarital sex, adultery cannot be condemned identically right across the board' (*New Internationalist* magazine, 158 (April 1986)).

The problem is that, without absolutes other than agapeic love, individuals can rationalise an affair, or say that the marriage had died before extra-marital sex was begun. Rule agapeists would recognise that condoning a one-night stand while away on business could develop into a pattern of deceit. Rule Agapeism would make sexual faithfulness a practical absolute because of the catastrophic potential for it to end a marriage and destabilise a family home. As William Barclay put it, 'It is much easier to agree that extraordinary situations need extraordinary measures than to think that there are no laws for ordinary life' (Barclay, *Ethics in a Permissive Society*, SCM Press, 1971, ch. 4, pp. 79–80). In his view, the 'terrifying freedom' of Situationism puts too much weight on the individual always acting out of agapeic love. It fails to take full account of the fallenness of human desires and motives, and our capacity for self-deception.

Kantian Ethics and extra-marital sex

N.B. The quotations in this section are from Kant's Lectures on Ethics, *Harper & Row, 1963, and from* The Metaphysics of Morals *(on Marriage Right), translated by Mary J. Gregor (Cambridge University Press, 1998).*

Kant speaks of marriage as a 'true reciprocity' which re-establishes the rational personality rather than 'making humanity an instrument for the satisfaction of lusts'. Marriage establishes a holistic view of the other person and a mutuality in which lawful monogamy offers and receives the whole of the other person, not the part offered in extra-marital sex.

Kant emphasises the **autonomy** of human beings. One might think that this would free people from the shackles of society's expectations and allow them to exercise their own subjective judgement as to the legitimacy of extra-marital affairs. Yet Kant sees our freedom exercised precisely in self-governing obedience to the moral law – 'There must be a basis', he writes, 'for restraining our freedom in the use we make of our inclinations so that they conform to the principles of morality'. **Promise keeping** is one of Kant's examples of the demands of the Categorical Imperative. Could the principle 'if you are unhappy in your marriage or the prospect of a better option arises, you ought to take it', be **universalised**? If not, it would be irrational to will it as a law-making member of the kingdom of ends. I would have to reject extra-marital sex as immoral.

The very form of this maxim is that of a **Hypothetical Imperative** governed by passional desires rather than moral duty. Universalising extra-marital sex would invalidate all promises made at the wedding. Kant also sees **goodwill** as crucial in relationships. As he writes:

> Human love is good will, affection, promoting the happiness of others and finding joy in their happiness. But it is clear that, when a person loves another purely from sexual **desire**, none of these factors enter into the love. Far from there being any concern for the happiness of the loved one, the lover, in order to satisfy his desire and still his appetite, may even plunge the loved one into the depths of misery.

Kant views human sexual appetites outside of marriage as immoral – driven, he supposes, by desire and not by reason or goodwill. As he writes,

> The desire which a man has for a woman is not directed towards her because she is a human being, but because she is a woman; that she is a human being is of no concern to the man; only her sex is the object of his desires. Human nature is thus subordinated . . . If then a man wishes to satisfy his desire, and a woman hers, they stimulate each other's desire; their inclinations meet, but their object is not human nature but sex, and each of them dishonors the human nature of the other. They make of humanity an instrument for

the satisfaction of their lusts and inclinations, and dishonour it by placing it on a level with animal nature. Sexuality, therefore, exposes mankind to the danger of **equality with the beasts** [emphasis added].

Extra-marital sex would therefore be, for Kant, unequivocally against the moral law.

Kant's second formulation of the Categorical Imperative is concerned with **not treating other persons as a means to one's end rather than as ends in themselves**. Human sexual desire is often directed not at the holistic welfare and happiness of another human being, but lustfully, to satisfy selfish desires. Kant sees marriage as placing sexual desire in a lawful relationship in which spouses are committed to 'the other person as a whole'. In giving your spouse the same rights over yourself that they give you over themself, there is a reciprocity and equality in marriage, and Kant concludes that: 'We can now apprehend by reason how a sexual union is possible without degrading humanity and breaking the moral laws. Matrimony is the only condition in which use can be made of one's sexuality.' The satisfaction of sexual desire is moral in marriage because it is the mutual and holistic giving and receiving of persons. Kant supposes extra-marital sex to be contradictory in treating oneself and the other person as a thing, 'for it is impossible to be [both] a person and a thing'. In marriage, sexuality leads to a holistic union of human beings. Extra-marital sex, in Kant's judgement, breaks this union and demeans persons as objects of desire.

Utilitarian perspectives and extra-marital sex

Utilitarianism is sometimes described as a 'thin' rather than a 'thick' ethic because of its minimal requirement to produce a great balance of pleasure over pain, or to maximise happiness or preferences. In *Having Love Affairs* (Prometheus, 1982, p. 12), Act Utilitarian philosopher Richard Taylor writes: 'The joys of illicit and passionate love, which include but go far beyond the mere joys of sex, are incomparably good. And it is undeniable that those who never experience love affairs, and who perhaps even boast of their faultless monogamy year in and year out, have really missed something.' Taylor even argues, on an Act Utilitarian basis that, if lying about an affair to one's spouse avoids emotional trauma and risk of the breakdown of the marriage, then one ought to conceal it.

A Rule Utilitarian approach would see Taylor's position as too permissive. Although individual liberty is a strong thread in the Utilitarian tradition of Bentham, Mill and Singer, the wider consequences of extra-marital sex for families, communities and society need to be taken into account. The problem with isolating individual actions is that the behaviour of a spouse has repercussions for a marriage and children. So rules prohibiting extra-marital sex or adultery produce less pain and more welfare when followed. The legal institution of marriage has proven through the centuries to be a useful environment in which to bring up children, and, in an individualistic society, it cautions against unchecked sexual desire that could damage flourishing families.

Homosexuality

Biblical teaching on homosexuality seems to be clear and uncompromising. Leviticus 20:13 says: 'If a man has intercourse with a man as with a woman, both commit an abomination. They must be put to death; their blood be on their own heads.' The story of Sodom in Genesis 19 has sparked much debate. Lot was visited by two angels (disguised as men), and the men of the city surrounded Lot's house, demanding that he send the angels outside so that the townspeople could 'know' them – that is, have sexual intercourse with them. God later destroyed the city because of the depraved behaviour of the people of Sodom (including the threat of gang rape), which is entirely at odds with today's loving, consensual same-sex relationships. In the New Testament, St Paul condemns homosexual relationships in Romans 1:24–32. This applies to female–female relationships as well (v. 26). Here again, liberal interpreters have seen Paul's criticism as being against lustful excess, whereas conservatives see Paul as being clear in his condemnation of all same-sex sexual relationships. He condemns 'homosexual offenders' as unable to inherit the Kingdom of Heaven, and claims homosexual relationships are a perversion resulting from the Fall (1 Corinthians 6 and Romans 1).

Christian perspectives and homosexuality

For Catholic and fundamentalist/conservative Protestant Christians, homosexuality is forbidden in the Bible and against the natural order of creation. God made humans male and female (Genesis 1:27), and Adam was given Eve as a companion. Heterosexual marriage (where the two become one flesh) is seen as the proper place for the sexual expression of this complementarity. For conservative Christians, Leviticus 18:22 and 20:13 condemns homosexual acts as being against the will of God. Paul also describes homosexual acts in Romans 1:26–7 as being unnatural and indecent. It is not that conservative Christians deny that homosexual orientation or same-sex attraction exists, but, rather, that they believe that, as for heterosexual singles outside of marriage, such sexual intercourse is forbidden in scripture.

Many Christian theologians, such as Michael Banner and John Milbank, seek to offer a critique of a secular culture that, in their view, pushes family and religious life to the margins while placing individual sexual orientation and expression at the centre of human identity. They argue that Christians need to focus on Christ, humbly aware of their fallen natures and how Jesus taught them not to judge (Matthew 7:1). Instead, heterosexuals and homosexuals alike should seek forgiveness for lustful desires that make others objects, and seek, with God's help, to be holy even as God is holy. The marriage between husband and wife is a reflection of Christ's love for the Church, which took him to the cross (Ephesians 5:22). It is here that the theological meaning of sex is properly understood. In the sacrament of marriage, the loving, creative union of husband and wife is not for self-gratification, but a calling to sacrificial service of one's spouse, the Church and the world. Within the Christian community, there is fellowship for those whose orientation, celibate calling or time of life rules out a sexual relationship.

By contrast, liberal groups within Christianity argue that the few biblical passages that refer to homosexuality need to be interpreted and contextualised if they are to be understood. They point out that there are very few references to same-sex consensual relationships in the entire Bible, and that Jesus never mentions homosexuality at all. Some liberal interpreters dispute the interpretation of the New Testament Greek words 'malakoi' and 'arsenokoitai' (1 Corinthians 6:9–11; 1 Timothy 1:10). They suggest that such texts do not refer to adult committed and consensual sexual relationships but to unequal relationships, such as with male prostitutes or minors, not uncommon in the ancient world. Furthermore, liberal thinkers would argue that Christians have altered their views over such questions as polygamy, divorce, conversion by military crusade, slavery, the role of women in leadership, evolution and hell. So, in the view of the US Presbyterian church (a liberal church denomination), 'Coming of age about sexuality requires affirming a diversity of responsible sexualities within the church, including the lives of gay men and lesbians.' Such churches, together with groups like the Lesbian and Gay Christian Movement, read Paul's statement in Galatians 3:28 – that 'there is neither Jew nor Greek, slave nor free . . . There is neither male nor female; for all are one in Christ Jesus' (an example of shifting attitudes towards the acceptance of non-Jews into the Church) – as a mandate to shift attitudes in today's Church and to promote an inclusive community.

There is a heated debate within Christianity about the status of same-sex relationships. In 2016, the Anglican Church voted to suspend its American branch from voting and decision-making because it had independently voted to allow its clergy to perform same-sex marriages without consulting the worldwide Anglican communion. In the UK, churches are not currently obliged to officiate in gay marriages (legalised in 2013 in the UK). In order to protect the freedom of belief of churches, the law allows them to 'opt in' to officiating at the ceremony, which can be performed in a civil or a religious setting in more liberal denominations. Some liberal Church leaders even argue that, in a society that has largely accepted homosexuality, the Church's rejection of this, as anything from 'intrinsically disordered' and sinful to 'short of the ideal', is a barrier to belief for wider secular society. The 1963 Quaker Report on Sex interpreted obedience to Jesus' command to 'love your neighbour as you love yourself' as faithful, self-giving love rather than exploitation or abuse; whether the relationship was heterosexual or homosexual was considered morally irrelevant.

Natural Law and homosexuality

Aquinas mistakenly supposed that there was no 'homosexual' behaviour in the animal world, concluding from this that homosexual acts went against the Natural Law. In his teleological view, sex could only be lawful within marriage where it was inseparably unitive and procreative. Aquinas argues that any sexual act must be of the 'generative' kind if it is to be moral. That is, legitimate sex must include vaginal intercourse. This clearly rules out male homosexual relationships. Natural Law theorists such as Paul Weitham say that homosexual acts, like contraception, impede the true purpose of the sex organs, which is to reproduce. This 'perverted faculty argument' may be what Aquinas meant. In the goal-orientated or teleological view of Natural Law, genitalia are aimed at procreation and, for Aquinas, homosexual relationships 'run counter to the natural mode of intercourse between male and female' (*ST*, 1a2ae, Q.94).

The Natural Law theorist John Finnis argues that homosexuality is always harmful and degrading. Homosexual sex cannot lead to procreation and, therefore, means that the couple's bodies are used instrumentally rather than for the purpose for which they were created. Therefore, no sexual activities outside heterosexual relationships are permissible. He also argues that the exclusive and lifelong commitment of marriage is a good thing in itself. The most telling argument against Finnis' view is that he puts procreation at the centre of marriage. If one were to put love or mutual support or companionship at the centre instead, there would be no reason to object to homosexual relationships. In agreement with Finnis, the Princeton law professor and Natural Law advocate Robert George comments that:

> Marriage is a comprehensive union of two sexually complementary persons who seal (consummate or complete) their relationship by the generative act – by the kind of activity that is by its nature fulfilled by the conception of a child. So marriage itself is oriented to and fulfilled by the bearing, rearing, and education of children. The procreative-type act distinctively seals or completes a procreative-type union.

He goes on to suggest that marriage has wider value beyond its primary purpose:

> Marriage has its characteristic structure largely because of its orientation to procreation; it involves developing and sharing one's body and whole self in the way best suited for honorable parenthood – among other things, permanently and exclusively. But such development and sharing, including the bodily union of the generative act, are possible and inherently valuable for spouses even when they do not conceive children.
> (George, *The Meaning of Marriage: Family, State, Market and Morals*, Scepter Publications, 2010, pp. 144 and 154)

Critics of Natural Law may argue that focusing sex acts on reproduction is too 'biologistic' and ignores the wider purposes of bonding, pleasure and expression of love fulfilled by sexual relations. They see this strict view of what is 'natural' to be a social construct. For Utilitarians then, judging an action good or bad depends not on the intrinsic nature of the action, but on its consequences.

Situation Ethics and homosexuality

Joseph Fletcher believed that 'Jesus said nothing about . . . homosexuality . . . Whether any form of sex, hetero, homo, or auto is good or evil, depends on whether love is fully served' (1966, p. 139). Critics have responded by saying that Jesus said that he had not come to abolish a word of the law and the prophets (Matthew 5:17), and that he would have been familiar with the prohibitions on homosexuality in Leviticus. Equally, in Matthew 19, Jesus quotes the Genesis 2:24 passage about a one-flesh union between a man and a woman and recalls that, at the beginning, the Creator made them male and female. So conservatives suggest that this 'argument from silence' is not the case.

Fletcher argued for the decriminalisation of homosexuality in an article on 'Sex Offences: An Ethical View', in which he proposed that criminal offences should be limited to: (a) acts with persons under the legal age of consent; (b) acts in situations that are a public nuisance / an infringement of public decency; and (c) acts involving assault, violence, duress or fraud. In his book *Moral Responsibility*, Fletcher urged that people be loved and things used, warning that 'promiscuity ignores and flouts the value and integrity of persons, turning casual sexual partners from true subjects into what some psychologists significantly call, "love objects". It turns them into things.' So Situationism would condemn the depersonalisation that can result from sexual objectification in relationships (whether heterosexual or homosexual), rather than take issue with a particular sexual identity as 'sinful'. In this same book, Fletcher states that 'Jesus showed more concern about pride and hypocrisy than about sex. In the story of the woman taken in adultery, her accusers were guiltier than she.'

Critics of the 'new morality' of Situationism, as it was termed, sought to show that its ends-justify-the-means relativism was unable to recognise intrinsic rights and wrongs. Whilst same-sex unions could be loving, even if they were, in the judgement of Natural Lawyers, intrinsically disordered, the fact that they were expressed in loving, virtuous and respectful ways would not make them right. Pope Pius XII saw the individualism of Situation Ethics as contrary to the official teaching of the Church and the authority of scripture, which were, in the Church's view, unequivocally clear on sexual ethics. Individuals sincerely disagreed, but they ought to submit to the higher authority of the divine and the Natural Law.

Kantian Ethics and homosexuality

Kant argued against the morality of homosexuality. He viewed it as a crime of the flesh against nature. In the *Groundwork to the Metaphysics of Morals* (1785; Harper Perennial, 2009), he wrote that 'Intercourse between sexus homogenii [i.e. same-sex partners] . . . is contrary to the ends of humanity; for the end of humanity in respect of sexuality is to preserve the species.' The Kant scholar Alan Soble explains that Kant's explicit condemnation of same-sex relations (found in his *Lectures on Ethics*) are grounded in the second formulation of the Categorical Imperative, which says: 'Act in such a way that you treat humanity, whether in your own person or in the person of any other, never as a means to an end, but always at the same time as an end.' Engaging in homosexuality is, in Kant's judgement, to treat the other person as a means to an end – your own sexual gratification – and this alone makes it immoral.

Others have argued that Kant's prohibition also arises from the first formulation of the Categorical Imperative: 'Act only according to that maxim by which you can at the same time, will that it should become a universal moral law.' If your maxim were that everyone should be homosexual, then this could not be universalised, as no children would be born and the human race would die out. This would obviously be contradictory.

Discussion Question

As Kant is not concerned about consequentialist reasoning or Hypothetical Imperatives, how would he respond to the following argument?

Today's global population is over 7 billion and rising. Furthermore, only a minority of the global population are gay, and, in any case, gay and lesbian couples can conceive children with the help of IVF and donor sperm / eggs / a surrogate mother, or they can adopt. So the argument that universalising homosexuality is a contradiction of the will is obsolete. If I state the maxim as: 'everyone ought to act in line with their sexual orientation and treat their partner as an end in themself not as a means to an end', what then, is contradictory about this?

Utilitarian Ethics and homosexuality

Jeremy Bentham wrote the first known argument for homosexual law reform in England. He argued for the decriminalisation of 'sodomy', which in his day was punished by hanging. His writings on this subject stretch throughout his lifetime, from his early twenties, but they were not published until 1931. He argued that homosexual acts should be judged on whether they contributed to happiness and alleviated pain. In 1795, he commented that 'I have been tormenting myself for years to find if possible, a sufficient ground for treating [homosexuals] with the severity [both in law and in morals] with which they are treated at this time of day by all European nations: but upon the principle of utility I can find none' ('Essay on Pederasty', quoted in J. R. Fitzpatrick, *John Stuart Mill's Political Philosophy*, Bloomsbury, 2006, p. 35). Bentham dismisses Voltaire's objection that homosexuality is 'prejudicial to the population', arguing that human population growth is under no threat and, if it were, then monks and nuns would be equally guilty. So Bentham sees no consequentialist grounds for objecting to homosexuality.

John Stuart Mill's 'Harm Principle' remains a crucial one in liberalising what consenting adults may do in private. The Utilitarian tradition replaces intrinsic right and wrong with the promotion of happiness/flourishing and the diminishing of unhappiness. It has been reformist with regard to sexual expression among consenting adults, and still campaigns for a reform of laws in countries where homosexuality or gay marriage is illegal. In his celebrated essay *On Liberty*, we read Mill's outline of what has become known as the 'Harm Principle' – 'the only purpose for which power can be rightfully exercised over any member of a civilised community against his will, is to prevent harm to others. His own good, either physical or moral, is not sufficient warrant . . . Over himself, over his own body and mind, the individual is sovereign.' Mill argues that, if homosexual acts between consenting adults cause no harm or distress (except to those people who are offended by homosexuality for religious or other reasons), then the law should leave people's private consensual relationships alone rather than criminalising them.

Discussion Question

1. No form of sexual behaviour can be regarded as unacceptable, sinful, or deserving of censure unless it has demonstrable ill effects on the individual who practises it or on others.

(Alex Comfort, *Sex and Society*, Penguin, 1964, p. 15)

Do you agree?

2. Writing on Christian marriage, Tim Keller suggests that people approach sexual relationships in one of two ways:

   (a) *A consumer or contractual mind-set – how can I trade my looks, wealth, intelligence, status for the best possible deal? What's in it for me?*

   (b) *A covenantal mind-set – in making promises of lifelong faithfulness and monogamy, mutual service creates a trusting and nurturing environment for personal, emotional, moral and spiritual growth.*

Do you think that there is truth in this analysis, or is marriage a blend of both?

3. It's not because we believe that desire-satisfaction is always good. Sexual desires in particular can powerfully incline people to favor short-term pleasure over long-term welfare, as Christian moral teaching has long and properly noticed. It's rather because we recognize that a small but significant portion of our fellow human beings are predominantly attracted to persons of the same sex, and that previous generations' tendency to ignore or hide or stifle this fact did far more harm than good. It's because we believe that romantic love is a good thing, and (more controversially) that the sexual expression of that love can bear good fruit even in relationships where procreation is neither intended nor possible.'

   John Corvino (a philosopher who has written and spoken extensively in defence of LGBT rights), *Commonweal Magazine* (21 July 2014)

How might Thomas Aquinas respond to Corvino's argument above?

FURTHER READING

Church of England House of Bishops (1991) *Issues in Human Sexuality*. Church House Publishing

Margaret Farley (2008) *Just Love: A Framework for Christian Sexual Ethics*. Bloomsbury Academic

Stanley Grenz (1998) *Sexual Ethics, A Biblical Perspective*. Westminster John Knox Press

Mark D. Jordan (2002) *The Ethics of Sex*. Wiley-Blackwell

Timothy Keller (2011) *The Meaning of Marriage*. Hodder and Stoughton

Neil Messer (2007) *Doing What Comes Naturally: Exploring Sexual Ethics*, Church Times Study Guides. SCM Press

J. S. Mill (1859) *On Liberty*

Pope Paul VI (1968) *Humanae Vitae*

Jonathan Rowe (2014) *Sexual Ethics Revision Guide*. PushMe Press

Peter Vardy (2013) *The Puzzle of Sex*. SCM Press

Michael Wilcockson (2001) *Access to Philosophy: Sex and Relationships*. Hodder Education

Thought Points

(1) Summarise the main issues in discussions on sexual ethics.

(2) Explain a Situation Ethics approach to sexual ethics.

(3) Discuss whether Natural Law is the most reliable approach to making decisions about pre-marital sex.

(4) To what extent do you agree that no ethical theory can completely solve the issues surrounding homosexuality?

(5) Assess the view that Kant's moral theory is of no help when making decisions about sexual ethics.

(6) In your view, which is the most successful ethical theory in dealing with the issues of sexual ethics?

(7) Evaluate the claim that Utilitarianism is the most successful approach to issues of extra-marital sex.

Glossary of Key Terms

A posteriori   What is known only after sense experience. Observation by the senses or technology is the basis of this type of knowledge.

A priori   Knowledge attained prior to sense experience and known through reasoning and logical deduction or innately. In understanding the definition of bachelors, one does not need to examine whether any particular bachelor is female or married by observing him. The statement 'Prime numbers are divisible only by themselves and one' does not depend upon knowledge of things in the world. A priori does not mean 'innate'.

Absolutist ethics   Moral standards are seen as unchanging and universal. Slavery and cannibalism did not become wrong at a certain period in history – they were always so. Divine Command and Kantian Ethics are examples of this stance and depend on principles not upon consequences.

Act Utilitarianism   This is Bentham's version of Utilitarianism, which considers how to maximise pleasure and minimise pain in each individual action or decision. There are no intrinsically good or evil acts. Instead we must act in each dilemma to achieve the greatest good of the greatest number of people involved. Rules cannot decide ahead of the specifics of time or place. We must judge what is useful (of Utility) in bringing about good consequences with the help of the Hedonic Calculus in any given dilemma.

Active euthanasia   When someone's death is deliberately brought about by an act (as opposed to an omission, as in passive euthanasia or mercy killing). In countries where this is legal, it is done for compassionate motives, and a terminally ill patient requests a physician to assist them in ending their suffering and 'dying with dignity'.

Advance directive   (also called a 'living will') This is a legal document in which a person specifies their wishes about what actions should be taken for their health-care in the event that, through illness or incapacity, they are incapable of doing so themselves.

Apparent goods   Real goods can often be mistaken for apparent goods such as seeking pleasure as an end in itself. Rather than fulfilling our nature, apparent goods (lust instead of love, revenge instead of justice) prevent us reaching our potentiality.

Arêté   Virtue, or any good characteristic or excellence. *Arêté* involves committed and purposeful training and practice, usually under the tutelage of a master-practitioner. Virtue ethics is sometimes termed 'Aretaic Ethics'.

Assisted suicide   A deliberate act that causes death, undertaken by one person with the primary intention of ending the life of another person, in order to relieve the second person's suffering.

Authoritarian conscience   Eric Fromm's term for the internalised voice of an external authority, something close to Freud's concept of the Super-Ego. This internal voice may be backed up by fear of punishment, or spurred on by admiration of an authority figure.

Cardinal virtues   These are the most important virtues. Plato and Aristotle, followed by many ancient philosophers, regarded temperance, wisdom, justice, prudence and courage as the most desirable character traits.

Categorical Imperative   Imperatives are commands: they are morally obligatory duties given to our reason by the moral law. The three formulations of the Categorical Imperative are Kant's tests to establish whether a proposed action is done out of duty to the moral law or from self-interest. They establish that an action is done out of goodwill if it passes the tests of being universalisable, treating others as an end in themselves and not a means to an end, and acting to bring about a kingdom of ends.

Cognitivism (moral)   Cognition refers to gaining knowledge through thought, experience or the senses. Moral Cognitivists believe that it is possible to have moral knowledge, or to know that moral judgements may be true or mistaken. This is a rejection of the non-cognitivist view that moral statements are simply attitudes of approval or disapproval and more like tastes than truth statements. This can lead in a positive direction, to the belief that we can know that obeying the golden rule is morally correct and true, or negatively towards the view that we have reason to believe that all moral statements are mistaken.

Conscience   The faculty said to enable us to make our own moral decisions and to judge those of others. Some have described this as the voice of God, or otherwise innate, but for Aquinas it is a species of practical reason. Its critics see this 'internal voice' as often just a product of one's upbringing and education, offering a less than reliable source of ethical insight.

Consciousness   Awareness of self, a key component of personhood.

Contraception   The deliberate use of devices or techniques aimed at preventing a woman from becoming pregnant as a result of sexual intercourse. Examples include the pill to prevent ovulation, intrauterine devices to stop implantation in the uterus, and barrier methods such as the condom, or male/female sterilisation.

Corporate Social Responsibility   In this concept, business is seen as having an obligation to society that extends beyond its duty to its owners or shareholders, beyond its legal and economic imperatives. It ought to protect society and minimise negative impacts that may arise from its operations (e.g., pollution, discrimination, dangerous products, misleading advertising); indeed, it should seek to improve the welfare of society. Businesses need to be economically viable and efficient in a competitive marketplace. But they also have discretion to act for the public benefit (e.g., through their wealth creation, sponsorship and philanthropy).

Darwinism   The theory of the evolution of species through natural selection developed by Charles Darwin. Without foresight, nature selects those traits that have a reproductive advantage in the competition for survival. Advantages such as strength, speed, camouflage, adaptability or high fertility are passed on to offspring.

Natural selection accounts for the variety and evolution of species. Neo-Darwinism offers more complete evidence from DNA and genetic mutations that explains the transfer of characteristics from parent to offspring.

Deontological Ethics Deontological ethics are concerned with fulfilling one's duty to obey the moral law ('deon' in Greek means 'duty'), as opposed to justifying an action in terms of its consequences. Duty presupposes a fixed and universal law, and the spirit of this approach is captured in the phrase 'Let justice be done though the heavens fall.' It asserts intrinsic rights and wrongs done for their own sake, and rejects instrumental ones done as a means to an end.

Determinism The view that every event, including human thoughts and actions, is the effect of previous causes without intervention of free choice. There are many determinisms depending on prior causes – of which God, genes and the environment are three examples.

Divine Command Theory The theory that moral standards of right and wrong have their origin in God's (or the gods') commands. *Theological Voluntarists* (e.g. William of Ockham) believe that right and wrong are whatever God commands and quite unaccountable to any human reasoning over a moral law. Aquinas, who thinks of morality as reason thinking rightly, would reject this view, believing instead that God commands what is right because his essential nature is lawful, loving and just.

Doctrine of Double Effect Where a doctor acts with good intentions (e.g. giving a therapeutic drug like morphine to help ease a patient's pain), and where foreseeable but unintended bad consequences arise (the dosage of morphine necessary to alleviate the patient's pain also accelerates the dying process). The proportionately grave reason for permitting the bad effect (relief from agonising pain) must not require an intrinsically wrong act to bring it about (e.g. the use of a lethal, non-therapeutic drug like potassium chloride whose effect is to stop the heart and thereby to end life).

Doctrine of the mean When talking about the moral virtues, Aristotle says that the virtuous man establishes a 'mean' or balance between deficiency and excess, e.g. courage is the mean between cowardice (deficiency) and foolhardiness (excess). This isn't necessarily the mid-point – for example, a virtuous person with practical judgement and experience would know to whom, when, how, and for how long and to what degree to express anger at injustices done.

Duty What every human must do if they are to act morally. Involves acting according to reason and the Categorical Imperative.

Egoism The belief that individuals have a moral duty to optimise good consequences for themselves.

Emotivism The theory, argued by Logical Positivists such as A. J. Ayer, that ethical statements merely express emotions and cannot be justified. Winston Barnes named this the '"Killing–boo!" theory'. In this view, any moral claim (e.g., 'Abortion is murder!') is essentially an emotional plea on the part of the one who expresses it for others to share this feeling, rather than a truth claim.

Ethical Naturalism An ethical Naturalist defines 'good' in terms of some natural property in the world, such as pleasure. A Naturalist could be a subjectivist, seeing moral statements as true in terms of the attitudes society approves of. Alternatively, they could be objectivist, identifying 'good' as the impartial viewpoint and giving equal consideration to the interests of all people.

Ethics of duty   The belief that right living means always performing one's rationally determined duty. The term is often used to describe Kantian Ethics.

Eudaimonia   The Greek word is commonly translated as 'flourishing', or actualising one's potential. It is a holistic idea of flourishing which is goal-orientated and continues one's whole life, requiring participation in wider community and society (the *polis*).

Euthanasia   Bringing about the death of a person in a painless and gentle way, for their benefit.

Euthyphro Dilemma   From a dialogue between Socrates and Euthyphro related by Plato – does God command an action because it is right, or is it right because God commands it?

Extra-marital sex   Sexual intercourse with someone other than one's spouse or marriage partner. Traditionally called 'adultery'.

Free will   Incompatibilists see free will as incompatible with determinism. For them, free will requires genuine alternative possibilities and self-formed actions originating in an individual's will or reason. This entails responsibility for one's choices. For compatibilists, free will is the absence of obvious external constraint or coercion. It is the feeling that one is acting freely even if one's will has been determined by prior causes one is unaware of.

Good Will   Kant's term for acting in accordance with the moral law and out of a motive of duty, rather than for a desired outcome. The Good Will is intrinsically good. Unlike other goods such as pleasure, wealth or health, the Good Will cannot be used for bad purposes, as it is good without exception. Honourable motives remain so even if the consequences do not turn out as one had hoped.

Hard determinism   This view combines universal causation (every event is part of a series of causes and effects) and causal determinism (prior causes determine future effects). Human actions, like Newton's laws of motion, are seen as predetermined by factors such as genetics and heredity. Such a view denies that there are any genuine alternative possibilities / actions that are internally decided upon and willed by a person.

Hedonic Calculus   Bentham's quantitative method of determining the right action to take in any circumstance in order to bring about the greatest good of the greatest number, the maximisation of pleasure and minimisation of pain according to a seven-part scale. This was intended to help an individual to calculate precisely the pros and cons of the possible consequences of an action.

Hedonism   The term comes from 'hedone', the Greek word for 'happiness'. In most forms of hedonism, happiness is interpreted as 'pleasure'. Early hedonists recognised the 'pleasure paradox' in which the single-minded pursuit of pleasure as an end in itself often left one dissatisfied or even in misery (e.g. addiction). Epicurus (341–270 BCE) proposed moderation in all things as a way of optimising long-term happiness. The peaceful life, surrounded by one's friends and avoiding fear and suffering, was thought to be the surest route to lasting pleasure.

Heteronomy Being subject to, or under the authority of, the 'law of the other', coming from outside of the rational will (autonomy) of a person. This might be from authority figures such as parents, teachers, the Church or societal codes, or it may be from appetites or desires that are not rationally willed. In saying that reason was a slave of the passions, Hume woke Kant up to reject his view of autonymy and argue instead that, outside of our self-governing reason, freedom of the will was impossible.

Homosexuality Attraction towards, desire for or sexual activity with a person of one's own sex.

Humanistic conscience Fromm's term for a person's own voice, present in every human being, and independent of external sanctions and rewards. This voice is a person's true self, found by listening to and heeding one's deepest needs, desires and goals.

Hypothetical Imperative In contrast to the Categorical Imperative (which sees moral commands as obligatory), Hypothetical Imperatives are conditional. They take the form of 'if . . . then' statements. Examples would be, 'If you want to avoid prison, then don't do the crime', or 'If you want people to think well of you, be honest.'

Informed consent When an informed and mentally competent person freely expresses a settled decision to enter into an action after being made fully aware of the risks and benefits that may result from it.

Intellectual virtues Aristotle listed five intellectual virtues: practical intelligence, scientific knowledge, intuition, wisdom and art or technical skill.

Intuitionism The ethical theory, associated with G. E. Moore, that one simply intuits the good. 'Good' and 'evil' are objective but indefinable. Basic moral truths are either self-evident or perceived similarly to how our senses experience the physical world, as a category of the human mind.

Involuntary euthanasia A criminal act in which euthanasia is performed on a person either when they are unable to give their informed consent or against their wishes. The infamous case of British doctor Harold Shipman illustrates this. Police investigating the high death rates among this GP's patients discovered that he was administering lethal doses of diamorphine, signing death certificates, and falsifying records to indicate that patients had been in poor health. In this manner, he murdered at least 215 patients.

Libertarianism Libertarians (such as Jean-Paul Sartre) oppose the view of Determinists that our choices are entirely the result of causes which came before us (such as our genes, parents, schools or the history of humankind). Yet, as Incompatibilists, Libertarians agree with hard determinists that, if true freedom exists, it must entail alternative possibilities (liberty of indifference) and choices originating within a person rather than wholly being the effect of a prior causal chain over which they had no control. Both reject the view of compatibilists like David Hume – that if a person feels a sense of free will and no obvious external constraint, this 'liberty of spontaneity' may count as free will.

Materialism / Physicalism The belief that existence comprises only of matter and energy. 'Scientism' is a term associated with a dismissive attitude towards knowledge that has not been verified or falsified by science. It restricts knowledge to material and efficient causes, rejecting formal and final causes as the pre-scientific legacy of Aristotle.

Meta-ethics   The Greek word 'Meta' can be translated as 'after', or 'higher/beyond'. Meta-ethics steps back from practical ethical issues and disputes between rival normative theories about how we ought to live. Meta-ethics considers the meaning of concepts and terms such as 'good' and 'wrong'. Are these objectively or subjectively known? Are there moral facts? Are they knowable by reason or intuition, are they innate, or are they unknowable? It is a second-order activity of thinking precisely about the reliability of our thinking. It arrives after the first-order disputes are underway and steps back to ask after the meaning of terms and concepts and what foundations these are grounded in (possible candidates include God, nature and intuition).

Moral objectivism   The opposite of subjective ethics, this view holds that moral statements are true independently of what people think or feel. It follows from this that it is at least possible to judge that moral claims are true or false.

Moral realism   The view that claims are true in respect of how they correspond to the real world. Moral realists hold that moral statements can in principle be verified or falsified – there is an objective reality about them. This may, for example, derive from God's created moral order or commands, but not all realists are theists.

Moral responsibility   The belief that persons are accountable for their actions. In law, a punishment may be lessened on the grounds of diminished responsibility due to a person's mental illness or immaturity. Praise and blame are seen by many philosophers (but not all) to depend upon moral responsibility if they are to be meaningful.

Natural Law   The view that morality is built into the natural order, or, as Aquinas put it, 'the rational creature's participation in the eternal law'. Innate within humans is a knowledge and inclination towards goods that enable them to flourish. These are universal and objective. Human laws may be said to be just insofar as they adhere to the Natural Law.

Naturalistic Fallacy   Claiming that what is good is arrived at by identifying a natural property – e.g., pleasure. It is fallacious in the sense that the mere fact that something is natural does not mean that we ought to do it.

Negative Utilitarianism   The view that the reduction of suffering is the only goal, or that it should take priority over the maximisation of happiness. In a world where people in absolute poverty die of preventable diseases or malnutrition, and where the scale of animal suffering is widespread in factory farming, Peter Singer has championed 'effective altruism' and challenged the rich to give away more of their income and do more to reduce human and animal suffering.

Nihilism   In terms of ethics, Nihilists believe that objectivity is impossible. No moral truth claims exist, or if they do they're unknowable.

Non-Cognitive language   Language about which it is inappropriate to ask whether it is true or false. This includes, for instance, such things as prayers, curses, poetry, etc.

Non-cognitivism   The view that moral judgements are not true or false as they do not make truth claims. Instead they express emotions, preferences, commands or attitudes.

Non-voluntary euthanasia   Where a decision is made to end the life of a person who is not in a position to make that decision themselves (e.g., they are in a PVS or a coma). Also known as mercy killing.

Normative ethics: Ethical theories that inform people how they should act. They don't merely describe, but have a sense of 'oughtness' to them – e.g., to maximise happiness (Mill), or to obey the moral law and do one's duty (Kant).

Objectivism For the objectivist, objects exist independently of a subject's perception of them. In the case of moral objectivism, the claim is that moral truths exist independently of culture or personal preferences.

Palliative care   Caring for a person with an incurable disease so that they maintain some quality of life and their pain is kept to a minimum until the moment of their death.

Passive euthanasia   A person (usually a doctor) allows another person to die painlessly by withdrawing treatment, which indirectly brings about that person's death. This can be controversial, as in using an intravenous line to provide hydration while withdrawing nutrition. The benefits in terms of pain relief and quality of life are weighed against the burden of unnecessarily extending the dying process.

Persistent Vegetative State (PVS)   Most of a person's brain functions are absent, but the body may still function (i.e. heartbeat, breathing).

Personhood   The distinguishing characteristics that make up an individual person. In Peter Singer's definition, some animals, e.g. chimps, can count as persons, and some humans can fall below the level of sentience and self-awareness needed for personhood. This leaves some sceptics thinking that the term's intention is to unsanctify human life as intrinsically valuable.

Phenomenon   That which is presented to us in sense experience. Kant, the most significant phenomenalist, argues that we can never know the world as it is, only as it is presented to us in sense experience.

Physician aid in dying   A qualified doctor administers lethal medicine in order to assist a person who wishes to commit suicide.

Physician-assisted suicide   A qualified doctor prescribes a drug which assists a person to take their own life.

Phronēsis   Practical judgement or wisdom generally built up through experience and observation, and seen in judgements that find the mean or middle course between deficiency and excess.

Pleasure principle   The Id's desire for instant gratification. Unchecked drives for food, sex, aggression and sleep are immediate and primal. Reality is not taken into account as the immature Ego pursues desires which are fantasies rather than realities, as they take no account of how others will react, often leading to painful conclusions. The Id is pleasure-seeking and indulges the biological and psychological needs of the immature Ego in an impulsive and uncritical manner.

Predestination   The belief that, as God is omniscient, he knows our choices from all eternity and therefore has already determined our eternal destiny. The belief is associated most commonly with Calvinism.

Preference Utilitarianism   An approach introduced by R. M. Hare and held by Simon Blackburn (Peter Singer used to hold this view, but now describes himself as a Hedonic Utilitarian, having been persuaded by Henry Sidgwick and Derek Parfit of objectivity in ethics). This is the version of Utilitarianism that aims to maximise the choices or expressed interests (preferences) of humans and animals. The interests of all sentient beings (not just humans) ought to be taken into account when ethical decisions are made. Often associated with minimising pain rather than maximising happiness (Negative Utilitarianism). A long-running debate exists in Utilitarianism between Hedonic Utilitarians, who prioritise caring about an organism's happiness and suffering (hedonic wellbeing), and Preference Utilitarians, who say we should ultimately value fulfilling what the organism wants (preferences), whatever that may be.

Pre-marital sex   Sexual relations prior to marriage. Also traditionally termed 'fornication'.

Prescriptivism   A non-cognitivist meta-ethical position developed by R. M. Hare which argues that moral statements are commands or imperatives, as opposed to descriptions. Moral terms are used to guide action and prescribe what people are to do in similar situations. Whilst agreeing with emotivists that access to moral facts and true-or-false moral statements is not possible, it progresses beyond this position to treat ethics as rational rather than a form of emotional manipulation. In contrast to emotivists, prescriptivists argue that we can regard some ethical prescriptions as being more rational than others, in the sense that they are better informed, more imaginative and consistent.

Prima facie duty   W. D. Ross' attempt to clarify a difficulty with Kant's theory. When there is a conflict of duties, Ross suggests that they be put in order of importance.

Primary Precepts   Beliefs arrived at by observing the goals towards which human action tends to gravitate (e.g. life, knowledge, social goals).

Principle of Utility   A phrase first used by Jeremy Bentham in his Introduction to the *Principles and Morals of Legislation*, to refer to the principle that should govern society and bring the greatest amount of happiness to the greatest number of people. Bentham was a social reformer and wished that all members of society could achieve as much happiness (and avoid as much pain) as possible during their lives. This is the fundamental idea behind Utilitarianism.

Proportionalism   An attempted moderation of the absolutism of Natural Law theory extension of the Doctrine of Double Effect. Aquinas allowed for theft in extremes to stave off starvation. His Just War theory also allowed for killing as long as the intentions were good and a greater good was thereby brought about.

Quality Adjusted Life Years (QALY)   A method used by physicians to calculate the Quality of Life of a patient to estimate the number of valuable months or years a patient may live.

Quality of Life (QoL)   This is a key concept in the debates concerning abortion and euthanasia. In the abortion debate, it can help decide whether a foetus has a 'life' distinct from the mother, and in the euthanasia debate it can help to focus the decision regarding whether someone's life has any value.

Reality Principle   Refers to the mature Ego acknowledging the Id's urges, whilst relating these to the real world so as to consider the risks and consequences of gratifying impulsive desires. This deferral of gratification represents the conscious mind exercising some control over the unconscious, primal instincts. The Ego reasons with the Id to say that what may be pleasurable in the short term may be painful in the long term.

Relativist ethics A rejection of moral absolutes that sees morality as relative to time and place. Descriptive relativism merely observes that moral disagreements exist among people and in society about ethics. Normative relativists go further to suggest that moral claims *ought* to be evaluated as right or wrong relative to the standpoint of a society, community or person that holds them. This view is expressed normatively in the phrase 'When in Rome, do as the Romans.' Here the diversity thesis (the existence of diversity in moral views between societies or cultures) has led to the dependency thesis (the belief that moral norms are dependent upon or relative to any given culture). Whilst Situation Ethics has relativism as a principle, Fletcher argued that it relativised the absolute rather than absolutised the relative, making agapeic love the one ruling absolute.

Rule Utilitarianism The greatest good of the greatest number is achieved when everyone follows rules, laws and customs that aim to maximise the happiness of everyone, not just individuals. Weak Rule Utilitarians (e.g. John Stuart Mill) evaluate the worth of rules as instruments in maximising pleasure/happiness or minimising suffering. Where they bring about greater harm than good, as a social reformer and parliamentarian, Mill sought to change them (speaking up for the right for women to vote, for example). Strong Rule Utilitarians believe that, as good rules are beneficial to most people most of the time, one needs very strong reasons to break them.

Sanctity of Life (SoL) The belief that human life is made in God's image and is therefore sacred in value and inviolable. It is a gift rather than a possession. Focused on human life, it places a uniformly high value on innocent life (though disagreements exist over when this begins), regardless of its quality.

Secondary Precepts These make Primary Precepts normative in terms of what ought to be done (e.g. provision of shelter, healthcare, protection for the vulnerable). Through practical knowledge, the primary goods come to be applied.

Sentience Having the ability to feel pain and a degree of self-awareness or subjective sense of oneself. Animals are sentient and, for thinkers like Peter Singer, could count as persons, whereas humans in a Persistent Vegetative State could fall below his criteria for or watermark of 'personhood'.

Situation Ethics A form of consequentialism not unlike Utilitarianism, except that instead of the Hedonic Calculus based on pleasure and pain, it judges the good on an agapeic calculus based on doing the loving thing, along the lines of four principles (positivism, pragmatism, relativism and personalism). Its originator, Joseph Fletcher, sought a middle way between legalism and antinomianism. A further distinction can be made between Act Agapism (very much letting individual situations guide us as to what the loving response is in their specific context) and Rule Agapism, in which greater attention is paid to rules and principles (because these bring a practical wisdom drawn from experience and remind us of wider duties in setting precedents). Mixed Agapism sees agapeic love as *a* principle (working alongside and transforming a natural human sense of justice and injustice) but not the *only* principle of Christian ethics.

Soft determinism / compatibilism Here a weaker definition of free will (liberty of spontaneity) than incompatibilists will accept is offered. The feeling of being free to act even if our will is decided by prior causes external to us, will suffice. In the absence of an obvious sense of constraint by an external cause, we feel our actions to be free. This said, the soft determinist agrees with the hard determinist that every event has a prior cause and that, merely because internal causes (such as genetics or psychology shaped by parents or one's wider social environment) are not as obvious as external causes, it makes events no less the effects of prior causes.

Subjectivism Subjectivists see morality in terms of personal preferences or tastes. They reject the idea that there are objective moral facts which can be said to be objectively true or false. Instead, they see moral values as rooted in human nature. Human behaviour is more passional than rational.

Suicide A person takes his/her own life voluntarily and intentionally.

Summum bonum The term Kant used for the highest good, which was the achievement of happiness and virtue together. This is a state rarely achieved in this lifetime (in which many virtuous people suffer and some vicious people prosper). Yet, for practical reasoning in morality, we have to assume that doing our duty is bound up with a moral order that is just and where happiness and virtue belong together.

Synderesis According to Aquinas, this is our inner knowledge of and natural disposition towards doing good and avoiding evil – 'that good should be done and evil avoided' – a natural disposition of humans to understand the first principles of morality instinctively.

Teleological ethics Making moral judgements based upon consequences. Actions are justified in terms of promoting desired outcomes. Actions are viewed as intrinsically good or bad not in and of themselves, but in terms of results. This is the opposite of deontological ethics in which actions are intrinsically right or wrong (e.g., Kant's emphasis on dutifully telling the truth even when the consequences could put someone at risk).

Telos The goal or end purpose of anything. All of nature is seen in Aristotle's thought as directed towards a final end – as goal-orientated.

Theological determinism The belief that God, who is sovereign over his creation, causes all events, and orders them according to his predestined will. How divine sovereignty and human free will may both be accommodated in such a view has led to differing opinions (e.g., those of John Calvin, with his double predestination of the elect and the damned, on the one hand, and those of Henry Molina, a Jesuit who thought that an omniscient God could align all human choices in any given possible world with his desired will in our actual world, on the other).

Theological virtues After the New Testament was written, the four ancient virtues became known as the cardinal virtues, while faith, hope and charity/love were referred to as the theological virtues. They were developed particularly by St Thomas Aquinas and became part of Natural Law theory.

Universalisability Refers to Kant's first version of the Categorical Imperative: what would happen if everyone were to do what is proposed? If a maxim is universalisable without contradiction, it is the moral thing to do.

Utilitarianism   An ethical philosophy that evaluates actions on their usefulness (utility) in maximising happiness and minimising suffering. It seeks to count each sentient person's interests equally and to bring about the greatest good of the greatest number.

Virtue Ethics / Aretaic ethics   This theory of ethics is agent-based not action-based. Its focus on developing character through training and practice sees the moral life as more complex than simply reading a textbook full of dilemmas and learning to calculate consequences. Aristotle's school (the Lyceum) was holistic and concerned to develop a disposition or orientation of character in its students. In the thirteenth century, Aquinas' great contribution was to synthesise Aristotelian virtue theory with Christian scripture, in what became known as Thomism (after his first name, Thomas). In the twentieth century, Elizabeth Anscombe began a revival of Virtue Ethics to which thinkers such as Alasdair MacIntyre, Robert C. Solomon and Martha Nussbaum have been significant contributors. The emphasis is on learning practical wisdom (*Phronēsis*) in exercising the virtues within a community or state (*polis*). With experience and expert mentors, one seeks excellence (*arêtê*) in the practice of virtue and the ability to find the perfect balance (*the golden mean*) between the vices of deficiency and excess.

Voluntary euthanasia   The practice of (ideally painlessly) ending the life of a person who wishes to die and usually referring to physician-assisted dying.

Whistle-blowing   A practice in which employees who know their company to be engaged in activities that are illegal (e.g. fraud/corruption), to violate human rights or to cause unnecessary harm inform the public or a government body. As long as they are acting in good faith and in the public interest, they are protected in law against retaliation.

Illustration Credits

Index